D1490996

BIRDS AND WOODS

Cock Pied Flycatchers in Sessile Oak

W. B. YAPP

BIRDS AND WOODS

LONDON
OXFORD UNIVERSITY PRESS
NEW YORK TORONTO
1962

Oxford University Press, Amen House, London E.C.4

GLASGOW NEW YORK TORONTO MELBOURNE WELLINGTON
BOMBAY CALCUTTA MADRAS KARACHI LAHORE DACCA
CAPE TOWN SALISBURY NAIROBI IBADAN ACCRA
KUALA LUMPUR HONG KONG

Printed in Great Britain

CONTENTS

TABLES

ILLUSTRATIONS

PLATES

TEXT FIGURES

FOREWORD

This book is in part an account of original observations, mostly previously unpublished; in part a review of other published work about woods and the birds that live in them; and in part an attempt to state, in more precise terms than have ever been used before, where woodland birds live and how they make use of the features of their habitats. I have indulged in some dangerous speculations, which may or may not, as knowledge increases, be supported. Without speculation science does not progress, and I ask nothing better for this book than that it should induce other ornithologists to go out into the woods to try to prove me wrong, and enjoy themselves in doing so.

The help of many people has been necessary and freely given, and I cordially thank all of them: my predecessors and contemporaries, whose work I have used and whose writings have stimulated me to thought, action, or exasperation; the taxpayers of Great Britain, whose contributions have made possible some part of my field work and the time in vacation to settle down to writing; and the officers and staff of the Forestry Commission, from the Secretary and Deputy Director-General down to many anonymous woodmen, none of whom has ever failed to give me the help for which I asked, often, I am sure, to their own inconvenience.

Specific acknowledgements are made in the references and list of illustrations, and I apologize to any whose names I have inadvertently omitted; I am especially grateful to Mr. C. F. Tunnicliffe for so accurately and beautifully interpreting my wishes in the frontispiece. Help of a different sort was given by Dr. Bruce Campbell, who first suggested that I might write such a book; Mr. James Fisher, with whom I discussed its plan many years ago; Captain and Mrs. H. R. H. Vaughan, who gave me hospitality and facilities in the woods of mid-Wales; and Mrs. W. K. S. Moore, who read and criticized an early draft.

Lastly, the officials of the Press have, as always, been helpful, understanding, and forbearing.

W. B. Y.

Church End,
September, 1961

Robin

1
INTRODUCTION

The reasons that lead one to a particular line of scientific investigation are many, but two were specially important in bringing me to work on woodland birds. One was a boyhood interest which could no longer be satisfied by simple list-making or aimless recording of observations; the other was exasperation at being unable to find in the books the answers to simple questions about the species of birds found in different sorts of woods and their relationships with each other. The present book is an attempt to answer some of these questions, and to suggest the sort of observations that are needed to answer others. But more than this, I hope it will communicate some of the delight that I have found in planned observations in the open air, and lead bird-watchers to a simple and scientifically useful but much neglected aspect of ornithology. It attempts to be on the one hand a serious contribution to animal ecology; on the other something that will interest the amateur who is already familiar with the names and looks of the commoner birds. There are many excellent books on the identification of birds, and I assume that the reader will have access to some of these.

When, a century and a half ago, Thomas Bewick named his

two volumes *The History and Description of Land Birds* and *The History and Description of Water Birds*, he was making an ecological distinction. Since then very little progress has been made on these lines. Land birds could be divided fairly easily into woodland birds and moorland birds, and books have been written about birds of gardens and of farmland, which are obviously artificial categories, but finer distinctions have seldom been made. Most of the surface of Great Britain was formerly woodland, of several different sorts, but the books seldom do more than say that a bird prefers deciduous or coniferous woods, as the case may be. To understand the distribution of birds one must know something of the woodlands themselves, and descriptions of these are therefore given in Chapter 3 and subsequent chapters.

Whenever my own observations are extensive enough I have used them as the basis of my lists and arguments, comparing them with the few published records by other people that are available. This has introduced some bias, in that most of my observations have been made in the north and west, but this at least does something to correct the bias in the other direction caused by the predominance of London and the Home Counties in twentieth-century bird-watching. Thus a well-known book on Bird Song published in 1936 says 'The nightingale . . . is a summer visitor to England (except parts of the north and extreme west)', but 'the pied flycatcher has a true song, which unfortunately the present writer has not had the opportunity of learning'. The truth is that the nightingale is just as restricted in its distribution and covers no larger an area than the pied flycatcher (Figs. 15 and 21), and the total numbers of the two are probably of the same order, but the nightingale lives in the south-east, surrounded by half the human population, the pied flycatcher in the hills, where there is no one to notice it.

It is difficult to say how many observations one needs before one can make valid statements about the distribution of birds, and I wish that for some types of woods I had more records than I have, but I am encouraged in finding that where the comparison is possible, the lists prepared for this book in 1960 differ very little from preliminary lists drawn up in 1954. In other words, though there are differences of detail, the main provisional conclusions that I drew six years ago have not been invalidated by further work.

This suggests that my samples have been large enough, though it is possible that they could have been better chosen geographically. Any bird may occasionally turn up anywhere, but such casual observations cannot be used to controvert statements made on the basis of many controlled counts.

All British birds have had their life and activities greatly affected by the presence of man, and woodland birds, more than most, have been forced to change their habits to suit the pattern which he has imposed on these islands. He has destroyed most of the original woodland habitat, by the processes of forestry and game preserving he has altered the nature of nearly all that is left, and he has provided new woodlands of trees formerly unknown in this country. Above all, in his parks, gardens, orchards, and hedges he has made a new type of habitat which has many of the features of woodland and yet is not woodland, so that some birds prefer to leave their natural place in the woods and make their home with him. The amateur bird-watcher, accustomed to look for the smaller birds in gardens or on agricultural land, is generally disappointed when he goes to the woods, for there often seem to be no birds at all, and it is very obvious that such birds as robins and blackbirds are to be found in much greater density in gardens than anywhere else. We cannot always be sure why this should be so; a greater production of food is perhaps important, but this simple explanation is not adequate, and subtle psychological factors seem also to be at work.

Whatever the reasons for this diversion of so many woodland birds from their natural home, it has had one important and scientifically unfortunate effect on their study: most of what we know about their habits has been learnt by watching them under artificial conditions, only a few steps removed from captivity. Not only are casual observations so much more frequent in places where man spends most of his time, but it has been common even for scientists to plan more extensive work where access is easy and long travel unnecessary. There are indeed relatively few published papers on the habits and activities of birds in woods, but it is with these that I am chiefly concerned in this book.

An example of the difference in habit between the same bird in woods and in gardens is given by the chaffinch. As a garden bird it begins singing and showing sexual behaviour usually during the first week in February, and occasionally earlier, but it does not enter the oakwoods, and so neither sings nor holds territory there, until the middle or end of March.

My earliest record for a singing chaffinch in twelve years' observations in the oakwoods of Wyre Forest in Worcestershire is 11 March. The entry of the breeding birds into the woods in 1960, so far as I was able to follow the events, was as follows. I took a walk of nearly the same course, covering about half a square mile, on each day except the first, when the distance was rather less.

March	12	21 minutes	No chaffinches
	16	40 minutes	One calling overhead
	20	38 minutes	Three calling overhead
	24	41 minutes	One calling overhead
April	1	39 minutes	One singing, 14 calling overhead or moving about in the wood
	4	39 minutes	Two singing, two calling
	15	47 minutes	One singing, one calling

This series of events means that during the last fortnight of March the cocks were exploring for territories, and that by the end of the month or the first week in April these were being occupied.

The chaffinch illustrates also the inadequacy of the ecological information even about common birds in the books, for the *Handbook of British Birds* does not mention that it is absent in winter from almost all woods except beechwoods, and on the other hand does not give woodland as one of the places where it breeds. The implication in fact is that it is a bird of gardens and orchards which is occasionally found in woods. The truth is the other way about. It is a bird of woods, especially oakwoods and birchwoods, in the breeding season, and of beechwoods and more open places in winter, but it is also found in orchards and gardens, habitats which are not more than a few hundred years old. Its density, unlike that of the robin and blackbird, is still as high in the woods as anywhere else.

There is a marked seasonal pattern of bird-life in the woods, which is much more than the mere arrival and departure of the recognized summer migrants. The population is at its maximum in summer, when the young are being fed, and after that there is a decline, both by death and by emigration. A few species may never leave the woods. The greater spotted woodpecker remains in the same part of the wood throughout the year, and the nuthatch is almost as constant; it is nearly always seen in pairs, but may move about to some extent with the tit-flocks. Both these species are found also in artificial habitats such as gardens and hedgerows, where they breed and remain throughout the year.

The chaffinch is quite different. Although it is not generally considered to be a summer migrant in this country, as a woodland bird it is. Breeding is over, and regular song ceases, by the end of June. Even allowing for the fact that silent birds are difficult to find when the leaves are still on the trees, there can be no doubt that soon after this the numbers of chaffinches in the woods begin to go down, and by October the oakwoods have none at all beyond an occasional solitary wanderer who drops in from a migratory flight above. There is no evidence as to where they go. They seem not to leave the country, but chaffinches are found throughout the winter in hedges and round farms outside the woods, and also in the woods if there are beech trees, often, but not always, in flocks; how many of these are our own birds from the oakwoods and how many are visitors from the north and east one cannot say.

The partial migration of the British chaffinch (*Fringilla coelebs gengleri*) is of special interest for two reasons. In the first place the continental race (*F.c. coelebs*) is fully migratory, at least in the north, flying west and south in large numbers, so that many reach Great Britain in autumn. Secondly, one would like to know how our birds behaved when oak forests covered almost the whole of England and there were no stack-yards and hedges to provide winter food. There are, I think, two possibilities: either all our birds moved to the beechwoods of the south-east, or, with or without a general movement in that direction, many emigrated to the Continent. In either case it looks as if our chaffinches have lost a migratory habit that they once possessed, and have become resident only within the time of dense settlement of these islands by man, a period of not much more than a thousand years.

Intermediate in behaviour between the greater spotted woodpecker and the chaffinch is the robin. Thanks to the work of Burkitt (1924–27) and Lack (1946) we know much more of its life-history than we do of those of most other birds. It is convenient to begin the story of the seasonal cycle in October. At this time all the robins in the woods, of both sexes, are holding territories, which are defended against intruders; the cocks sing, with rather less vigour as the year dies, and so do many of the hens. About Christmas or early in the new year the song of the cocks revives and the behaviour of the hens changes; they cease singing, leave their territories and go in search of a mate, sometimes merely moving into an adjacent territory held by a cock, at other times disappearing from the district and presumably going further afield. After the pair is formed the song of the cock declines in frequency and vigour, as is often the way with birds.

Nest-building begins in mid-March. The young begin to fly at about the beginning of May, and a second brood is reared and sometimes even another. The young scatter, being traditionally driven out by their parents, and after the moult in July and August both young and old begin to chase other robins so that new territories are established. At this time the cocks sing again with a characteristic autumn song, which to many human ears sounds more melancholy than that of spring, and some of the hens sing too. Other hens, though they win and hold territories, are silent, but the majority, two-thirds or three-quarters of the total female population, migrate. There is little information on where they go; probably not far, as there are a few recoveries of British-ringed robins from Holland and France and none from further south. It is possible that a few cocks also migrate. The migratory hens return and pair with territory-holding cocks at the same time as do those which have not moved away. It seems that the robins of England are on the borderline of country which is suitable for wintering, since none of those in the Canary Isles and the Azores migrate, while in most of Scandinavia all do. It is said that a high proportion of robins leave the north of England and Scotland in autumn, but there is no statistical evidence of this. It must be added that the figures on which this account of migration is based are for robins in mixed country—small woodlands, orchards, and fields; no precise information is available for pure woodlands, but the robin is certainly an occasional winter resident of most types of woodland. There is, however, variation. In Wyre Forest the number of robins in winter changes from year to year, with no very obvious connexion with weather. My records do not suggest that there are any more in the woods of Exmoor than in those of the north of England.

The tits have a quite different type of life-history. The blue tit, which will serve as an example, is, except in the breeding season, social in its habits, and although not all individuals flock in the winter, solitary birds are rare. An account of the life-cycle is best begun with nest-building, when the birds have already been paired for some time. This starts at a time which varies according to the earliness of the season, from mid-March to the third week in April. The young leave the nest about the end of the first week in June, and there is very rarely a second brood. Within a week or two of leaving the nest the young of different families mix, and within a further ten days they mix with the young of other species of tit. Goodbody (1952) found by counting ringed birds that there is a rough random dispersion throughout the summer and early autumn from June to September; the later in this period the count was made, the more birds were found away from their birthplace and the fewer nearer it. It might be expected that this sort of behaviour would continue through the winter, but Hinde (1952), who made intensive observations in a restricted area of Wytham Wood near Oxford in the winter of 1948–9, concluded that from the autumn onwards most tit-flocks were stable in composition and kept to a roughly-defined area about 10 acres in size. In Wyre Forest there is certainly less constancy than this in the flocks, and the flock areas, if they exist at all, are very much larger. A large flock often breaks up, partly but not entirely into different species, and Hinde found that this tends to happen more and more as the day goes on. Tit-flocks also link up with flocks of other species such as goldcrests, and often pick up pairs (but not, so far as my observations go, flocks) of nuthatches and treecreepers, and these composite flocks again fragment. Some blue tits, probably adults, do not flock, but remain as pairs throughout the winter.

Gibb (1950) made regular weekly counts of the tits in Wytham Wood; this consists chiefly of neglected pedunculate oak (see Chapter 4) with a thick shrub layer, and is fairly typical of such woods in the south of England. He concluded that the population declined from October to January or early February and then rose in March and April, but he gives no account of the methods used to make the census. Since the total area surveyed was only about 75 acres, of which a quarter consisted of strips 50 yards and 20 yards wide, the decline may mean no more than that in severe weather the tits are attracted to adjacent farmlands where there is more to eat. My own transects in the much larger area of Wyre Forest show no regular decline through the winter, but do show large fluctuations, suggesting that the flocks wander rather widely, and Beven (1953) found the same thing in Surrey.

On any sunny day in late autumn or winter snatches of song may be heard, and there is a good deal of presumably sexual chasing, two birds leaving the flock and pursuing each other for a hundred yards or more through the trees. Gibb found that hole-inspection also occurs throughout the winter on warm days, but becomes more frequent in February. The cock bird leads in this and displays to attract the hen. Eventually one hole is fixed upon as the nest site and building begins. The changeover from flock to pair life is gradual, and Hinde found that in spring there was a period when the birds lived in pairs in the morning but joined other pairs to form a flock later in the day. Once a pair has been formed it usually lasts for life, even though the second-year birds join in a flock in the winter. This means that there must be some efficient mechanism of individual recognition. Possibly the sexual chases seen on sunny days in winter are of birds already paired.

Finally, there are the typical migrants, which are summer residents only. The willow-warbler normally arrives in the first half of April and, like many other immigrants, often stops to sing in areas where it will not breed; at this time, for instance, it may be heard and seen feeding in mature oakwood without a shrub layer. By the end of April breeding has begun, and by the middle of June, or a little later, the young are flying and, although they are quiet and difficult to see, family parties are now about in the woods. Soon after this the birds probably begin to move south. At the end of July or the beginning of August they are often seen in places where they are never otherwise found, and at this time too there is a secondary outburst of song. My own town garden has no breeding willow-warblers, but for several autumns one has stayed and sung for a week or so in the shrubbery. The *Handbook* says that departure of residents lasts until the end of September, but they are gone long before this from all the woods that I know. The Sutherland birch-woods, so full of them in June, are empty by the end of the first week in September. May (1949) found that few remained on his Surrey common after July, and that those which did so were juveniles and kept company with flocks of tits.

At present one can do little more than guess at the reasons for these different patterns of life-history. Clearly, less food is available in winter than in summer, so that it is a good thing for some birds to leave, but why it should be one species and not another is not so obvious. The greater spotted woodpecker feeds on large boring larvae which take two or three years to reach the adult stage, so that as much food may be present for it in winter as in summer. The diets of the blue tit and the willow-warbler in summer are, in general terms, very similar, and although the former takes some seeds in winter which the soft-billed warbler could not attack, it is not certain that it is this which makes it possible for the tit to survive in the woods through the winter while the warbler does not. The related chiff-chaff does sometimes persist throughout the winter in the south of England, which suggests that temperature is more important than food-supply. There seems no reason why the robin, which has a much wider diet, should not stay throughout the year, as indeed some individuals do, and the emigration of the chaffinch, which in winter is largely seed-eating, seems to be in part a psychological preference, since it can feed on many other things.

There would be no fun in science if all the answers were known, but the materials for writing an ecological history of woodland birds are more than usually scanty. In fifty years' time it may be possible to write the sort of book on this subject that I should like to write. Meanwhile, I hope that my readers may be encouraged to watch birds in a new and exciting way.

Great Spotted Woodpecker

2

METHODS OF STUDY

The fundamental requirements for the study of woodland birds are the same as in any other branch of field ornithology—common sense, careful observation, and a good pair of eyes and ears, aided where necessary by field glasses and a notebook—but for a fuller understanding of the woodland bird community it is important to be able to make verifiable statements about the numbers of birds present and the proportions of different species, and it is the methods of estimating these that I shall discuss in this chapter. For field records a card-index system is essential, and the manipulation of the records is made easier by the use of simple punched cards, such as those of the Cope-Chatterson Company.

The word CENSUS is often used loosely to mean any estimation of the numbers of individuals present in a particular place, but it is best restricted to actual counts of heads, and it is in this sense that it will be used in this book; a figure for the total population of a given area arrived at in any other way is called an ESTIMATE, and the crude figure from which the estimate is decided is called a SAMPLE COUNT, whether that figure is itself obtained as a census of a smaller area or in some other way.

The Registrar-General's census of the human population made at ten-yearly intervals is the best-known example of a census and also one of the most accurate, but even this is subject to slight errors; those who are sleeping out, for example, may not be recorded, and there may be some lack of truthfulness in the householders who fill up the forms. Censuses of birds are much less accurate; one can seldom be quite certain, even with the most conspicuous species, that no individuals have been overlooked, and many birds, especially small woodland species and nocturnal sorts such as the owls and the woodcock, may be present for a long time before they are seen. It is seldom possible to investigate more than a small area in one day, and over a period of a week or a fortnight there may be changes in the population by death, immigration or emigration; the result of the count is then not a census of those present on one day, and may be either larger or smaller than the true figure, since some of the birds that have come into the area are counted as well as those that have died or left. In the breeding season there is a further difficulty because the number of young birds changes rapidly from day to day, and it is then usual to count only the adults.

The habits of many birds in the breeding season are often very different from what they are in the rest of the year, so that the methods that can be used, and their accuracy, also differ widely. In the breeding season most woodland birds are territorial; they seldom leave a relatively small patch of ground, and even if they do they have a fixed point, the nest, to which they return with some frequency. Repeated visits to a grove or a small wood will enable a careful observer to say exactly how many pairs of birds are present, as even inconspicuous species such as the treecreeper will show themselves in time. Some idea of the degree of concealment of small birds can be got by comparing the apparent relative numbers of cocks and hens of species where the sexes are markedly different; the cock chaffinch, for instance, usually attracts attention by his song, but in spite of his brighter colours he does not seem to be any more readily seen than the hen, since it is the white wing-bar, possessed by both sexes, which attracts attention. A series of counts of chaffinches and pied flycatchers in sessile oakwoods is shown in Table 1. For the chaffinch the auditory conspicuousness is about five

TABLE 1

Relative numbers of cocks and hens in sessile oakwood

	Cocks heard singing before they were seen	*Cocks seen before heard*	*Hens seen*
Chaffinch . . .	104	22	23
Pied flycatcher . . .	58	8	8

times the visual and for the flycatcher it is about seven times. There may be some slight excess of males, but it is certainly not what the crude totals of cocks and hens recorded imply, and the fact that the numbers of the two sexes which are seen before they are heard are so nearly equal, suggests that in fact the sexes are about equal in numbers, which is what one would expect on general biological grounds.

It has been claimed that in some species, notably the blue and great tits, the counting of breeding pairs is made easier by saturating the area with nesting boxes; the birds so much prefer the artificial holes to the natural ones that none of the latter is occupied, and all one has to do to take the census is to walk round and see how many of the boxes have nests in them. The defect of this method is that one is dealing with highly artificial conditions: the census is indeed accurate but it is an unnatural ecological situation.

For larger areas, or where repeated visits are impossible, the sweep is the main method that has been used. It requires a number of observers, who walk in a line like beaters at a shoot, so that they hope to put up all the birds in the area, to record those seen, and not to record the same bird twice. Of these hopes only the second is likely to be fulfilled. Unless the beaters are very close together skulking birds such as wrens may refuse to fly, and it is impossible to make any allowance for birds which fly ahead and are seen for a second or third time. I have not used this method in the breeding season, but my attempts to use it in the winter suggest that it is so inaccurate as to be valueless, except perhaps for a few conspicuous and easily flushed species. Moreover, it is quite inapplicable to woods with a thick shrub layer.

The Americans have made much more use of a method which

they call 'cruising', and this seems to me to be more promising. As used in the winter this is really an extension of the line-transect (see p. 16) and as such is a sampling method, but in the breeding season it is accurate enough for most species to be considered as a census. The observer walks slowly, with as many halts as may be necessary, on a number of parallel lines which make part of a grid covering the wood; their distance apart is chosen by experience and depends on the spacing of trees and shrubs in the wood and the species of bird present. For hillside sessile oakwood 50–80 feet is suitable; in pedunculate oakwood the lines should be closer together, and in beechwood without a shrub or field layer they could be further apart. Every bird heard or seen is recorded, together with its approximate position. To enable this to be done the observer must know where he is; he can fix the beginning of his line of walk, at his entry to the wood, from a large-scale map; his direction by a compass, or on hillsides by making use of contours; and the distance he has walked since entering the wood in one of three ways. In woods with little undergrowth, where a normal stride can be taken, he can count paces (which is tedious and very liable to error), or wear a pedometer; in tangled woods the only method is to use a surveyor's tape, preferably of 100 feet. The loop at the end of this is hooked on to a firm but not very strong twig, and the tape is allowed to run out as the observer walks; he can then record his distance from the starting point at any moment. At the end of 100 feet a sharp pull on the tape will break the twig to which it is attached, and it is wound in for the process to be repeated.

To interpret the records a tracing of the outline of the wood as shown on the 25-inch plan is made on graph paper, and the positions of all the birds seen or heard are marked on this. It is usually clear that many of these belong to the same bird or to the same pair, and a little common sense will enable one to put a maximum and minimum on the numbers of pairs present. An example of a census made in this way is shown in Fig. 1. The 14 acres of this wood, which is more difficult to work in than most, took four hours.

A census that is relatively easy to make in the breeding season is that of singing males, and there has been much discussion about the accuracy of estimations of the total population derived from such counts. Two fundamental difficulties arise: that not all the cock birds in the wood may sing while the observer is within earshot, and that the total population may not be exactly twice that of the males. The first can be minimized by making the count soon after dawn, when nearly all the birds sing, or by choosing a suitable sunny day, or by spending long enough in the area, but as the distances at which the songs of different species can be heard differ widely, the method cannot really be used to give a census unless it is combined with some form of cruising technique. The second difficulty can only be fully overcome if we are able to compare estimates of the population of a given species made in this way with accurate censuses made at the same time of year and under the same conditions. We know that many migrants sing loudly when they are resting on their journey northwards, and so do unmated males, so that song counts made at the beginning of the season are unreliable, but we do not know for most birds what the sex-ratio really is, or what may be the percentage of non-breeding adult birds. Nice (1937) in her very careful study of the American song sparrow (*Melospiza melodia*) found that the sex-ratio (males to total) ranged from about 51 per cent. in April to 54 per cent. in June, and the percentage of non-breeders was not more than 10. I have suggested above that the numbers of male and female chaffinches and pied flycatchers in English and Welsh woods are very nearly equal.

A comparable method to the song count has been used by Southern for a census of brown owls. These birds almost invariably call a few times when they wake in the evening and before they begin flying. A large number of observers distributed through the wood recorded the time and compass bearing of each bird they heard. Subsequent plotting on a map gave the positions of all the birds and their numbers. Since the hoot of the owl carries well it is reasonably certain that no birds were missed, but the accurate estimation of the bearing of the hooting bird is difficult.

The simplest sort of sample is itself a census of a small area: a full count is made of the birds of, say, 5 acres of a wood, and this is multiplied by the number of times that five will go into the total acreage. The theoretical side of this sort of sampling is well known, and can be studied in any textbook of statistics; the larger the size of the sample the more accurate it is. There are also two practical considerations which are more often neglected. In the first place,

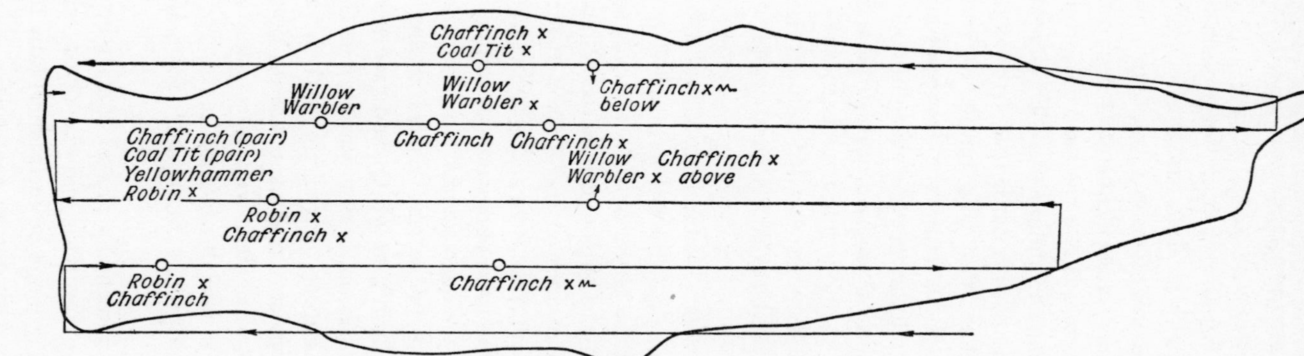

FIG. I. Cruising census in hillside sessile oakwood. The approximate track of the observer, and the positions where birds were recorded, are shown. x=bird singing; the chaffinch song shown x~ had an unusual trill in the middle. Probable pairs are yellowhammer 1, robin 1, chaffinch 4 (minimum 3), coal-tit 1, willow-warbler 1.

the method in its simple form will work only if the whole area is uniform, a condition which in this country is approached only on moorland and in the Forestry Commission's plantations, and even in these there are frequent local variations in height or luxuriance. This difficulty can theoretically be surmounted by the use of a number of small samples, either deliberately designed to include in proportion all the irregularities of the total area or distributed in a mathematically determined random way. The special features of a wood which affect the nesting birds may be so small, and are so various and obscure, that a very large number of samples would be needed to meet them all. Secondly, the density of bird populations is such that one can seldom get adequate numbers for statistical treatment either in the time at one's disposal or within an area of uniform climate. The methods that have been worked out for use with creatures such as wireworms, with millions to the acre, must be used with caution for birds which number only tens per square mile.

A type of sampling which has been much used is the line-transect, or, as it is sometimes called, the belt-transect. This resembles the cruising census in that the observer walks as nearly as possible on a straight line and records the birds which he sees or hears, but he does not need to record his position or the position of the bird. Various authors, notably the Finns Palmgren and Nordberg, have attempted to derive figures for the total population from their line-transects, but more often they are used simply for comparative purposes. Colquhoun, for instance, in a series of papers, attempted to compare the bird populations of different woods, and gave some attention to the theory, but his discussion, which was the first to be written in English, did not take into account all the factors. Since an understanding of the line-transect is fundamental to any quantitative work on woodland birds, I shall deal with it at some length. I have given a fuller discussion elsewhere (Yapp 1956). The mathematical theory has been developed by Masuyama (1957) and by Skellam (1958).

The problem is fundamentally one of contact between moving particles of two types, the birds and the observers. A record is made when these two impinge on each other; how frequently they do so will depend theoretically on four things only, the size and speed of each of them. Without going into mathematics we can say that the faster either is moving and the larger they are, the more contacts there will be in unit time. We can simplify things a little by giving all the size to the bird and none to the observer; the latter is regarded as a mere point, and the bird as having a radius equal to the average distance at which it is first seen or heard by him. This covers part, but not all, of what Colquhoun and others call conspicuousness. The recognition-radius of birds which are chiefly picked out by song or call note is clearly the distance which the sound will carry; it depends on the species and on the auditory acuity of the observer, and will be reduced when wind, waterfalls, or other background noises (including other bird song) tend to drown it. The visual radius depends largely on the density of the foliage, and so will obviously vary greatly from season to season, and from one type of woodland to another, and will also depend on the habits and coloration of the bird.

In the breeding season the bird may be considered as approximately stationary, for it does not move outside its territory, and the diameter of this is generally small in comparison with the size of the wood or the distance travelled by the observer in an hour. The winter speed of such wandering birds as the tits is of the same order of magnitude as that of the observer, and must be taken into account.

There are two other practical considerations. Clearly, if the observer walks too fast he will be unable to observe properly and will miss many birds that he ought to see or hear. Colquhoun thought that this was the only effect of the observer's speed, and he says that the slower the speed the more the contacts in unit time. This is only true at speeds which are never likely to be used, and up to about 2 miles per hour the simple theoretical relationship holds. The other consideration is the remaining portion of what has been called conspicuousness. A bird may have a song which carries a long way, but spend much of its time in silence; it may be easily seen when it moves but spend much of its time stationary and out of sight, as for example does a bird sitting on the nest. It is probably impossible at the present time to evaluate these effects in any way which is worth while.

This may make gloomy, as well as difficult, reading, but although line-transects made under uncontrolled conditions are quite worthless, under certain circumstances the method can give useful information. The points to be borne in mind are these: (1) It is probably always dangerous to compare the results of different observers unless these have been well matched by comparison in the field. (2) The method works best with birds that are fairly frequently making some sort of sound, such as singing males of many species in spring and winter flocks of tits. (3) The observer's speed must be controlled and known; 2 miles per hour is a useful value that can be maintained in nearly all woods. In calculating the speed all time spent standing still, whether this is used in note-making or in identifying birds, and all time spent in deviations from the straight line to get a better view of a bird for identification, should be deducted from the time taken to travel the mapped distance. (4) Comparison cannot be made between one species and another unless they are known, from general observation, to have roughly the same degree of conspicuousness. This is approximately true of many of the small singing passerines and of the tits in winter. (5) Comparisons can be made from one type of woodland to another only if the conspicuousness of the bird is the same in each. Where the height of the trees and the thickness of the shrub layer are different the visual conspicuousness will obviously be different also, but the auditory conspicuousness will not normally be greatly affected. Even this will be reduced to some extent in high woods, where birds are calling or singing in the canopy.

It will be seen from this that the line-transect is probably of use for comparing numbers of singing passerines, especially the chaffinch, pied flycatcher, robin, wren, redstart, thrushes, and warblers, both with one another and from one wood to another; and in winter for comparing numbers of tit *flocks* (the number of *tits* can only be determined or compared if we know the composition of the flocks; this aspect is discussed more fully in Chapter 11). As with all sampling methods, it only becomes at all accurate if fairly high numbers—of the order of 100 or more—are dealt with. Its application to birds such as owls and hawks, which are present only in small numbers, is very doubtful. Tucker (1947) in a series of careful counts in Epping Forest showed that during daylight the time at which the transect was made had no significant effect, but at some seasons, when birds are singing for only part of the day, this may not be true.

It must be added that although one cannot always use a line-transect to make a definite statement about the frequency of occurrence of birds, the cumulative evidence derived from a number of transects may be impressive. No one who has used the method can doubt, for instance, that, inconspicuous though they are, such birds as the treecreeper and the spotted flycatcher are really rarer in woods than the blue tit and pied flycatcher. In the lists later in this book I have used my line-transects chiefly in a comparative way, expressing the number of contacts for each species as a percentage of the total contacts, which may be called the relative abundance. The consistency of this for several species over the years suggests that this method gives a useful, if slightly distorted, picture of the densities of birds actually present in different types of woodland. The distortion arises because quiet inconspicuous birds such as the treecreeper are underestimated, while large, wide-ranging birds such as the carrion crow and the buzzard are overestimated.

The Americans have made some use of the 'call count' method. For this a suitable circuit is mapped out, with counting stations at regular intervals; for the mourning dove (*Zenaidura macroura*) in mixed wood and farmland, for which the method has chiefly been used, a circuit on minor roads with twenty stations at 1-mile intervals has generally been used. The circuit is followed, in the same direction, at the same time of day, in successive weeks or months, and a halt of standard time (3 minutes for the mourning dove) is made at each station. The number of birds heard calling, or the number of calls heard, at each station is recorded. Both of these must bear some relation to the total population, but what this relation is we do not know. It appears that although more birds call just after sunrise than just before sunset, there is more variation in the proportion of birds calling in the morning, so that more consistent results are obtained from evening counts. This method has possibilities for rapid covering of large areas of uniform woodland, such as Forestry Commission plantations.

A method of estimating populations which has been fairly widely used for invertebrates and small mammals but little for birds is that of 'marking and recapture'. The animals are trapped, marked in some way so that they can be recognized (coloured rings on the legs are generally used for small birds), and released, the number so marked being recorded. After a short time marking is stopped and the observer records the number of marked birds, as well as the total number of birds, which are trapped. If x birds have been marked and released and y birds are subsequently trapped, of which z are found to be marked, $\frac{x}{P} = \frac{z}{y}$, or $P = \frac{xy}{z}$, where P is the total population.

The validity of the method depends on a number of assumptions: (1) that there is uniform dispersion of the released birds; (2) that birds which have once been trapped do not become either trap-shy or trap-happy; (3) that the population is not altered by birth, death, immigration or emigration during the period of the experiment. Methods for dealing with the difficulties that arise when the third of these is not true are discussed by Bailey (1952). An account of the application of the method to a woodland bird (but not in a wood) is given by Blackwell and Dowdeswell (1951). It might well be more widely used by those who have the facilities for ringing and live near appropriate habitats. It would clearly fail if more than one person used similar colour rings in the same neighbourhood, and anyone who contemplates working on these lines should make contact with the British Trust for Ornithology, who maintain a register of colour-ringers.

Botanists have made much use of a figure called the 'percentage frequency' as a type of measure of the distribution of plants. In a given habitat, as large a number as possible of sample plots called quadrats is observed, and the species present in each of them are recorded. No notice need be taken of the number of individuals present. The number of plots containing a particular species is expressed as a percentage of the total number of plots, and the resulting figure is called the percentage frequency of the species. The size of the plot must be adapted to the size of the plants with which one is dealing; it will be larger, for instance, for trees than for grassland, and it must always be stated. Clearly, if it is too large many species will have a percentage frequency of 100, and the technique will not distinguish between them. The method has been used for invertebrates, but very little for the larger animals. It has advantages and ought to be tried more widely than it has been for birds. It will generally be impossible to lay out artificial plots, but fortunately nature and the forester have provided them for us. This introduces a complication, for the plots will not all be of the same size and shape, as they should be, but if one groups woods within the same range, say 5 acres and less than 10, 10 acres and less than 20, and so on, the error is likely to be small. The method could be used, for example, to compare the occurrence of birds in woods of different type. It has the advantage that it is much quicker than any system based on counting, and to some extent eliminates the difficulty caused by varying conspicuousness. My experience suggests that twenty minutes in a wood of the order of size of 10 acres will usually reveal all the species present except perhaps a few of the most secretive.

The percentage frequency can also be used for what may be called time-quadrats. Every species observed in a time-unit, which may conveniently be 20 minutes, is recorded, and the number of time-units containing each species is expressed as a percentage of the total number of time-units. I have used this method in later chapters, but have had to make some approximations since many of my records cannot be used in this simple way. Instead, I have taken each visit to a wood as representing so many time-quadrats, according to the time spent in it; anything up to 29 minutes is one quadrat, 30 to 49 is two, and so on. The birds are regarded as distributed uniformly over these quadrats so that if there are three contacts in 60 or 80 minutes there are three quadrats with that species present, but three contacts in 34 minutes would mean only two quadrats. The similarity of orders of abundance given by this method to those obtained by line-transects is striking.

The presence or absence of a species in a quadrat may also be used to find out whether two species are associated together more often than would be expected by chance. If one multiplies together the total number of quadrats and the number in which both species occur, and divides the product by the product of the numbers of quadrats containing each species separately, one gets a number which cannot be less than zero.[1] If it is unity, the association of the two species

[1] In algebraic language, $r=\frac{ad}{bc}$, where r = the coefficient of association or correlation; a = total number of quadrats; d = number of quadrats containing both species; b = number containing one species; c = number containing the other. More complicated formulae for dealing with the same problem exist.

is what would be expected by chance; if it is less than one, the two occur together less often than would be expected; and if it is more than one, they occur together more often than they would by chance. Such mathematics tells us nothing about what causes the attraction or repulsion. The two species may be dependent upon each other, or actively repel one another by their competition for nest sites, or may simply require conditions that are generally similar or different, as the case may be. As with all quadrat work, the results obtained will depend on the size of the unit. It is obvious that liking for the same type of habitat and competition for nest sites will work in opposite directions, the first tending towards association of the species, the second towards their separation. Which effect predominates will depend on the size of the quadrat, and in small areas where only one suitable nest site might be available, the two species would never be present together. For this reason a value of the coefficient of about one or less may mean nothing at all, but a high value does probably indicate either an attraction of one species for the other or, more probably, similar requirements.

When the quadrats used are not of equal size the results are even less precise, but again a value larger than one can only indicate that the two species are found together more often than they would be by chance. I have worked out coefficients of this sort, based on occurrences on 142 visits to woods of various sizes, for 13 of the commonest woodland species. Of the 78 combinations, 65 have values between 0·8 and 1·3, so that no conclusions can be drawn from them. Seven, with values of 1·5 or more, are mentioned in the accounts of the habitats of the birds at the end of the book.

A point to which some attention has been paid in recent years is the zonal distribution of the birds in a wood. The estimated height of the bird from the ground when it is first seen, or its position in one of five horizontal zones or layers, is recorded, or a stop-watch may be used to determine the time which it spends in each layer. In most types of wood convenient layers are: A, the canopy (the topmost branches of the trees); B, the main part of the trees; C, the shrub layer and lower branches of the trees; D, the field layer; and E, the ground. Colquhoun and Morley (1943), who first used these five divisions (but with slightly different names), defined them by height, but as the bird is unlikely to be influenced so much by the actual height from the ground as by the general type of vegetation, it is probably better to define them qualitatively, at least for woods with the normal four-layered botanical structure. In many beechwoods and sessile oakwoods zone C does not exist.

Counting, in one way or another, is necessary if we are to give precision to any of the statements which we make about the distribution of birds, but it is only too easy for the observer to be led away by mathematics into statements which are meaningless or misleading. Much published work on birds contains mathematical manipulation which only obscures the facts.

The only safe rules for numerical work in biology are to record accurately; to keep all your original notes; if you publish, to publish as far as possible the crude figures, or to give such information in your tables that the crude figures can readily be calculated (if you give percentages, for instance, always give the total number of observations from which they were obtained); and to avoid all mathematics that is not straightforward, simple, and perfectly clear in its meaning.

The first comprehensive attempt to determine the birds found in different types of woodland was the co-operative inquiry organized by the British Trust for Ornithology, and written up by Lack and Venables in 1939. Unfortunately the observers were not given adequate instructions, so that although they used the line-transect, they did not record their speed or the time spent in the woods, or the size of the woods, and the results will not bear many of the conclusions that were drawn from them. Lack and Venables say, for example, that the highest bird density in woodlands is that of the chaffinch in highland firs, but as these counts were made in Rothiemurchus and Glenmore (see Chapter 6), which have a total area of about 40 square miles, while most of the other woods were of a few acres only, it is not surprising that more birds were recorded in the former. In fact, the density of birds of whatever species in Rothiemurchus is lower than that in most other woods, and very much less than that in the highland birches. Nevertheless, the lists in this paper are valuable as records of presence or absence of a species and of relative abundance in a particular type of wood. They cannot be used for comparing densities in different woods.

Coal-Tit

3

THE ENGLISH WOODLANDS

Nearly all birds live among vegetation of one sort or another, and woodland birds, more than most, are affected by the trees, bushes, and other plants that surround them. Whether it is the apparently lifeless forests of spruce in winter, in which one can sometimes walk for miles without seeing or hearing a bird, or the summer birchwoods of Sutherland, in which the ripple of the willow-warblers' song is so continuous that one can no more count the singers than one can the flashes of sunlight on the surface of the burn, it is the trees which largely determine, directly or indirectly, the birds' pattern of life. To understand the ecology of birds one must know something about the ecology of plants, and this chapter is about the woodlands of Great Britain. Plant ecology is a much older science than animal ecology, and it was the botanists who developed the concept of the community, that is, of a collection of plants living together in such a way as to be recognizable and so worthy of having a name attached to it. Communities are of various sizes and degrees of complexity. At one extreme, the division of the surface of the earth into woodland and moor, marsh and steppe, was made by common men long before the days of scientific botany; at the other, the collection of green Algae of a single species (*Pleurococcus viridis*) found commonly on the north sides of tree trunks, is of little interest except to specialists.

In descriptions of the habitats of birds two types of community of intermediate position are especially important: the consociation, a community dominated by a single plant species (or sometimes two or three in more or less equal mixture), but containing many others, and usually found over a wide area where climatic and edaphic[1] conditions are suitable; and the society, which is similar to a consociation but occurs as a small local unit within a consociation. An oakwood is a consociation, while a patch of birch within the oakwood is a society. It is convenient to give a name to every type of consociation which can be recognized, and this is done by taking the generic name of the dominant species and adding *-etum* to its stem, and then putting with it the trivial name in the genitive case. For example, the oak of southern England is *Quercus robur* and the oakwood is *Quercetum roboris*; the beech is *Fagus silvatica* and the beechwood *Fagetum silvaticae*.

In describing their consociations, botanists have often been interested only in the species of plant which are present, but for birds other features, known collectively as the structure of the plant community, are more important. Most woods have a four-layered structure: the trees; the shrubs; the field layer, consisting of herbs and undershrubs; and the ground flora, or inconspicuous plants, chiefly mosses and liverworts, growing in close contact with the ground. For ornithological purposes it is often convenient to divide the first of these into two: the canopy, or extreme top of the trees from which the sky would be visible, and the main part of the trees between the canopy and the upper surface of the shrubs. The presence or absence of any shrub layer, and the height and thickness of the field layer, are likely to mean more to a bird than the particular species of which they are composed. The advantage to an ornithologist of knowing something of the classification of vegetation is that a given consociation generally has, at least under fixed climatic conditions, a definite structure, so that a botanist knows, for example, that a typical pedunculate oakwood (*Quercetum roboris*) has a thick

[1] edaphic = pertaining to the soil, from Greek ἔδαφος, the ground.

shrub layer and a leafy field layer, while a sessile oakwood (*Quercetum petraeae*) usually has no shrubs and a heathy field layer. There are always some exceptions, and any consociation shows many variants which must be described to give a full picture.

Birds are also influenced by other features, such as the size and shape of a wood, or its age (and so its height), which are of no particular interest to the plant ecologist since they are transitory or imposed on the wood by man. A small number of such things as rocks, climbing plants, and decaying trees with holes may have a great influence on birds by serving as nesting sites. Birds are largely dependent on invertebrates for their food, and the presence or absence of these is largely determined by such things as the dampness or acidity of the leaf-litter. These in their turn are in part determined by the trees and in part by the edaphic and physiographic features which help to determine what trees are present. Although we cannot, as we should like, determine all the features that are important in the life of a species of bird, the botanical nature of the environment in which it lives is probably as good a summary of its needs as we are likely to get.

I have already used the word 'dominant' in defining consociation. It is applied to the species which gives the characteristic appearance to a community and which often, by its presence, determines the presence or absence of other species. In all woodlands the dominant plant is a tree, for other plants are not visible from outside, and the tree often influences, by the depth of shade which it casts and other factors, the plants which can grow beneath it.

Almost any part of Britain which is not cultivated by man and which is protected from the attacks of his grazing animals soon becomes covered with bushes and then with trees. This was well shown in many of the roads which were laid out in the building boom of the early years of this century and then abandoned. Many such on the western side of Bristol were by the nineteen-twenties carrying an impenetrable scrub of ash, hawthorn, and bramble, and would no doubt in time have developed into something very similar to the ashwoods characteristic of the coombes of the adjacent parts of Somerset. In almost all the large towns of England the bomb-sites of the Second World War soon bore a comparable vegetation, although there was often a predominance of exotic shrubs owing to the ready availability of their seeds from gardens, and the sites were not left long enough without interference for large trees to develop. Neglected farmland too soon ceases to be grass. Spiny shrubs such as thorn and briar usually come first, and then trees of whatever sorts are in the neighbourhood.

These facts all suggest that woodland was once much more widely spread than it is now, and the historical evidence supports this conclusion. Not every place described in early records as a forest was wooded, for in medieval times and later a forest was a place which was reserved for the king's hunting and differed from the surrounding land only in that the pursuit of game and other activities in it without licence incurred special and severe penalties. Some such areas, such as Dartmoor Forest and Exmoor Forest, were probably never, at least in historic times, covered with trees, but others, such as Inglewood in Cumberland and Feckenham in Worcestershire, were more or less thickly wooded. From documentary evidence and from general observations we can in fact be reasonably certain that at the time of the Saxon settlements almost the whole of our land was woodland. The exceptions were the hill tops of Wales, Scotland, and the north and west of England, and the river valleys. These last were swamps, although many of them probably bore fair numbers of alders and willows, and so, from a bird's point of view, counted as woodland. There may also have been some grassland on the thin chalk soils and heaths on the shallow sands. Fig. 2 is an attempt to show the probable distribution of woodland in about A.D. 500.

It was by the clearance of the woodlands that farms were made, and the history of the Saxon and Norman settlements is a story of progressive destruction of the trees. By Tudor times little extensive woodland was left except in the royal forests and on the estates of a few great nobles, and complaints were already being made of the shortage of timber for building and, above all, for smelting of iron. Planting began on a small scale in the seventeenth century and was greatly extended in the eighteenth, from which time many of our apparently natural woodlands may be dated. This century saw also the introduction from Central Europe of our first important alien forest tree, the larch, although this was planted extensively only in Scotland, where, for example, Lord Strathmore made much use of it at Glamis.

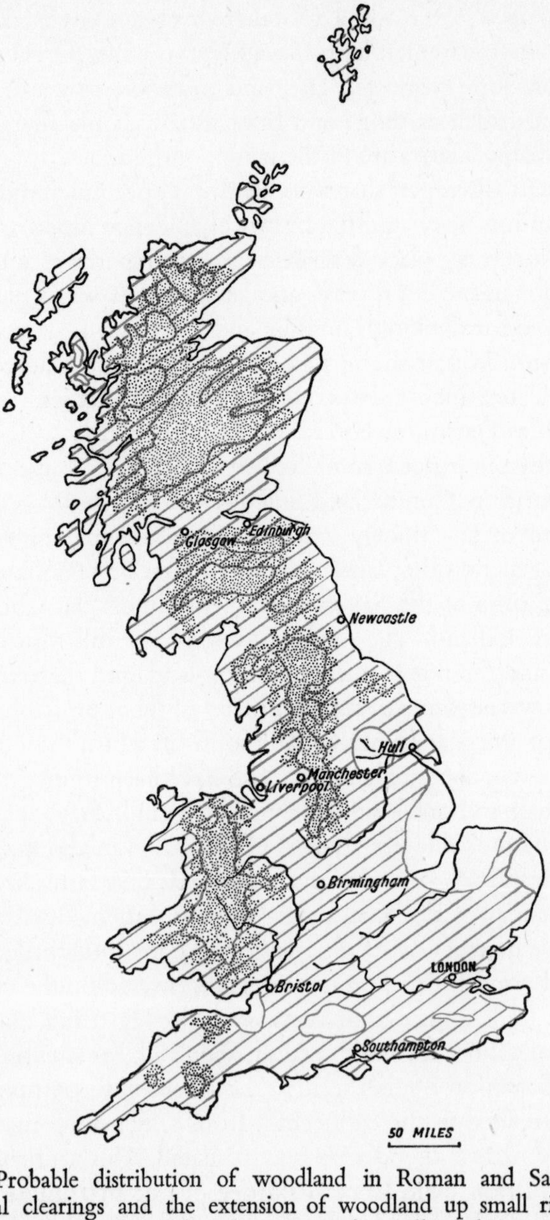

FIG. 2. Probable distribution of woodland in Roman and Saxon times. Agricultural clearings and the extension of woodland up small river valleys cannot be shown on this scale. The extent of woodland shown is a probable maximum, and is greater than that suggested in the Ordnance Survey maps of Roman Britain (1st edition) and Britain in the Dark Ages. The condition of the chalk uplands (Salisbury Plain and the Downs) is doubtful. They may have been covered with ash or beech, or may have been cleared by the Neolithic and Bronze Age peoples who inhabited them in relatively high numbers.

In the nineteenth century the woodlands were neglected, but the establishment of the Forestry Commission in 1919 began a great development in planting which has changed the appearance of many parts of England and Wales, covering many thousands of acres with foreign trees such as larch, spruce, and Douglas fir. Woodlands in 1949 covered 5·8 per cent. of the land of England, 6·2 per cent. of Wales and 6·6 per cent. of Scotland, and there have been slight increases since then. These are known to be higher proportions than have existed at any time since 1871, and are probably higher than any since the reign of the first Elizabeth. These figures include, however, woods of all ages, including young plantations, and also clear-felled areas which are awaiting replanting and have not regenerated. This last category accounts for 19 per cent. of the whole so that the actual area of woodland available for birds is much less than the above figures suggest. Most of the felled areas were the result of the heavy demands for timber during and immediately after the Second World War. Rather surprisingly, the clearance of conifers has been so great that the area under high forest in 1947 was only 77 per cent. of that of 1913–14, in spite of the activities of the Forestry Commission. By contrast, the area of broadleaved high forest had increased in the same period by 5 per cent.

The areas under the chief species are shown in Table 2. In the past decade the Forestry Commission has made considerable use of lodgepole pine (*Pinus contorta*) but no figures for its acreage are available.

The distribution between counties is very uneven. The most thickly wooded part of Great Britain is an area of east Scotland, where the adjacent counties of Inverness (excluding the islands), Nairn, Moray, Banff, Aberdeen, and Kincardine all have more than 10 per cent. of their surface under woodland, with Angus, Fife, and Perth only a little below. The most thickly wooded counties are Moray, with 21·6 per cent., and Nairn with 19·1 per cent. There is another relatively heavily wooded area in south-east England, where Kent, Sussex, Hampshire, and Surrey all have more than 10 per cent., and Berkshire a little less; the most densely wooded English counties are Sussex with 15·5 per cent. and Surrey with 15·0 per cent. A third minor concentration is found in Gloucestershire, Herefordshire, and Monmouthshire, with about 8 per cent. of

TABLE 2

Areas of woodland, five acres and over, by dominant species, from the Forestry Commission Census of 1947–9

Broad-leaved species	England			Scotland			Wales			Great Britain		
	Area Acres	Percentages of broad-leaved	Percentages of all species	Area Acres	Percentages of broad-leaved	Percentages of all species	Area Acres	Percentages of broad-leaved	Percentages of all species	Area Acres	Percentages of broad-leaved	Percentages of all species
Oak (*Quercus robur* and Q. *petraea*)	337,088	52	33	45,103	38	8	49,304	60	26	431,495	50	24
Ash (*Fraxinus excelsior*)	69,575	11	7	4,947	4	1	10,244	12	6	84,766	10	5
Beech (*Fagus silvatica*)	108,219	17	11	47,043	40	9	6,503	8	4	161,765	20	9
Birch (*Betula verrucosa* and *B. pubescens*)	51,352	8	5	6,578	6	1	9,216	11	5	67,146	8	3
Spanish chestnut (*Castanea sativa*)	9,930	2	1	27	–	–	107	–	–	10,064	1	1
Sycamore (*Acer pseudoplatanus*)	43,687	7	4	7,668	6	1	4,798	6	3	56,153	7	3
Elm (*Ulmus* spp.)	13,256	2	1	6,064	5	1	813	1	–	20,133	2	1
Other broad-leaved trees	9,450	1	1	1,185	1	–	1,695	2	1	12,330	2	1
Total all broad-leaved trees	642,557	100	63	118,615	100	21	82,680	100	45	843,852	100	47

Coniferous species	Area Acres	Percentages of coniferous	Percentages of all species	Area Acres	Percentages of coniferous	Percentages of all species	Area Acres	Percentages of coniferous	Percentages of all species	Area Acres	Percentages of coniferous	Percentages of all species
Scotch fir (*Pinus silvestris*)	148,361	38	14	208,930	46	36	6,861	7	4	364,152	39	20
Corsican pine (*P. nigra*)	31,543	8	3	3,494	1	1	3,466	3	2	38,503	4	2
European larch (*Larix decidua*)	73,158	19	7	48,069	10	9	11,676	11	6	132,903	14	8
Japanese larch (*L. leptolepsis*)	21,269	5	2	18,034	4	3	15,755	15	8	55,058	6	3
Douglas fir (*Pseudotsuga taxifolia*)	17,716	5	2	11,194	2	2	8,918	9	5	37,828	4	2
Norway spruce (*Picea abies*)	41,557	11	4	70,785	16	12	20,811	20	11	133,153	14	8
Sitka spruce (*P. sitchensis*)	48,188	13	5	85,182	19	15	33,669	33	18	167,039	17	9
Other conifers	5,208	1	–	9,033	2	1	2,070	2	1	16,311	2	1
Total all conifers	387,000	100	37	454,721	100	79	103,226	100	55	944,947	100	53
Total all species	1,029,557	–	100	573,336	–	100	185,906	–	100	1,788,799	–	100

woodland. Most of the other counties, which include many of those with the best agricultural land and many of those with large areas of moor or mountain, have much less than the average for the country as a whole. All these figures are taken from the Forestry Commission Census of 1947–9 which included woodlands of 5 acres or more. A sample survey showed that the total area of woods from 1 to 5 acres in size was only 5 per cent. of that of the larger woods, so that no great inaccuracy is introduced by their omission. Fig. 3 shows the total acreage of woodland by counties. The Forestry Commission's Annual Reports show that the chief increase since 1949 has been in Scotland, Wales, and the northern parts of England.

The changes produced first by clearance and then by planting must have had big effects on the bird population. Grass-nesting birds such as skylarks and lapwings must have been rare in the early Middle Ages, and the less adaptable woodland species, such as woodpeckers and the sparrow-hawk, were probably commoner than they are now. Other woodland birds, such as the thrushes and most of the tits, have been able to make use of the hedgerows, orchards, and gardens which have largely replaced the woods, and are perhaps no less abundant now than they were 500 years ago; the increased food-supply which man has provided has probably compensated for the decreased area of suitable cover. The extensive twentieth-century planting of conifers in the south of England has already led to the nesting of the crossbill, formerly only a casual visitor, and other comparable changes may follow.

Great Britain is not large enough to show any great difference in climate from one part to another. There is a general increase in rainfall and in winter temperature as one goes from east to west, and a general decrease in sunshine and summer temperature as one goes from south to north, but the differences are small (Figs. 4, 5, 6, 7). In these circumstances the plant community which the land naturally bears depends much more on the soil than on anything else, and this in its turn depends largely on the underlying rock. A vegetation map of Britain therefore corresponds very closely, except in the far north, to the geological map. The exception is that altitude, which increases precipitation and exposure to wind while it decreases temperature, has a depressant effect on the growth of trees, so that above a certain level they are stunted, and higher still they will not grow at

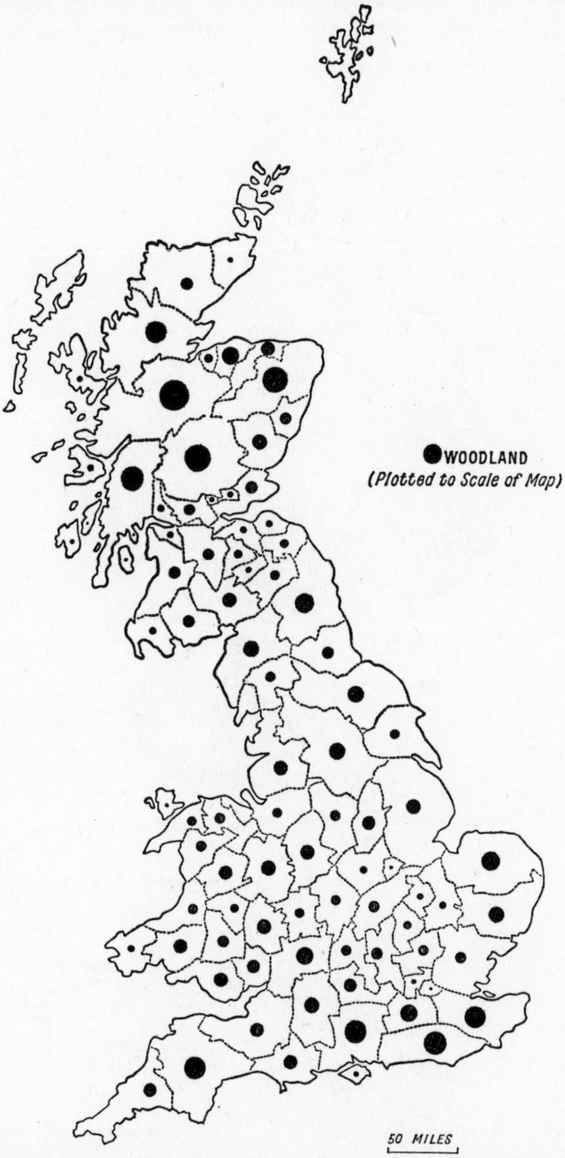

FIG. 3. Woodland areas, 1947–9. The black circles show the total area of woodland in each county, on the scale of the map. The chief changes since then are probably increases in the area of woodland in the counties of the Scottish border, on the hills of central Wales, and in those counties of Scotland that already had a large area. From Forestry Commission Census Report No. 1 (1952); Map 1 (p. 239).

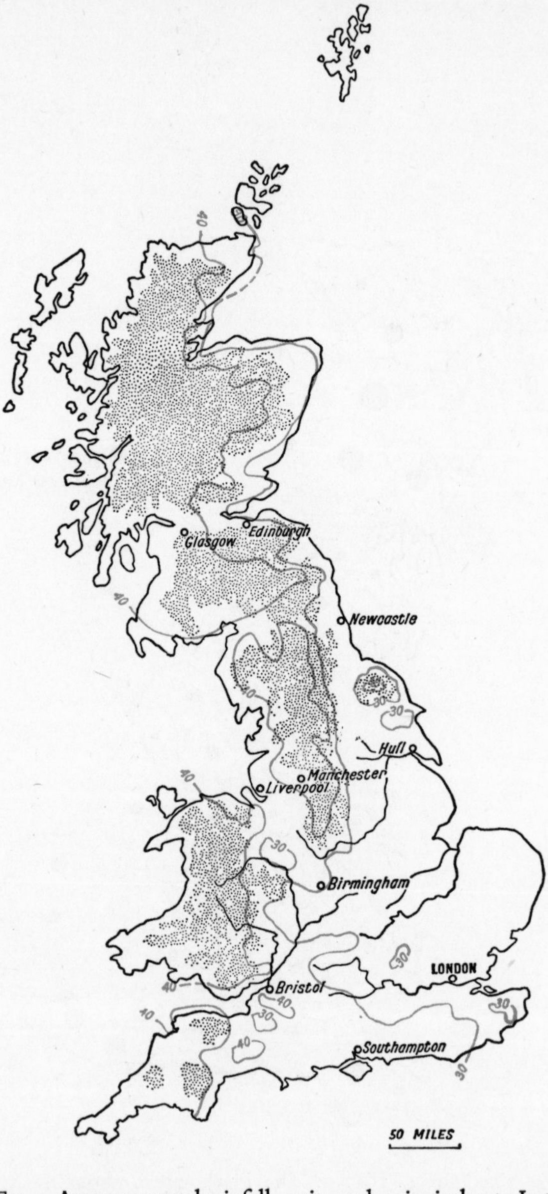

FIG. 4. Average annual rainfall. 30 in. and 40 in. isohyets. In this and the following maps the main upland areas are stippled.

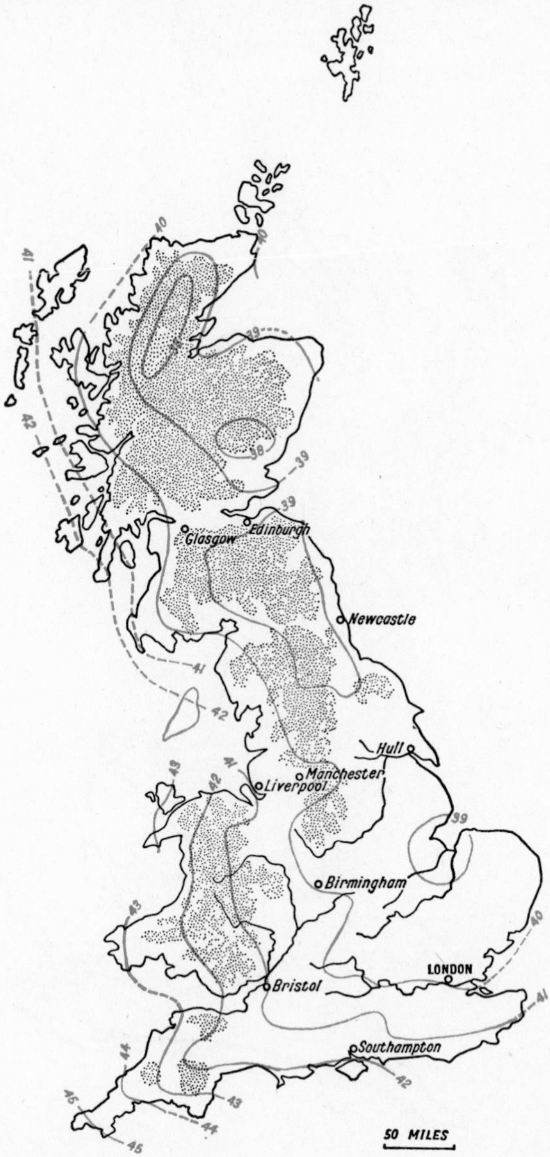

Fig. 5. Average means of daily mean temperature, January. Deg. F.

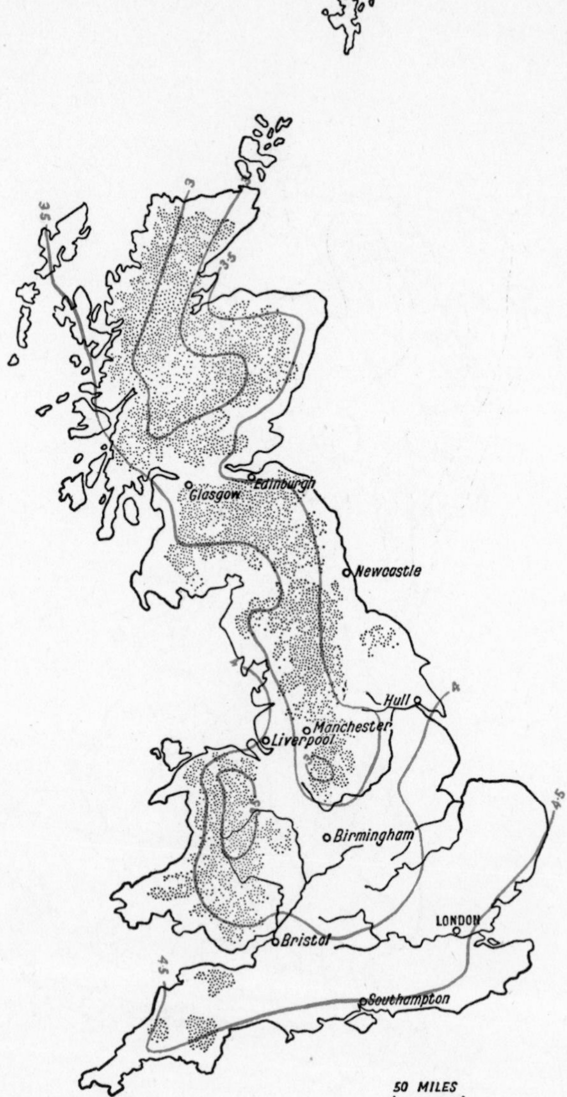

FIG. 6. Average yearly means of daily duration of bright sunshine, hours.

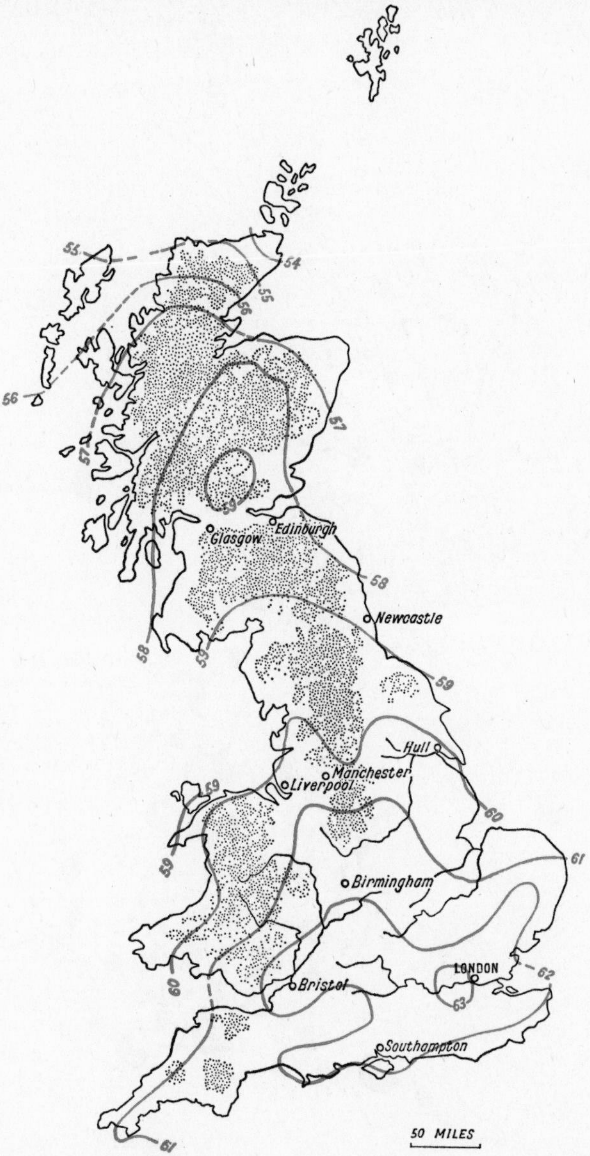

FIG. 7. Average means of daily mean temperature, July. Deg. F.

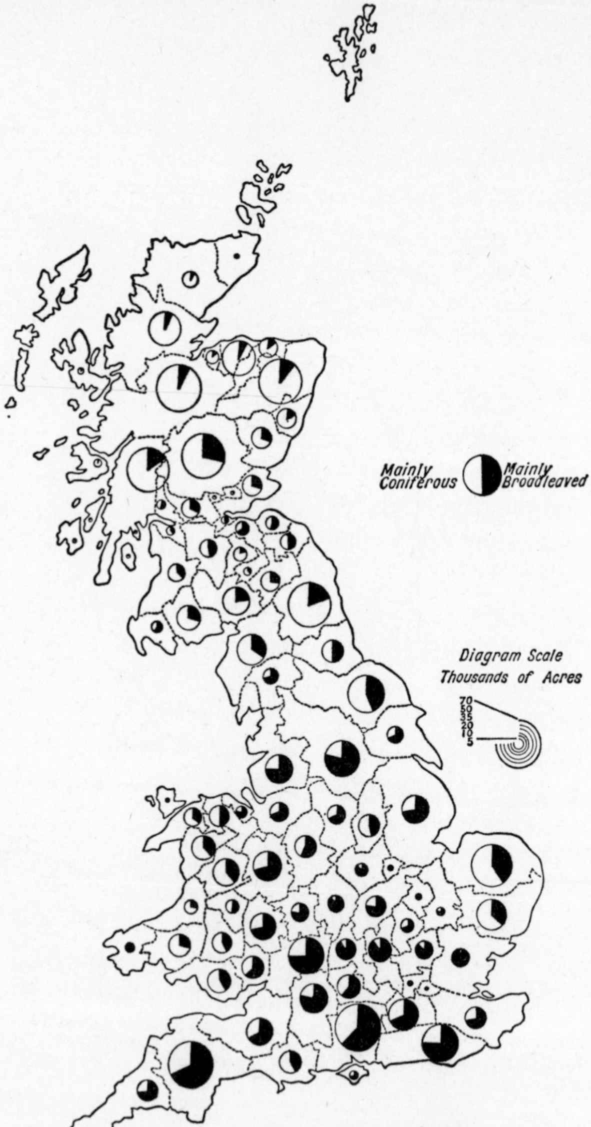

Fig. 8. The distribution of coniferous and broad-leaved high forest, 1947–9. See note to Fig. 2; most of the increase referred to there has been in conifers, and there has been some general decrease in broad-leaved woods. From Forestry Commission Census Report No. 1 (1952): Map 5 (p. 243).

all. The level at which this happens varies from one part of the country to another less than might be expected: it is at about 1,500 feet above sea level on Dartmoor, in the Lake District, and in Ross and Sutherland, although the trees found at this altitude are not of the same species in the three places. The highest natural woodlands in Britain are in fact in Inverness-shire, where the Scotch firs of the Forest of Rothiemurchus go to nearly 2,000 feet above sea level.

The distribution of the various types of woodland is very uneven. It depends not only on the natural distribution of the dominant tree-species, as discussed in later chapters, but also on the planting which has gone on. Fig. 8 shows the distribution of high forest, including plantations of all ages, by counties between mainly coniferous and mainly broadleaved trees. It will be seen that broad-leaved trees predominate in the south and Midlands of England, conifers in the rest of England and in Wales and Scotland. Another important feature of the distribution is that while the broadleaved woods are mainly old or uneven-aged, the coniferous woods are predominantly young. Whatever planting or regeneration takes place, the woodlands of Britain will be very different in fifty or a hundred years' time from what they are now, and their bird life will change accordingly. The age at which woods become mature from an economic point of view obviously varies with species, soil, and climate, but it is taken by the Forestry Commission to be eighty years on the average for coniferous woods and 120 years for broad-leaved. At neither of these ages are the trees fully grown, and with the spread of industries which convert timber to pulp, paper, and chip-board, the age of cutting tends to come down. It is possible that in future the rotation for conifers, especially spruce, will not be more than fifty years. There is also a tendency to earlier and heavier thinning, which will itself cause changes in the bird life.

England has four main types of deciduous woodland, and smaller areas of some others, which are described in more detail in later chapters. Over almost the whole of the land which is neither water-logged nor rich in lime, the natural cover seems to be either *Quercus robur*, the pedunculate oak, or *Q. petraea*, the sessile or durmast oak, and large woods of both of these, at least semi-natural in origin and appearance, still exist. On the older limestones, especially of Somerset, Derbyshire, and the Craven district of Yorkshire, the dominant tree is the ash, while on the chalk of the south-east the characteristic tree is the beech. Birches of two species form smaller woods largely on sandy or poor soils, and in wet places there are small woods of alder. All these species have been much planted, especially beech and the two oaks.

The various elms (*Ulmus* spp.) which, although native, have not formed extensive woods within historic times, have been planted to some extent, and are important elements in groves (see p. 42) and lines of hedgerow trees.

The only exotic hardwoods that have been much planted are the sycamore (*Acer pseudoplatanus*) and the sweet chestnut (*Castanea sativa*). The former is generally in small blocks, and forms woods which from the bird's point of view must be unpromising. The large leaves lie flat on the ground and decay slowly, so that other vegetation is effectively inhibited. The sycamore regenerates freely, and frequently extends into the native woods. The leaves of the chestnut also decay slowly, and as it also casts a deep shade, woods formed of it have some resemblance to beechwoods. The Forestry Commission is now making considerable use of the red oak (*Quercus maxima*) (though chiefly in amenity planting along roadsides rather than in large blocks), and various species of *Nothofagus*, which are interesting relatives of the beech from the southern hemisphere, are now being used experimentally.

The only coniferous tree that forms natural woods in England is the yew.

Many species of tree, both deciduous and coniferous, are planted for ornament or for occasional use in forestry, and may have some effect on the bird population by providing food or shelter. An example is the Wellingtonia (*Sequoia gigantea*) in whose deeply fissured bark the treecreeper has developed the habit of making roosting holes.

The woodlands of Wales do not differ greatly from those of England, but the western position and generally upland character of the country make for some deficiencies. There are no natural beechwoods of any size, and, so far as I am aware, no natural pedunculate oakwoods, though it is difficult to be certain of this as very few Welsh woods have been described in the literature. Oakwoods of one or other sort are found in all the counties. The few birchwoods resemble those of England. The ash was possibly once found extensively on the limestone soils, but the only Welsh ashwood that has been described is near Cader Idris. It has little resemblance to the typical ashwoods of the mountain limestone and contains much oak. Wales has no natural coniferous woods.

The woods of Scotland, like those of Wales, are almost undescribed botanically. It has been customary, ever since the time of Dr. Johnson, who was an unreliable witness in Scottish matters, to write of Scotland as if it were treeless, but this is an exaggeration and a libel. As in England, there has been much destruction of timber, but nearly all the larger valleys are well wooded, and the planting of the eighteenth-century landlords was on a greater scale than in England.

In many of the glens and straths there are woods of oak, both pedunculate and sessile, which resemble in structure and field layer the lowland sessile oakwoods of England. They seldom go far up the hillsides, and there are no woods comparable to those of the mountains of Cumberland and Wales. Instead, the birches, which as elsewhere are frequent associates of the oak, form a fringe above the oakwoods, and sometimes go to considerable heights, occurring also as isolated woods in the hills, up to an altitude of 1,600 feet above sea level.

Scotland has a surprising amount of planted beechwood—9 per cent. of its total area of high forest—which is concentrated in the eastern counties from Banff to Roxburgh. Only 1 per cent. of the high forest of Scotland is ash; and that is chiefly in Wigtown and Kirkcudbright.

Scotland has one type of woodland which is now absent from the other parts of Britain; it is the dark wood, or black wood of Scottish history, dominated by the Scotch fir (*Pinus silvestris*). It is commonly called in books pine forest, and the tree the Scots pine, but these are names which have no existence in the vernacular but became common in the nineteenth century as translations from the Latin. Occasional roots dug out of the peat show that this type of wood formerly existed over much of the hill country of northern England, and in some lowlands, such as the East Anglian fens and Warwickshire bogs. In Scotland also firwoods were once much more extensive than they are now, probably covering all the highlands above the oaks to an altitude of perhaps 1,000 feet in the west, and 2,000 feet in the east.

A bird may be influenced not only by the trees of which the wood is composed, by their height, and by the other vegetation, but also by the shape and size of the wood, for these determine the amount of 'edge' which the wood has, and have effects on the feeding grounds which are available. There is no consistent or agreed system of nomenclature for the shapes and sizes of woods, but the one which is used in this book is based on the usage of the Forestry Commission and is designed to be precise and easy to use without doing violence to the English language.

FOREST is chiefly used, as it inevitably must be, as part of a place-name with a topographical name in front of it. It is used in this way not only for the old forests, which may or may not be woods, but also for the large planted estates of the Forestry Commission. If the word stands by itself it means a very extensive area of trees, at least 1,000 acres and often much more. Within such an area there may be several types of woodland, and some areas which are not wooded at all.

WOOD implies a smaller area of trees, usually a single consociation, with only small patches of other types of vegetation, or none. It is not used specifically for woodland which comes under the next heading; but it is also used as a general term without regard to size.

GROVE is used for patches of woodland of half an acre and less than 5 acres. Woods of this size were excluded from the Forestry Commission Census, which is the reason for taking 5 acres as the limit.

A group of trees of less than half an acre is called a CLUMP.

For rough estimation in the field it may be remembered that a square half-acre has sides of 49 yards, and a square of five acres has sides of 156 yards.

A LINE of trees consists of trees growing in single or double file with their crowns touching, or nearly so.

When the trees grow naturally, or suffer only moderate thinning, so that their crowns are in contact and leave no spaces through which light can penetrate to the shrubs or ground beneath, they are said to be growing in CLOSE CANOPY or to form HIGH FOREST (Plate I). If all the trees are cut over at intervals of several years, so that they grow again from the stumps and there is a rotation from almost bare land to scrub, or something between scrub and high forest, the result is a COPPICE. Cutting of most of the crop, with a few trees left to grow on to full size, makes COPPICE-WITH-STANDARDS. 'Copse', which is the same word as coppice, but is vulgarly used to mean a small wood, is best abandoned, and is not used in this book.

PLANTATION means an artificial woodland, with the trees mostly of one age and planted usually in straight lines. There may be some irregularities in height of the trees in a plantation, for where the original transplants die in any quantity the Forestry Commission fills the gaps at a later stage, a process known as 'beating up'. There are also a few woods where the 'double-storey' system is practised—heavy thinning followed by some replanting, so that the wood has trees of two ages only.

SCRUB is vegetation of woodland type but less than 26 feet (8 metres) tall. There is little difference in form between scrub which is on the way to become woodland by a natural process of regeneration, so that it is a stage in the succession to high forest, and scrub that is depressed in height by altitude or other adverse conditions, although the associated climatic differences may be great. 'BUSH SCRUB' is lowland scrub which is stable and appears not to be progressing towards woodland. It is characteristic of 'tumbledown' pastures and abandoned arable land on heavy clays, and possibly only maintains itself because tree-seeds are absent. It is often largely made up of thorny plants, and when entirely so may be called a SPINNEY, as it has sometimes been by ornithologists. The term 'scrub' should not be used for the shrub layer of woodlands and it is probably also best avoided for the early stages of plantations, although the birds of these are often similar to those of natural scrub. For plantations which are almost impenetrable before brashing foresters use the word THICKET. The Forestry Commission defines scrub in a rather different way as 'inferior growth unlikely to develop into a utilizable crop of coppice, poles or timber'. So defined it makes up 15 per cent. of all woodlands. My definition of it, which would include some regenerating woods and simple coppice, would probably give a rather larger area. Whichever way it is looked at, it is an important habitat for birds. Fifty-eight per cent. of what the Commission classes as scrub is birch, but there are considerable areas of oak, alder, and hazel, and minor, but locally important, areas of thorn, elderberry, willow, and *Rhododendron ponticum*.

Where conditions are unfavourable, as on wet land or at the altitudinal limit, woodland seldom ceases abruptly, but passes gradually into the adjacent type of vegetation, with scattered trees which are often reduced in size. Such a mixed zone is called an ECOTONE. A similar ecotone is sometimes produced at the edge of woodland on farms where the standard of husbandry is not high and the grazing pressure is relatively low, so that trees and shrubs can regenerate to some extent in the grass. Two types of woodland ecotone are important in British ornithology. The term PARKLAND is used here for a mixture of trees and grass, whether shrubs are present or not, and TREE-HEATH for a mixture of trees and heathy plants such as heather and bilberry. The only extensive parklands are those which have been planted, but even a narrow woodland-grassland ecotone may be important in determining the species of bird present. Tree-heath is more extensive and perhaps semi-natural; it is found on the sands of the south of England, for example in much of the New Forest, and as part of the Scottish firwoods.

The actual edge of a wood is also an ecotone, but of a somewhat different type.

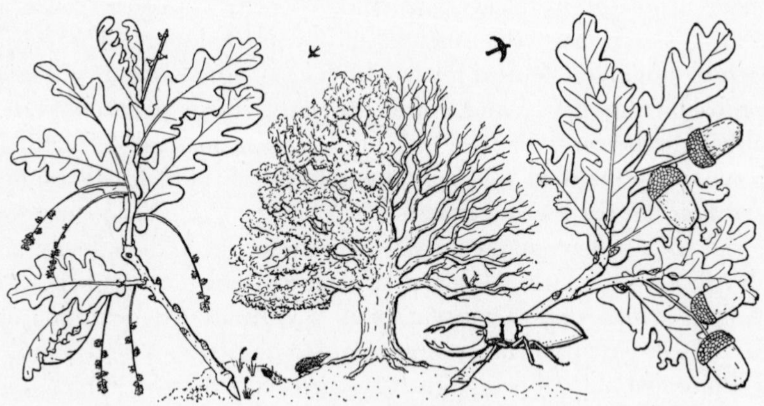

Pedunculate Oak

Jay

4

THE BIRDS OF OAKWOODS

The natural woodland of much of southern England and almost all the Midlands appears to be *Quercetum roboris*, dominated by the pedunculate oak, *Quercus robur* (Plate II). It is found particularly on clay soils and on deep sands such as those of the Cheshire plain (Fig. 9). The tree may be recognized by its leaves, which have wings or auricles at their base and have no stalks (or sometimes very short ones) and only a few simple hairs, and by its acorns which, when fresh, are striped, and have stalks which are an inch or more long (see p. 44). Pedunculate oakwood is seldom pure: that is, there are usually other trees, especially ash and both species of birch, and in some places, such as Epping Forest, hornbeam (*Carpinus betulus*) is abundant. There is usually a very thick shrub layer, consisting chiefly of hazel (*Corylus avellana*) but including also the hawthorn (*Crataegus monogyna*), blackthorn (*Prunus spinosa*), and at a lower level species of bramble (*Rubus*) and rose (*Rosa*). This may be so thick as to be quite impenetrable. The climbers ivy (*Hedera helix*) and honeysuckle

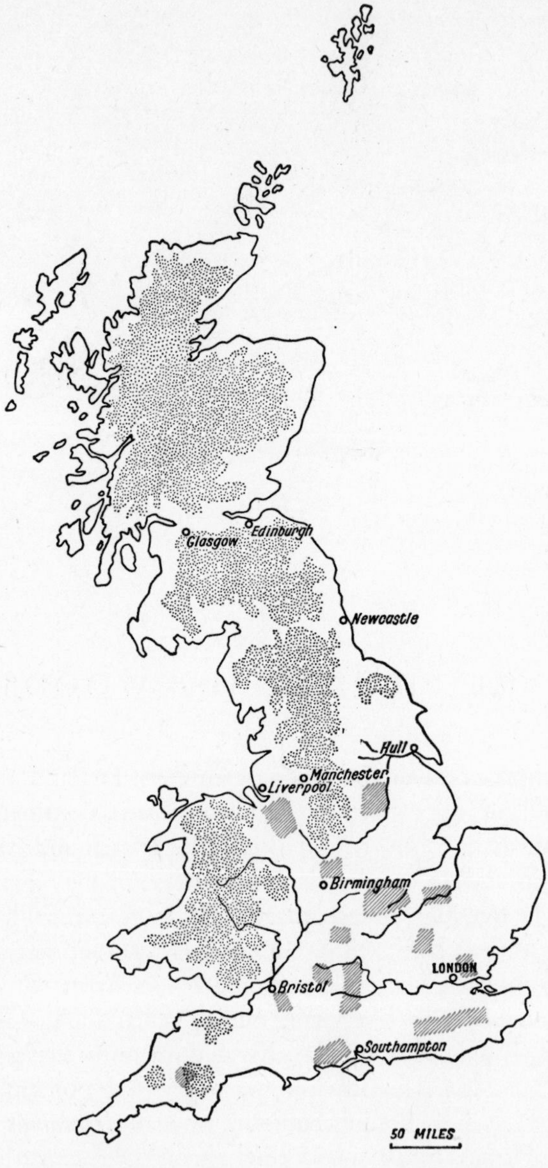

FIG. 9. Map to show where there are large or important blocks of semi-natural pedunculate oakwood. Since no complete botanical survey has ever been made it is probable that there are some omissions from this and the next three maps. The shaded areas do not represent continuous woodland.

(*Lonicera periclymenum*) are abundant, and may be important in providing nesting sites. The field layer is rich and herbaceous: that is, the stems of the plants are not markedly woody and tend to die back in autumn. There is often a succession of different types of herb in spring and summer, a 'prevernal aspect' of lesser celandine or wood anemone being followed by such plants as bluebell, wood spurge, and bracken.

Natural oakwoods, like all those of temperate climates, grow in close canopy. The more vigorous individuals become taller than their competitors, suppressing them and finally killing them by their shade; the crowns of the successful trees spread out so that they touch, and there are no large spaces through which light can reach the lower layers (Plate I). Mature pedunculate oakwood of this sort in southern England has from 60 to 100 trees per acre, with an average height of 70 or 80 feet, although under good conditions the oak may reach 100 feet.

The traditional method of forestry of the pedunculate oakwoods, which has persisted from the Middle Ages to the present day, did not allow such a canopy to develop. The oaks were reduced to about 12 per acre, with the result that they became much more spreading, were often as broad in the crown as they were tall, and did not exceed 40 or 50 feet in height. At the same time, the resulting absence of shade allowed the shrubs to become much more luxuriant. This type of coppice-with-standards owes its origin to the value of the 'knees', formed in the oak timber where the big lateral branches grew out of the trunk, in ship-building and roof construction, and to the value of the hazel cut as coppice. This cutting usually took place about every fifteen years and led to a cycle of luxuriance and dying-out of the field layer as the shade increased with the growth of the shrubs.

There must have been a corresponding cycle in the bird population but so far as I know this has not been investigated. Many of the old coppice-with-standard woods, especially of the Home Counties, are now neglected, and valued more as pheasant coverts than as sources of timber. Large areas of coppice-with-standards are found only in the heavily-wooded counties of Kent, Sussex, Surrey, and Hampshire, and moderate amounts in Dorset, Berkshire, and Suffolk. The density of the standards is now much higher than formerly, being 40 or 50 to the acre.

To the north and west, pedunculate oakwood is replaced by woods dominated by the durmast or sessile-fruited oak (*Quercus petraea* = *Q. sessiliflora* (Fig. 10). This is a species closely related to the pedunculate oak, and of the same range of size; some variant forms, a few of which may be hybrids, cannot be easily assigned to one species or the other. In winter the two can hardly be distinguished, but *Q. petraea* has leaf and flower characters the opposite of those of *Q. robur*. The leaf has long hairs on the lower surface along the midrib, and small stellate hairs (which can be seen clearly only with a lens) on the lamina, and has a stalk or petiole which is seldom less than half an inch and may be an inch, while the flowers (and hence the acorns) are stalkless or sessile, or nearly so, and the acorns are a darker brown and without stripes (see frontispiece). The leaves tend also to be larger than those of *Q. robur*, to have a less deeply waved edge, and to have a peculiar shiny appearance which gives a characteristic green to the woods in which they grow.

Some durmast oakwoods are found in Sussex and Hertfordshire and elsewhere in the south of England, but these do not differ from the nearby pedunculate woods in many respects that a bird is likely to notice. Conversely, some pedunculate woods are found far to the north and west (for example, on Dartmoor), but many of these greatly resemble the durmast woods around them. In the eighteenth century much planting went on, and it is known that acorns were sent from one end of the country to the other; much, although not all, of the apparent overlap is therefore likely to be artificial. Foresters seem to have a preference for the pedunculate species, and it has certainly been planted, as in the Forest of Dean, where the other is the native tree. Indeed, Professor M. L. Anderson believes that the pedunculate oak is not native to this country at all, but was introduced in the Middle Ages and gradually spread with civilization north and west. The pollen of the two species cannot yet be distinguished, and until this becomes possible no firm decision on the date of entry of the pedunculate oak to England can be made, but Anderson's hypothesis is certainly the simplest explanation of some otherwise puzzling facts about the distribution of the two species.

The typical durmast oakwood is quite different from the typical pedunculate wood (Plate III). The trees are usually in close canopy, but their height does not exceed 40 or at the most 50 feet, and may

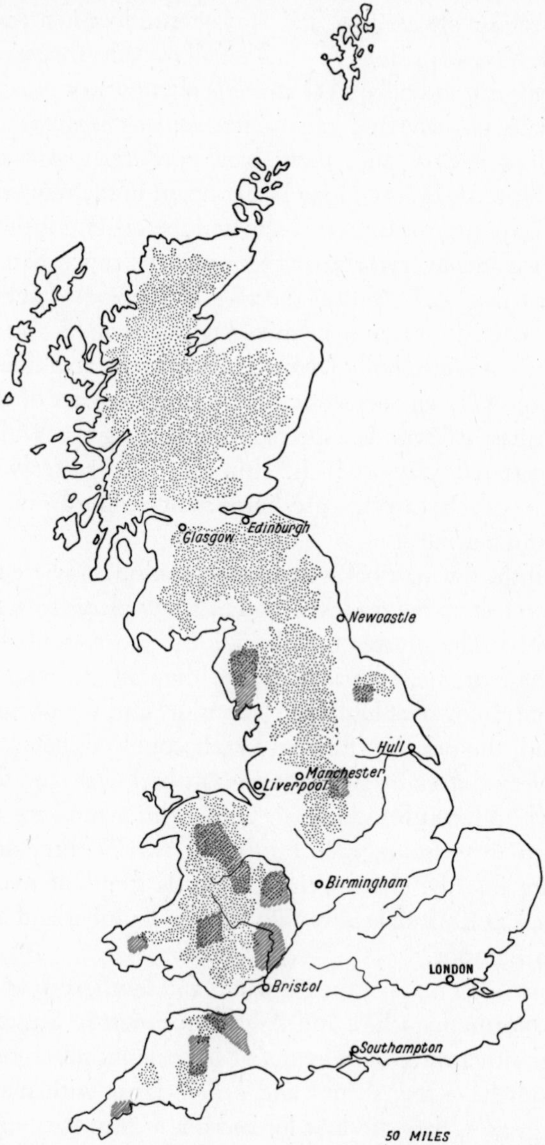

FIG. 10. Map to show where there are large or important blocks of semi-natural durmast oakwood in England and Wales.

be less; large shrubs are few, and may be entirely absent; and the field layer is heathy, consisting of such small woody shrubs as heather (*Calluna vulgaris*) and bilberry (*Vaccinium myrtillus*), or grassy, containing especially sweet vernal grass (*Anthoxanthum odoratum*), wood soft grass (*Holcus mollis*), and wavy hair grass (*Deschampia flexuosa*). At lower altitudes bracken may be abundant in the more open parts. The field layer may be thin or absent and the ground is then covered with mosses and liverworts, or there may be much bare shale and rock. The oak may be almost the only tree present (when planting may be suspected) or it may be mixed with rowan (*Sorbus aucuparia*), both species of birch, holly (*Ilex aquifolium*), ash, and alder. The last two are especially characteristic of the damper parts of the woods. Many durmast oakwoods, especially those along the Welsh border, contain scattered yews, which, although they scarcely affect the appearance of the wood, are important to birds in providing roosting and nesting sites.

Many of the durmast oakwoods are on hillsides, where they range up to 1,000 feet above sea level, and in a few places to 1,250 feet or a little more. The greater the altitude the more stunted the trees, until in the extreme, especially where they are growing on crags, they are only a few feet high. In Devonshire and the north-west and in Scotland, the oak was formerly itself coppiced, being cut to the ground every sixteen or twenty years; its bark was used for tanning and the wood burnt for charcoal. Under this system the trees grew again from the stumps, each producing two or three new shoots. To this are due the characteristic multiple stems of many hillside woods, such as Keskadale near Newlands in Cumberland, and Shillet Wood on Exmoor.

On some sandy areas of the Midlands and south, such as Sherwood Forest in Nottinghamshire and Ashdown Forest in Sussex, the two oaks grew either as co-dominants or in societies side by side. Since these woods have few shrubs and a field layer with many heathy plants or grasses, they are best looked on, at least for our purposes, as a special type of the durmast woods.

Oakwoods of one or other type make up 33 per cent. of the total high forest of England and are common in all the counties. Forty per cent. of all the oakwoods in Great Britain are 90 per cent. or more pure.

In Snowdonia and central Wales there are several good sessile oakwoods, many of which have a heathy field layer and resemble those of the Lake District, but others have a more luxurious herbaceous field layer, with large sheets of bluebell, which is almost absent from comparable hillside woods in the north-west of England.

There has been much discussion about the position of the pedunculate oak in Scotland, but as it seems to be absent from the remoter valleys, and as the woods are never, as far as I know, of the pedunculate type, it is at least possible that its presence is always due to planting. This would certainly make the distribution of the two species easier to understand. Many of these valley oakwoods are in process of being destroyed by the Forestry Commission, which seems a pity as the oakwoods are often well-grown and presumably yield useful timber. Some counties are entirely without oakwoods, and only in Inverness, Argyll, Perth, and Stirling, where the oak is the characteristic tree of the larger valleys, do they form a significant proportion of the total woodland.

I have records of birds for April, May, and June (called hereafter 'the breeding season' or 'summer') from 13 pedunculate oakwoods, all in the south of England, and from 32 durmast oakwoods distributed over the Lake District, north and mid-Wales, the English counties of the Welsh border, Somerset, and Devon. When the counts are dealt with as explained in Chapter 2 they produce 23 and 85 time-quadrats for the two types of wood. Most of the counts are fully-timed line-transects and for these I have worked out the relative abundance for each species. Table 3 shows for each type of wood every species which scores either a percentage frequency of at least 20 or not less than 4 per cent. of the total contacts. Most birds in the table in fact score both.

It is reasonable to ask how far these results are valid; would they be different if we doubled our observations or took a different set of woods? The lists for the durmast oakwoods cover enough woods for us to be confident that they do present a reasonably accurate picture of the birds of these woods, so much so that after a few years' work I knew what to expect in any fresh wood that I visited and was seldom disappointed. A preliminary table produced on the same principle when the woods visited were much fewer differed only in detail from that now presented.

TABLE 3A

Dominant birds of pedunculate oakwoods: summer

13 woods, 23 quadrats, 579 contacts in 423 minutes

	Percentage frequency	Contacts	Relative abundance
Anthus trivialis (tree-pipit)	22	6	1
Corvus monedula (jackdaw)	22	6	1
Erithacus rubecula (robin)	78	43	7
Fringilla coelebs (chaffinch)	87	74	12
Garrulus glandarius (jay)	22	10	2
Parus coeruleus (blue tit)	39	23	4
P. major (great tit)	39	17	3
Phoenicurus phoenicurus (redstart)	22	12	2
Phylloscopus collybita (chiff-chaff)	31	11	2
P. trochilus (willow-warbler)	56	8	9
Sturnus vulgaris (starling)	4	40	7
Sylvia atricapilla (blackcap)	22	5	1
S. borin (garden-warbler)	22	6	1
Troglodytes troglodytes (wren)	70	43	7
Turdus merula (blackbird)	65	43	7
T. philomelos (song-thrush)	35	11	2
T. viscivorus (mistle-thrush)	22	8	2
Columba palumbus (wood-pigeon)	48	7	1
Cuculus canorus (cuckoo)	35	11	2

TABLE 3B

Dominant birds of sessile oakwoods: summer

32 woods, 85 quadrats, 1,033 contacts in 1,100 minutes

	Percentage frequency	Contacts	Relative abundance
Anthus trivialis (tree-pipit)	48	39	4
Corvus corone (crow)	25	30	3
Erithacus rubecula (robin)	58	57	6
Fringilla coelebs (chaffinch)	92	180	18
Muscicapa hypoleuca (pied flycatcher)	61	85	8
Parus ater (coal-tit)	54	39	4
P. coeruleus (blue tit)	25	20	2
P. major (great tit)	34	26	3
Phoenicurus phoenicurus (redstart)	39	37	4
Phylloscopus sibilatrix (wood-warbler)	62	85	8
P. trochilus (willow-warbler)	47	57	6
Troglodytes troglodytes (wren)	46	55	5
Turdus merula (blackbird)	28	27	3
Buteo buteo (buzzard)	20	23	2
Columba palumbus (wood-pigeon)	19	39	4

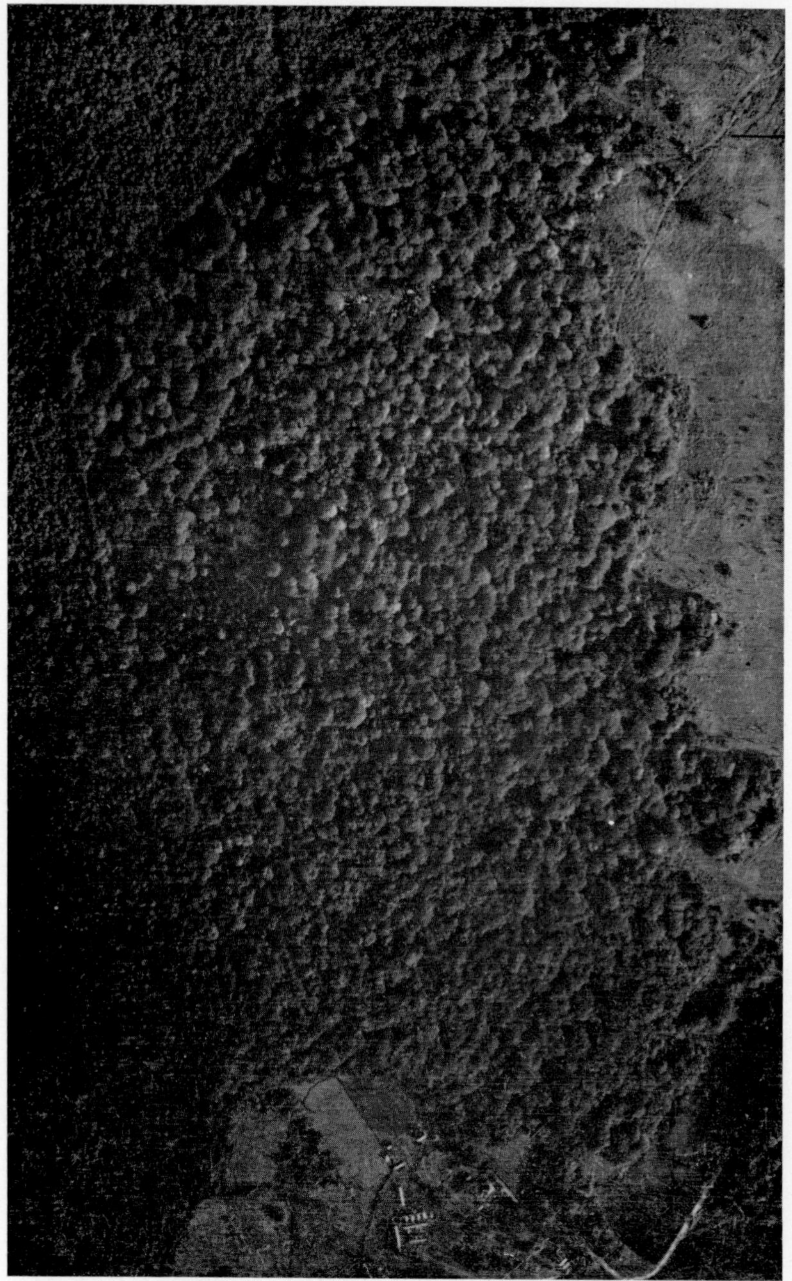

I. Aerial view of deciduous woodland in close canopy in September, New Forest, Hampshire. The larger crowns in the middle of the photograph are about three-quarters to four-fifths beech and the rest oak; the smaller crowns, to the left, are a plantation of oaks 96 years old.

II. Pedunculate oakwood in February, Surrey. The trees are about 150 years old; there are many shrubs, largely hazel, and in the middle distance the dead fronds of bracken.

The table for the pedunculate wood can be compared, if we make some assumptions, with one produced from Lack and Venables' lists. They did not distinguish between the two species of oak, but some of their woods can be identified from the original records (which by the courtesy of the Director of the Edward Grey Institute, I have had the privilege of seeing), and others can be confidently assigned to one species or the other by their geographical position. There are 33 which are pretty certainly of pedunculate oak, and the nine species of bird that occurred in 20 or more of these are those which occupy the top nine places in order in my lists of percentage frequency, with a value of 35 per cent. or more. There are differences in order within these nine, but the first five in my list are also the first five, though in a different order, in Lack and Venables' list. At lower frequencies the differences are, as would be expected, greater, but of 24 birds that occurred in 25 per cent. or more of their woods, 15 score a percentage frequency of not less than 20 in mine; since we know nothing of the sizes of their woods or the time spent in them, or how far the bird population may be distorted by human influence, this may be considered as very good agreement.

If attention is paid both to the percentage frequency and to the percentage of total contacts, it is clear that the pedunculate oakwoods are dominated in summer by seven species: robin, chaffinch, blue and great tits, willow-warbler, wren, and blackbird. In the same way ten species are dominant in the durmast woods: tree-pipit, robin, chaffinch, pied flycatcher, coal-tit, great tit, redstart, wood-warbler, willow-warbler, and wren. Four of the species common to the two lists (robin, chaffinch, willow-warbler, and wren) are amongst our commonest birds, and, as the lists in the next chapter will show, are also dominant in other types of wood. The appearance of the great tit, not the blue, as the dominant tit common to both woods is perhaps surprising, but it does seem to be in general slightly more adaptable.

The seven dominant species of the pedunculate woods appear to have little overlap in either food or nest sites, except that the blue and great tits may sometimes compete with each other. The ten of the durmast woods have much more in common. They are all predominantly insect-eating, and there are a number of similarities in nest site. This subject is discussed in Chapters 9, 10, and 11.

One striking thing is that, of the twelve birds in the two lists, only the chaffinch and blackbird make typical nests in trees or bushes, and both of these generally nest low down, the blackbird sometimes on the ground.

The larger birds are necessarily present in smaller numbers than the smaller ones, but it is striking that even on the basis of percentage frequency, which allows for this difference, the only birds of even medium size that appear in the table for pedunculate oak are the wood-pigeon and cuckoo, and in that for the durmast woods, crow, buzzard, and wood-pigeon. The wood-pigeon is solitary in the breeding season, though sometimes a small group of nests may occur together, and it is rare to find more than a few birds in even a large wood, partly, perhaps, because they prefer the edges, where there is access to open country for feeding. The buzzard is certainly not as common in the durmast wood as the contacts imply. When the observer is near the nest it has a habit of repeatedly flying overhead, so that it is scored several times. Nevertheless, many woods in the hill country contain a nest.

The only bird in the table that needs to be explained away is the starling. I found it in one wood only, but here a flock of about 40 were feeding in the canopy. This sort of occurrence of highly gregarious birds distorts the picture and is more important in the winter.

No large woods have been intensively investigated over several years, but the London Natural History Society have worked in a pedunculate oakwood on Bookham Common in Surrey (Beven, 1951, 1953). In each of the years 1949–52 they found that the seven species that were dominant in my lists were the commonest birds, and that in the four years taken together, they made up 71 per cent. of 3,141 birds recorded. This compares with 49 per cent. in my lists; it is to be expected that a series of woods will show more species and a smaller proportionate population of the common ones.

None of the birds in the table for pedunculate woods, and only the crow and buzzard in that for the durmast oaks, normally nest in or anywhere near the canopy of the trees, and few feed there to any great extent. Hartley (1953) has shown that blue tits feed during the summer chiefly at middle heights, and only the wood-warbler is a consistent feeder in the canopy. The tree-pipit, redstart, chiff-chaff, blackbird, and song-thrush make much use of the tops of trees as song posts, but are not confined to those of any great height, all of them singing occasionally from shrubs only a few feet high.

Of the less common birds in the oakwoods the nuthatch and greater spotted, lesser spotted, and green woodpeckers are all birds of the tree-tops, and the treecreeper as it climbs a tree usually ascends to a fair height before it flies to the base of the next.

It seems that the birds of English pedunculate oakwoods, and to a lesser extent those of the durmast woods, are largely a community of shrubs rather than trees. This is in striking contrast to the communities of tropical forests, where many species live all their lives in the canopy.

Some birds are as common, or nearly so, in the sessile oakwoods as in the pedunculate woods. The chaffinch is all but universal and the willow-warbler, robin, and wren are found in the majority of woods of both types. These are presumably unexacting or catholic species which can find their few specific requirements in a wide variety of habitats. Except for the willow-warbler they are also found in more than half the deciduous woods of all the other types, and all are also common in gardens and other derived woodland habitats. The only other birds which rank high in both types of oakwoods are the great and blue tits, which are also adaptable species. The blue tit inhabits a smaller proportion of the sessile oakwoods than of the others, and in numerical abundance, compared with the chaffinch, it is very much lower in the former. The coal-tit is present in more sessile oakwoods than are the great and blue tits, and this is especially marked in the hill-woods, where it is the characteristic tit, exceeding in numbers the other two species put together. Its preponderance is most marked in the Lake District; in mid-Wales and on Exmoor its numbers are much greater than those of the blue tit but equalled by those of the great tit, while it was not recorded in the two north-Welsh woods for which I have figures. These hill-woods provide plenty of the cracks between rocks and the ground which the coal-tit likes as nesting sites, but there must, I think, be some other factor which encourages it in the north and west. It is possible that it is rather more of a northern species than the other English tits.

Of the birds that appear in the table for pedunculate woods but not in that for the durmast woods the jay, blackcap, and garden-warbler, and (in Lack and Venables' list but not mine) the long-tailed tit, hedge-sparrow, bullfinch, and whitethroat, all require dense cover, and their scarcity in the sessile woods may need no other explanation than the absence of shrubs. This is illustrated for some of these species by column 5 of Table 14 on p. 103, which shows the total contacts (including juveniles) for a number of visits to Wyre Forest (Worcestershire) during the months of April, May, and June 1950–3. The figures are slightly weighted in favour of the residents and early summer migrants, since some of the others, notably the wood-warbler, do not arrive until May. The area in which these observations were made is about five-eighths of a mile square; it is subject to forestry treatment, but is in a fairly natural state except that it has been underplanted with beeches. Where these are young they make no practical difference to the wood and are hardly visible amongst the bramble, bilberry, heather, and bracken which make up the natural field layer; but in a few places, where they were twelve or more years old, the beeches made a thick shrub layer 10 feet or more high. It is in these areas that the jay, whitethroat, garden-warbler, and blackcap were found. The dunnock was still absent, in spite of the growth of these beech thickets, and the bullfinch nearly so, and some additional explanation seems needed.

I have few records of starlings from sessile oakwoods. Some nesting sites must be available, for woodpeckers are present, and although starlings have spread to the west only within the last century they have been plentiful in Cumberland since the time of Macpherson and occur in the Pennine ashwoods, so that we cannot explain their limitation as merely geographical. A possible explanation is that the food supply is inadequate. Starlings are omnivorous, and a characteristic method of feeding is to dig in turf for earthworms and insect larvae. The acid soils of the sessile oakwoods and their surrounding grasslands contain very few worms, and probably fewer larvae than the richer mull soils of the clays and loams on which pedunculate oak is dominant, and it is likely that the starlings choose not to live where they cannot get a suitable supply of this sort of food. Dr. Carrick (*in litt.*) informs me that starlings in captivity do not thrive unless they are provided with a piece of turf in which they can dig.

A similar explanation probably accounts for the great reduction of mistle-thrushes and song-thrushes in the sessile oakwoods. Earthworms and molluscs are important in the diet of both of these, and in the sessile oakwoods there are few earthworms and practically no snails. The absence of berry-bearing shrubs may also be important, for both thrushes take much fruit, but this is more likely to affect the distribution in the autumn than in the breeding season. The list of foods given in the *Handbook* suggests that the blackbird is more nearly dependent on insects than the other thrushes, and its occurrence in the sessile oakwoods agrees with this. It is present in more than a quarter of them, but is much less common than in the pedunculate woods.

The marsh-tit just fails to merit inclusion in the table for pedunculate woods, though Lack and Venables' lists rate it higher, and it is much less common in the sessile oakwoods. If the note in the *Handbook* on breeding, 'Usually nests in natural holes of willows, alders, etc.', is to be taken literally, no other explanation is needed, for while Tansley lists alder as occasional and species of willow as frequent in *Quercetum roboris*, these trees are not usually found in *Quercetum petraeae* except in especially damp places. Where the ground is damp enough for either of them the oak generally ceases to be dominant and gives way to a belt of alder, or in the less extreme places to a mixed woodland of ash, birch, and alder.

The only other notable passerine absentee from the sessile woods is the chiff-chaff, to which I shall refer below.

There are fewer woodpeckers in the sessile woods, but this is perhaps partly a geographical limitation, for the green woodpecker has spread north of Derbyshire only within the last century and it is only since about 1900 that the greater spotted has become at all numerous in Cumberland and Westmorland. Another possible reason is the fact that many of the fell-woods which come into my list consist of relatively small trees whose boles are scarcely large enough to contain holes adequate for the woodpecker. It remains remarkable that both species are uncommon in the Welsh woods, to which this does not apply.

The relative scarcity of the wood-pigeon in the durmast woods may be accounted for by the fact that the sessile oaks in the more exposed places are much less prolific of their acorns than the valley trees, and the almost complete absence of pheasants by the same reason and by the general neglect of game-preserving in the north and west.

Five species appear in the sessile oakwood list which are not in the other. The carrion crow and buzzard are present in less than half the woods but are nevertheless quite characteristic; they are large birds and each pair makes a solitary nest and requires a big area for feeding. The scarcity of the crow in the pedunculate woods and the absence of the buzzard are probably due at least in part to their persecution. Both are shot by gamekeepers, and the crow is common enough in the hedgerows of the Midlands and south, so that it is likely that the highly-preserved woods of the Home Counties hold fewer than they would under natural conditions. The hill country provides also more suitable food in the form of dead sheep and afterbirths for both crow and buzzard, and for the buzzard especially the rabbits of the hills (until 1954), though less numerous than in the valleys, were probably easier to catch. The buzzard had become rare even in the wilder parts of Great Britain by the beginning of this century, but it has undergone a strong revival. Since the old records show that it was formerly common in the lowlands, it is possible that it may in time colonize the pedunculate oakwoods.

The other three, coal-tit, wood-warbler, and pied flycatcher, are present in half the quadrats of the sessile oakwoods, but in hardly any of those of the pedunculate species. They are, in fact, with the tree-pipit and redstart, which only just come into the pedunculate table, the characteristic birds of the durmast oakwoods, and give this type of woodland a charm which, for myself, I would not change for the beautiful but luscious songs of nightingale and garden-warbler. The tree-pipit and the wood-warbler always nest on the ground, and the redstart often occupies the same sort of cracks between rocks and the earth as does the coal-tit. It is possible that ground-nesters in general dislike too thick a shrub layer, perhaps because the nest would be too difficult to find. The pied flycatcher and redstart have been said to need space between the canopy and the ground for their method of feeding, but this is not entirely true as both are found in some of the fell oakwoods (and birchwoods) in which there is no true canopy, but a network of branches at all heights from ground level to 20 or 30 feet. Where the trees are tall the wood-warbler feeds mostly in the canopy, but it is not greatly restricted by the height of the trees and is found in woods where the trees are only about 24 feet high. In parts of the country where there is contrast between shrubs, with or without tall trees over them, and tall trees with no shrub layer, as between the birches and the well-grown sessile oaks of Wyre Forest, the wood-warbler and the willow-warbler share the country between them, but where, as in the sessile oaks and birches of the hill country, there is no such clear division, the two species are found together and may be in approximately equal numbers. The chiff-chaff is practically absent from the sessile oakwoods, for my only records are for Wyre Forest. Here, although there are plenty of birds singing in early April, it does not, I think, breed. It possibly requires a combination of tall trees and a thick shrub layer which these oakwoods do not give.

The treecreeper, tawny owl and, under natural conditions, the sparrow-hawk, are almost certainly commoner in both sorts of oakwoods than the lists suggest. The same is perhaps true of the nightjar and, at least for the more northern woods, of the woodcock. Neither species is likely to be seen by day unless it is actually flushed.

The detailed lists show that the sessile oakwoods are fairly commonly inhabited, or at least visited, by some birds which are generally considered to be characteristic of bushy heaths or open moorland. The yellowhammer has been seen well inside some of the woods in all the main regions; I have no evidence that it actually makes its nest in the woods but they are certainly within its territory, for I have seen food-gathering and chasing of one cock by another at least 100 feet in from the edge, and the cocks sing throughout the Keskadale oaks in Cumberland, which are about 14 acres in extent. Further reference to this is made below (p. 100).

The general impression given by the large sessile woods of the lowlands, as was remarked by Taylor (1938) of the Forest of Dean, is one of a general poverty of birds. This is not always true of the fell-woods, in which the density and brilliance in song or plumage, or both, of chaffinch, tree-pipit, pied flycatcher, and redstart, make up for any possible shortage in total numbers. I am not sure that there is really a shortage, but there are few adequate figures for comparison. In 423 minutes at about 2 miles per hour in pedunculate

TABL

Birds of pedunculate oakwoods of Dartmoor. Total contacts, all birds. L &V = Lack and Venables 1939; LAH = Harvey 1953; others original. N = nest, ∞ = many, ★ = present, numbers not recorded.

					Summer
	Wistman's Wood				*Piles*
	1938 L &V	3.6.48	6.49 LAH	12.6.52	10.4.47 LAH
Anthus pratensis (meadow-pipit)				3	
A. trivialis (tree-pipit)	1	1		2	
Certhia familiaris (treecreeper)					
Cinclus cinclus (dipper)					1
Corvus corax (raven)				2	N
C. corone (crow)	4			4	
Emberiza citrinella (yellowhammer)			★	1	
Erithacus rubecula (robin)	1			2	
Fringilla coelebs (chaffinch)	2	1		6	∞
Muscicapa striata (spotted flycatcher)					
Oenanthe oenanthe (wheatear)				8	
Parus ater (coal-tit)	2				
P. coeruleus (blue tit)					1
P. major (great tit)					1
Phylloscopus sibilatrix (wood-warbler)			★		
Prunella modularis (hedge-sparrow)					3
Regulus regulus (goldcrest)					
Sitta europaea (nuthatch)					
Sylvia communis (whitethroat)					
Troglodytes troglodytes (wren)	6			5	
Turdus merula (blackbird)					
T. pilaris (fieldfare)				12	
T. viscivorus (mistle-thrush)				5	
Buteo buteo (buzzard)				1	N
Columba palumbus (wood-pigeon)				5	
Cuculus canorus (cuckoo)	1	1		2	
Dendrocopus minor (lesser spotted woodpecker)					
Falco tinnunculus (kestrel)				1	2
Scolopax rusticola (woodcock)					

				Autumn and Winter						
ood		*Black Tor Beare*			*Wistman's Wood*			*Piles Wood*		
9	3.7.52	6.49	29.5.53	27.8.53	1938	2.12.53	1.9.53	11.11.56	2.12.53	16.1.46
H		LAH			L&V					LAH
	2			1						
		★								
							2		2	★
	2		1	2			2			
	2			1			4		2	
	4	★								
	1				1		2	1	4	
	8		14				1			
			1							
		★								
								12	2	
	4		1					11	11	★
									4	★
		★								
								2	2	
	1								2	★
		★								
	2		4	1		4	2	6	7	
	3								3	★
	8			5						
	3		N	1				2	N	
	6									★
			1							
	1								2	
	1									
					2			2	1	★

oakwoods I made 579 contacts, or 82 per hour. In the high sessile oakwood of Wyre Forest (see Chapter 8) the contacts in 1950–3 were 52 per hour for a total of 431 contacts. My total contacts of 347 for the fell oakwoods of mid-Wales in May give an average of 50 per hour. This suggests a density about the same as in Wyre, which agrees with my subjective impression; but when a wide range of sessile woods, both on hills and in valleys, from Cumberland to Devon, is taken, there are 56 contacts per hour for a total of 1,033, so that many woods must have a higher density than those of Wales. Beven (1951), after a series of careful counts made by a modified cruising technique in 1949 and 1950, estimated the breeding population of Eastern Wood on Bookham Common in Surrey, which is described as a typical pedunculate wood with much hazel and hawthorn, as 130–40 birds on 40 acres. I made very similar surveys of the Keskadale oaks in the same years, and estimated 50 birds on 14 acres, which is a very slightly higher density, but within the limits of error may be taken as about the same. The general conclusion is that while the lowland sessile oakwoods have fewer birds than the pedunculate woods, the density of these may not be much higher than that in some of the fell-woods.

It is interesting to compare the bird population of the sessile oakwoods, especially those of the hills, with that of the ancient and possibly natural pedunculate oakwoods of Dartmoor. Here, Wistman's Wood above Two Bridges, Black Tor Beare south of Okehampton, and Piles Wood north of Ivybridge, are all on the open moor a mile or more from any houses. The first two are more than 1,200 feet above sea level, and Piles Wood lies between 850 and 1,050 feet. They are thus in a situation where one would expect to find the sessile oak, especially as this is the dominant tree of many of the valleys on the fringe of Dartmoor. In general structure they resemble somewhat the sessile oakwoods of the Lake District, but they differ in that they are all growing on block scree, which is locally called clatter or clitter—large blocks of stone from one to several feet across—in the crevices of which the trees are rooted.

The birds of these woods have been recorded a number of times in recent years, and the figures are shown in Table 4. There is a general similarity to the community of the sessile oakwoods, except for the striking absence of the pied flycatcher and redstart. Devonshire is at the extreme limit of the range of these two species. There are fair numbers of redstarts and some pied flycatchers on Exmoor, but in the early years of this century the redstart was uncommon as a nester west of Exeter and Ilfracombe. White (1931) described it as 'fairly numerous on some Dartmoor slopes', and it still nests in the oakwoods round the Moor. The pied flycatcher was reduced in the south-west some years ago, but is now increasing. It nested near Chagford, on the edge of Dartmoor, in 1950 and is now present in a number of the valley woods. It will be interesting to see if either of these species spreads to the high-level woods, which appear very suitable for them. It is remarkable that the four visits to Wistman's Wood have shown only two tits, both coals. There is the same invasion by heath birds, this time yellowhammer, meadow-pipit and wheatear, as we have noticed in the sessile woods. As might be expected, the general structure of the wood seems to be more important to the bird than the particular species of oak which is dominant.

THE WINTER POPULATION

The breeding season of most birds ends in June, and after that there is a period of moult, wandering, and emigration before the population of the woods settles down to its winter aspect. The post-nuptial instability is over by October, and I include all counts made from the beginning of this month until the end of March as belonging to the winter. There may be some breeding activity before the end of the latter month, but this is less marked in the woods than in the man-made habitats surrounding houses.

I have winter records from much the same lists of durmast oakwoods as in summer, but there are fewer visits and only 33 quadrats, with a total of 402 contacts in timed counts. The dominant species, determined on the same basis as before, are shown in Table 5.

The absence of the recognized summer migrants is obvious and needs no comment, but the robin and chaffinch, ranking high in summer, are also now missing from the list. It has long been known that many robins leave their breeding quarters, and these observations confirm it. I have no records of winter robins from any Cumberland oakwoods, and even many of those in Devonshire seem to be without them.

The emigration of the chaffinch, which is not so well known, is even more complete. I have records from three woods, all in Wales, and none later than the middle of November. It comes back, as shown on p. 4, at the end of March or beginning of April.

TABLE 5

Dominant birds of sessile oakwoods: winter

15 woods, 33 quadrats, 402 contacts in 545 minutes

	Percentage frequency	*Contacts*	*Relative abundance*
Aegithalos caudatus (long-tailed tit) .	15	48	12
Corvus corone (crow) . . .	30	15	4
Parus ater (coal-tit) . . .	57	63	16
P. coeruleus (blue tit) . . .	54	29	7
P. major (great tit) . . .	21	11	3
P. palustris (marsh-tit) . . .	21	10	2
Pyrrhula pyrrhula (bullfinch) . .	9	15	4
Regulus regulus (goldcrest) . .	21	24	6
Troglodytes troglodytes (wren) . .	36	24	6
Turdus merula (blackbird) . .	24	15	4
T. pilaris (fieldfare) . . .	6	41	10
Columba palumbus (wood-pigeon) .	36	21	5

There is also a fall in frequency of the buzzard, which feeds in the open at all times and is obviously less tied to the woods than in the breeding season, and of the yellowhammer, which leaves all those woods near or in which it nests.

The absence of summer migrants and of the chaffinch is bound, unless there is a corresponding influx of winter visitors, to raise the relative abundance of the species that remain, but it need have no effect on the percentage frequency, and broadly speaking this is what is found. In the oakwoods, as in all others, the chief winter population consists of the mixed flocks of tits and goldcrests. In the durmast woods much the commonest species is the coal-tit, which scores the very high relative abundance of 16 per cent. The blue tit comes next, with a big increase in its percentage frequency, and then the goldcrest and long-tailed tit, the last being high in relative abundance but low in percentage frequency. The great tit has a lower percentage frequency than in summer, and is now little commoner than the marsh-tit.

Tit-flocks are probably more conspicuous than breeding pairs, but even allowing for this it seems certain that goldcrests and long-tailed tits must be winter visitors to the woods. The increases in coal-tits and blue tits suggest that they also are migratory. This is confirmed by the record of individual woods, some of those in the north being completely devoid of tits in some winters.

The conspicuous tit-flocks often call attention to the tree-creepers and nuthatches that accompany them, and this is probably enough to account for the apparently greater winter frequency shown by both species in my counts.

Both the migratory thrushes use the oakwoods for roosting rather than feeding, and the high relative abundance of the fieldfare is caused by the occurrence of one large flock in a Welsh wood. The high score of the bullfinch is caused similarly by a flock of birds feeding in the canopy of a Devonshire wood. The increase in the wood-pigeon is also due to the presence of feeding flocks, which are much larger in years when there is a good crop of acorns.

I have no winter observations on pedunculate oakwood suitable for comparison with these, but Beven found some similar changes on Bookham Common. There was an almost complete absence of chaffinches, a slight invasion of goldcrests, and a disproportionate increase of long-tailed and blue tits. There were practically no coal-tits, but there was no recognizable loss of robins. So far as they can be used, Lack and Venables' winter counts agree with Beven's results, except that they found some increase in coal-tits.

I have September records for eight durmast oakwoods, some of them with more than one visit, and none show any chaffinches or summer migrants. One lowland durmast wood in August contained a few willow-warblers.

My only records for pedunculate oakwoods in September are for two enclosures in the New Forest, both with an admixture of other trees, especially beech. Neither showed either chaffinches or summer migrants. Piles Wood on Dartmoor, visited for me by Mr. D. M. Griffin, showed one chaffinch in September, but six chaffinches and four yellowhammers in July. Wistman's Wood at the end of August was almost empty, with no chaffinches, yellowhammers, or robins. It seems from these observations that by September the birds have almost reached their winter pattern.

The overall picture presented by the winter counts is not so greatly different from that of summer as might have been expected. It is not perhaps surprising that a wood can support as many vegetarian birds in winter as in summer, for the quantity of vegetable matter does not change appreciably as the year dies, and a greater proportion of it is present in the more succulent form of seeds and fruits. The same might also be true of birds feeding on miscellaneous small animals, for worms and molluscs do not have great seasonal variations in abundance, but it is more difficult to understand how the wood can support so many species that feed chiefly on insects. Tits seem to find something to eat on trees from which beating the branches produces nothing at all; they are presumably both assiduous and skilled at finding minute eggs and pupae embedded in or attached to the bark, and have developed a special type of microphagy, that is continuous feeding on small particles. They do not have the warblers to compete with for food, but their own numbers on the whole are higher in winter than in spring; this must be so if the breeding population remains static, for of the summer family of $2+x$, where x is the number of young reared, x must die before the next breeding season, and it is even more markedly so in those woods in which, as we have seen to be probable, there is an influx of tits and goldcrests from elsewhere. What the woods do not have to do in winter is to provide enough food for the growing young. This is needed at a very high rate, for not only do the young, being largely unfeathered, lose heat rapidly, but they grow rapidly as well. Gibb found that his great tits, which weighed about 1·3 grams at hatching, added a fairly steady 1·5 grams a day for the first ten days of their life. This sort of increase can only be kept up with an abundant food supply, such as is provided by growing moth larvae in spring. These in their turn are dependent on the opening leaves, so that the breeding population of a deciduous wood is dependent, apart from anything else, on the seasonal growth of the vegetation.

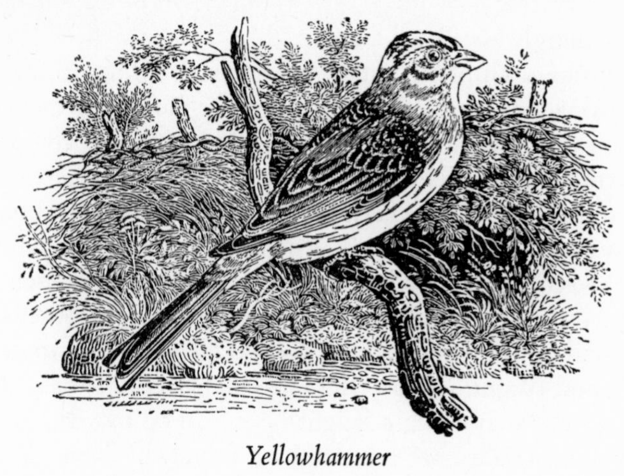

Yellowhammer

5

BIRDS OF OTHER DECIDUOUS WOODS

BIRCHWOODS

There are two species of birch tree in Britain, *Betula pubescens* and *B. verrucosa* (=*B. alba*=*B. pendula*), but unfortunately they have no constant vernacular names; *B. pendula*, as its name implies, has a more weeping habit than the other, with graceful drooping branches, and is sometimes called the silver birch, though the other also sometimes has a whitish trunk. The best distinguishing feature is that the mature bole of *B. verrucosa* splits up into prominent rectangular bosses; the young twigs of *B. pubescens* are generally covered with a soft hairy down, but this feature is absent from many specimens in the north. Intermediate and possibly hybrid forms occur. In general *B. verrucosa* is more abundant in the south, *pubescens* in the north. Neither forms important woods in England or Wales, although in prehistoric times they probably formed a fringe above the oakwoods in all the hilly districts, and there are a few relict woods of this sort in the Pennines and in the Lake District, in some of which one species is dominant, in some the other, while some are mixed. The only other commonly associated trees are the rowan and the alder. There are no shrubs or climbers and the field layer is similar to that of the nearby oakwoods, but with a tendency to be more grassy and damp.

Birches are common constituents of oakwoods, and as they regenerate more readily than the oaks they spread wherever there has been a clearing, especially if mice or pheasants are present in large numbers to eat the acorns. The result is that many oakwoods contain societies, more or less temporary in nature, of birch. Birch also makes a scrub, mixed with rowan, holly, ash, and other species, where conditions are too difficult for woodland proper to develop. Under good conditions, or when growing amongst oaks, birches of both species may reach a height of at least 60 feet, but stands of good forestry quality are rare, and are found chiefly in the south-eastern counties of England and in Cumberland, Yorkshire, and Shropshire. Most of the birchwoods, especially of the hills, are little more than 25 feet high and are classed as scrub (p. 43). For this reason there are no useful figures for their total area.

Many of the larger Scottish valleys have open birchwoods, largely of the silver species, but only in Perth is there much birchwood that is of any value from the point of view of forestry. The most characteristic Scottish birchwoods are not these, but isolated woods which occur in the hills of several highland counties and are most frequent in Ross and Sutherland (Plate IV). Some are almost pure *B. pubescens*, the trees seldom exceeding 30 feet in height; some have many rowans and occasional hollies, but there is never a shrub layer. The field layer varies: in some woods there is none, the rocky surface of the ground being covered with mosses and liverworts; in others it is heathy, with bilberry as the dominant; and in still others it is herbaceous, with a thick carpet of bluebells and primroses. In the far north these are in full bloom in the first and second weeks of June, an indication of the shortness of the Highland summer.

I have records from thirteen English and Welsh birchwoods, mostly in the hills but including four in the lowlands of southern England, and when these are treated as described in the previous chapter they yield 20 time-quadrats and 253 contacts. The birds that score a percentage frequency of 20 or more, or that have a relative abundance of not less than 4 per cent., are shown in Table 6. Of

III. Durmast oakwood in May, Brecon. The trees, about 30 feet high, are near the altitudinal limit and lichen-covered; there are no shrubs, and the field layer is sparse, with moss, grasses and bluebells.

IV. Hairy birchwood in June, Ross. The trees are 20 to 30 feet high, there are no shrubs, and the field layer is rich, including heathy species (heather, bilberry), herbaceous ones (primrose, bluebell, geum, shamrock, grasses, bracken), and mosses.

TABLE 6

Dominant birds of English and Welsh birchwoods: summer

13 woods, 20 quadrats, 257 contacts in 302 minutes

	Percentage frequency	Contacts	*Relative abundance*
Anthus trivialis (tree-pipit) . .	60	22	9
Corvus corone (crow) . . .	40	9	4
Emberiza citrinella (yellowhammer) .	30	9	4
Erithacus rubecula (robin) . . .	70	20	8
Fringilla coelebs (chaffinch) . .	100	52	21
Muscicapa hypoleuca (pied flycatcher) .	40	12	5
M. striata (spotted flycatcher) . .	20	2	1
Parus coeruleus (blue tit) . . .	40	10	4
Phoenicurus phoenicurus (redstart) . .	45	8	3
Phylloscopus sibilatrix (wood-warbler) .	40	11	4
P. trochilus (willow-warbler) . .	90	40	16
Troglodytes troglodytes (wren) . .	65	13	5

the thirteen woods four are chiefly hairy birch, the others chiefly the silver birch. I have analysed the birds for the two series separately and there is no clear difference. It is therefore reasonable, until longer series of figures are available, to take them all together. In fact there is little difference between the two types of wood, and one has to look very closely to decide which tree is dominant. The list is very similar to that for the sessile oakwoods; the yellowhammer and spotted flycatcher are added, and the coal-tit, buzzard, and wood-pigeon are missing. The sample is small, and the yellowhammer was present in six of my oakwoods, so that there is probably little difference in its status in the two types. The birchwoods show the same tendency to invasion by heath birds as do the oakwoods. The absence of the coal-tit from both the Lake District birchwoods and all those of Wales is very striking. In both these areas it is the commonest tit in the oakwoods, and that it does not dislike birchwoods as such is shown by its occurrence in those of Scotland (p. 71).

The detailed lists show some interesting features. Both chaffinch and willow-warbler are present in all the woods, but the former is rather more abundant; this is in marked contrast to the position in the Scottish birchwoods and in Wyre Forest. In the latter, as a result of coppicing, there is a large area which is now predominantly birch about 25 feet high; when this part of the wood is viewed from an opposite hillside it looks as if about two-thirds of the trees are birches, the remainder being sessile oaks with a few yews. Table 14, column 3, shows the total contacts made in this area during the months of April–June 1950–3. The willow-warbler is here four times as abundant as the chaffinch, which comes only ninth in rank. The only reason that I can suggest for this is that the forest as a whole is not saturated with chaffinches, and that the nearby oakwoods are more attractive than the birchwoods. It is possible that the homing instinct, whatever that means, brings a bird to the general neighbourhood in which it was reared, and that then ecological factors determine the choice of breeding territory. If this is so, it should follow that the hillside oakwoods contain as many chaffinches as can make adequate territories in them, so that the others are forced to go to the less congenial birchwoods. The chaffinch was easily the commonest bird in the Wyre sessile oakwoods, and scored 58 contacts in 466 minutes, or a little under 8 per hour at 2 miles per hour. The corresponding figures for the Welsh hill oakwoods are 80 contacts in 497 minutes, or a little under 10 per hour. The difference is not large enough to give much support to the hypothesis but is not incompatible with it, especially if, as is likely, conditions are more rigorous in the hills so that the minimum possible size of territory would be larger. A similar explanation may apply to the wood-warbler; it ranks high in the hill birchwoods, but is hardly present in the Wyre birches.

The position of the tree-pipit will probably surprise most ornithologists who do not know the mountains, as indeed it did me when I first started exploring these woods. It is present in seven out of nine hill birchwoods and in one lowland wood, and ranks third, just above the robin, while in the Wyre birches it is also third, but below the robin. All these woods, except for Scober, the one Pennine birchwood which has some taller oaks, have trees from about 24 to 30 feet in height, which is clearly quite adequate for the pipits. The pied flycatcher is present in both the Cumberland birchwoods, but is absent from those of the Pennines and Wales. Birchwood is not generally thought of as the typical habitat for this bird, but as it apparently thrives in birches in the Lake District there seems no reason why it should not do so elsewhere. The spotted flycatcher has about the same position here as in the Scotch woods described below. The redstart also is absent from most of the Welsh birchwoods, but otherwise occupies much the same position in rank and numbers as it does in the oakwoods. The relatively high values for the song-thrush are remarkable, and are repeated in the Scotch woods.

The wood-pigeon was present in the birchwoods only when some other trees, such as oak, were available. Presumably the fine twigs of birch are unsuitable to support its bulky nest. The same is true of the buzzard, and I have no evidence of it nesting in birchwoods, though I have recorded its presence in a few birchwoods in the hills. The position of the greater spotted woodpecker is noteworthy, especially as it is a recent immigrant to the northwest.

The isolated birchwoods of the Highlands are a characteristic feature of north-west Scotland, and are especially thick in Coygach and the adjacent parts of Sutherland. They are almost pure *B. pubescens*, but of a form which is often not hairy and should possibly be regarded as a distinct species. I have records from 26 woods, ranging from the Minch to the North Sea, and in altitude from sea level to 1,600 feet. Since the status of the birds in these woods has been changing rapidly in the past it is important to note that my visits were in 1951 and 1952. The dominant birds, determined in the same way as before, are shown in Table 7.

TABLE 7

Dominant birds of Ross, Sutherland, and Caithness birchwoods: summer

26 woods, 54 quadrats, 739 contacts in 1,060 minutes

	Percentage frequency	*Contacts*	*Relative abundance*
Anthus trivialis (tree-pipit)	61	65	9
Erithacus rubecula (robin)	56	46	6
Fringilla coelebs (chaffinch)	89	85	11
Muscicapa striata (spotted flycatcher)	20	11	1
Parus ater (coal-tit)	39	22	3
P. coeruleus (blue tit)	24	12	2
P. major (great tit)	28	16	2
Phoenicurus phoenicurus (redstart)	30	18	2
Phylloscopus trochilus (willow-warbler)	100	262	36
Troglodytes troglodytes (wren)	59	35	5
Turdus philomelos (song-thrush)	35	25	3

The willow-warbler is easily the most abundant bird and the chaffinch comes second with only about a third of the willow-warbler's number of contacts. The tree-pipit is in third place and above the robin; it is present in more woods and was recorded half as many times again. It is possible that it is still increasing in numbers since it was apparently unknown in these birchwoods until about 1900.

In general the list is similar to that for the English and Welsh birchwoods. The chief difference is that the coal-tit is easily the most abundant, as well as the most widely spread, of its family, as was noticed as long ago as 1887 by Harvie-Brown and Buckley. The great tit has probably increased since they wrote, but the blue tit is still distinctly uncommon. I saw no long-tailed tits, but they are said to be present in Coygach in some years. Perhaps when I was there they had not recovered from the effects of the frosts of 1947. The song-thrush, although not present in large numbers, was recorded in a much higher proportion of these birchwoods than of the sessile oakwoods or even of the English and Welsh birchwoods. I know of no information on the soil of the northern birchwoods, but it is at least possible that in many of them it is near enough to neutrality to permit the presence of a moderate fauna of earthworms and snails. The field layer is seldom heathy, and in many of the woods a thick carpet of primroses and bluebells, which is reminiscent of a southern oakwood, suggests a much richer soil than that which usually supports the sessile oak. By contrast the blackbird is almost entirely absent. If, as Baxter and Rintoul suggest, it has only arrived in the north-west within about the last hundred years, it has possibly not yet penetrated to the hillside woods, but I do not think this is likely. It has established itself on most of the islands off the west coast, and according to many authors lives and nests in many of these in situations which appear at first sight much less suitable for it than the birchwoods. It is impossible to believe that in the northward spread no blackbirds have seen or visited the woods, and the fact that these have not been colonized must mean that in some way they are unsuitable.

The crow of this part of Great Britain is the hooded species (*Corvus cornix*), or subspecies (*Corvus corone cornix*) as it should be called if the term has its usual meaning. It does not appear in the birchwood lists quite as commonly as does the carrion crow in the sessile oakwoods and English birchwoods, but is present in a number of them. Its rather smaller numbers may be due to the much lower density of sheep on the hills of Scotland than on those of England and Wales.

A bird which was present in nearly a quarter of these woods but does not occur in any of my other lists, is the lesser redpoll. It is gregarious even in the breeding season, so that its distribution is clustered instead of scattered. There seems no reason why it should be found in some woods and not others, but if its numbers were reduced by some climatic or other factor its social behaviour would make it fill up one wood before it colonized the next. It seems to be largely dependent on the seeds of birch, but its greatest density in Ross was in the grounds of the Hotel at Drumrunie Lodge, where those of various shrubs presumably attract it. The wood-warbler is a recent addition to the birds of this area, but by 1952 it was regularly present in some of the birchwoods as far north as they go. As in the English and Welsh birchwoods, it lives side by side with the willow-warbler, but it will be interesting to see if it becomes at all abundant in these woods, and if so, if there is any reduction in the density of willow-warblers. At present this is very high indeed and must be the highest of any species in any British wood; on a sunny day it is impossible to make anything like an accurate transect-count, as so many are singing within earshot at once.

These northern birchwoods show once again an invasion by heath birds, ring-ouzel, wheatear, and whinchat. I saw no yellow-hammers, but Mr. R. S. R. Fitter found it in a few of the woods in 1951.

The north of Scotland is well beyond the geographical range of the pied flycatcher in Great Britain, though it goes to higher latitudes on the Continent. The spotted flycatcher is, however, present in these woods, somewhat surprisingly. It is not common, but is more widely spread than in any English wood.

It seems from the lists in Lack and Venables that the fauna of birchwoods at Aviemore on Speyside, which probably occupy the site of felled oak or oak–fir woods, is intermediate between that of the English and Welsh woods and that of the north-west Highlands. The chaffinch is commoner than the willow-warbler, but the coal-tit is the commonest tit. The only discrepancy is that there are relatively few tree-pipits.

It is interesting to compare our birchwoods with those of northern Europe. There as here the silver birch is a common successional tree where other species, such as oaks and conifers, have been cleared or burnt, and the hairy birch (or a close relative—the birches still need investigating, as Gilbert Carter pointed out in 1936) forms scrubby woods in the far north, well beyond the climatic range of the firs.

Nordström (1953) has described the birds of a wood of the first sort on an island in the Gulf of Bothnia at 62°19′N. The willow-warbler was the commonest species, with chaffinch, spotted flycatcher, garden-warbler, fieldfare, and redwing all having a relative abundance of more than 4 per cent. Tree-pipit, yellow-hammer, great tit, and pied flycatcher were present in fair numbers, but only one coal-tit and four robins were recorded in five years. The total of species recorded was 36, so that the fauna was richer than in Scotland, where I recorded only 21 species.

Jenkins (1953) found that the dominant birds in birchwoods on the island of Andøya, at 69°N off the Norwegian coast, were the meadow-pipit, mealy redpoll, willow-warbler, fieldfare, and red-wing, no other species making 4 per cent. of the total. His woods were somewhat affected by man, and the presence in them of nest-boxes perhaps accounted for a few pied flycatchers. He did not record either robins or tits, and there was only one bluethroat. The fauna seems to be somewhat restricted, as is general on islands. During 40 minutes in birchwoods at sea-level on the Norwegian mainland at Nordkjosbotn (69°13′N), which although of the hairy birch are very similar to those of Aviemore, I recorded eleven willow-warblers, five bramblings, three yellowhammers, and one or two tree-pipits, wheatears, willow-tits, magpies, garden-warblers, fieldfares, and redwings.

The extensive woods of hairy birch at Kilpisjarvie in Finland, at 69°N and 1,500 feet above sea-level, are no more than scrub, but are in many ways similar to those of Sutherland. The dominant birds are willow-warbler, redpoll, brambling, and bluethroat, in that order, and there are fair numbers of pipits. Both tree- and meadow-pipits are present, but it is not always possible to tell to which species a bird belongs when it is silent and not close to the observer. Redstarts, hedge-sparrows, redwings, and yellow wagtails are present, but there are no tits except a few willow-tits. If the brambling is taken as a substitute for the chaffinch and the bluethroat for the robin, this is a very similar fauna to that of the Sutherland woods. Further reference to this is made in Chapter 13.

ALDERWOODS

Just as the birch replaces the oak at higher places on the hills, so the alder (*Alnus glutinosa*) replaces it in wet river-valleys and by stream sides, and it is found in waterlogged soils all over these islands. Before most of the river-valleys were drained it must have been much commoner than it is now. Alderwood is now found as the 'carr' of East Anglia, where it contains many willows (*Salix*) and other trees, especially birch and ash. Species of sedge (*Carex*) are dominant in the field layer, and alderwood is normally closely associated with swamps in which sedges or reeds (*Typha*) are dominant and small specimens of alder and willow are only occasional.

A more open alderwood is also found as a fringe along the edges of many rivers, especially in the north, and Cumberland has at least one fairly large hillside alderwood. Here there are few shrubs, and the field layer is dominated by rushes (*Juncus*) and grasses (*Anthoxanthum*), but there is a long list of associated species. The trees in alderwoods seldom exceed 40 feet in height.

In some of the valleys of the western Highlands are damp woods dominated by alder with an admixture of ash and a few sessile oaks. They have no high shrubs but a rich and tangled field layer in which brambles are usually dominant, and grasses, male fern (*Dryopteris filix-mas*) and ragwort (*Senecio jacobaea*) are abundant.

The birds of the stream-side belts of alders are dealt with in Chapter 7. Four summer visits to the Lake District alderwood, in Martindale, have produced the total contacts shown in Table 8. The fauna is mostly similar to that of the English birchwoods, except that there are no redstarts or thrushes.

I have not been able to visit the Scottish alderwoods in summer and can find no information on their birds. Since they are floristically rich, it would be very interesting to know what birds they contain.

TABLE 8

Birds of a Lake District alderwood. Total contacts, all birds

	26.6.48	28.5.49	25.5.50	4.4.55	14.12.50
Anthus pratensis (meadow-pipit)			2		
A. trivialis (tree-pipit)	1		2		
Certhia familiaris (treecreeper)			1	1	4
Corvus corone (crow)				2	
Emberiza citrinella (yellowhammer)			4		
Erithacus rubecula (robin)		1	1	2	1
Fringilla coelebs (chaffinch)		1	4	4	
Muscicapa hypoleuca (pied flycatcher)			3		
M. striata (spotted flycatcher)			2		
Parus ater (coal-tit)			2	1	4
P. coeruleus (blue tit)		1		1	2
P. major (great tit)	1			1	
Phylloscopus trochilus (willow-warbler)	1	1	2		
Troglodytes troglodytes (wren)			2		1
Turdus merula (blackbird)					1
Buteo buteo (buzzard)			2		1
Cuculus canorus (cuckoo)	1				

ASHWOODS

The ash (*Fraxinus excelsior*) is characteristically a tree of limestone soils. It demands plenty of bases in the soil, and correspondingly it is itself rich in mineral ash when burnt; this is probably the justification for the former use of its green boughs as manure for grassland. Perhaps because the land on which it grows is too good to be left under trees, there are now no extensive ashwoods, but it was probably formerly the dominant tree of most of the mountain or carboniferous limestone, and of chalk and other limestones where beech is not present. Fragments of ashwood, seldom more than a few acres, still exist on the carboniferous limestone of Somerset, the Derbyshire dales and the northern Pennines, and in the Isle of Wight, Wiltshire, Dorset, and Devonshire (Fig. 11). For the most part these are on steep hillsides which cannot be cultivated and the soil is shallow and stony, with much bare rock. There may be a

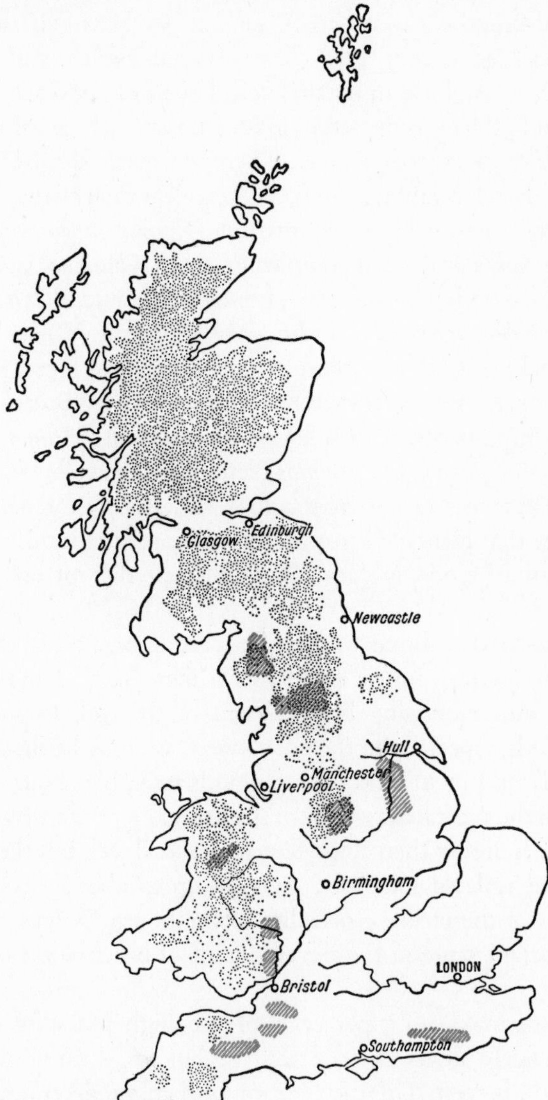

FIG. 11. Map to show where there are large or important blocks of semi-natural ashwoods.

number of other associated trees, such as wych elm (*Ulmus glabra*), whitebeam (*Sorbus aria*), bird cherry (*Prunus padus*), and yew, but some of these are local in occurrence. The ash may reach 80 feet in height, but in the poor situations in which many of our ashwoods are found it seldom exceeds 40 feet. There are many shrubs, especially hawthorn, hazel, bramble, and roses, as well as such characteristically lime-loving small trees as dogwood (*Cornus sanguinea*), spindle (*Euonymus europaeus*), and wayfaring tree (*Viburnum lantana*). All three of the woody climbers, ivy, honeysuckle, and old man's beard (*Clematis vitalba*) are present and may be abundant. Where the shrub layer is thick, as it often is, there is hardly any field layer, but where it is more open there is an extremely long list of herbaceous species. Common dominants in this layer are ramsons (*Allium ursinum*), dog's mercury (*Mercurialis perennis*), and lily of the valley (*Convallaria majalis*). These are all less than a foot tall, and it is generally only in clearings that plants of knee-height or more are found, so that the inside of an ashwood is very different from that of an oakwood (Plate V).

As has been said above, ash is a frequent associate of both species of oak, occurring more often with increasing dampness, and probably with increasing base content of the soil. In some small mixed woods, especially in the north-west, ash may be the chief tree. Floristically and in structure these woods resemble sessile oakwood rather than the typical ashwoods of the limestone. Pure ashwood does not go much higher than 1,000 feet above sea-level, but these mixed woods, and isolated ash trees, straggle up to about 1,200 feet. In some areas of the chalk, especially on the South Downs, ash scrub is an important stage in the development of beechwood from bare grass.

Ashwoods make up 7 per cent. of the high forest of England. They are fairly generally distributed, but are commoner in the west and south-west. This distribution probably reflects not only the distribution of basic soils, but also the liability of the tree to frost damage. Because of its susceptibility to this and because, owing to its opposite method of branching, destruction of the leading shoot, whether by frost or a browsing animal, leads to a forked stem, the ash is not much liked by foresters, in spite of the high quality of its timber. Very few ashwoods are pure.

There are few ashwoods in Wales, the best known being Coed Craig y Benglog, near Cader Idris. It is very open and probably not more than 80 or 90 years old. It contains many sessile oaks and some birch, and has other features in common with the regenerating mixed woods of the Lake District (such as Side Wood in Ennerdale, which is certainly not more than 150 years old, and may be less) but is richer in species in the field layer.

The alderwoods of the western Highlands described above (p. 75) are replaced on slightly drier, but still damp, soils by ashwoods, though some alders are always present. The ashwoods are very similar to the alderwoods, but the male fern is dominant, the brambles are taller, and there is much hazel. There are also ashwoods (which I have not seen) in Wigtown and Kirkcudbright, but only 1 per cent. of the high forest of Scotland is under this tree.

TABLE 9

Dominant birds of ashwoods: summer

13 woods, 25 quadrats, 366 contacts in 414 minutes

	Percentage frequency	*Contacts*	*Relative abundance*
Anthus trivialis (tree-pipit)	32	15	4
Corvus corone (crow)	24	8	2
Emberiza citrinella (yellowhammer)	24	7	2
Erithacus rubecula (robin)	24	9	3
Fringilla coelebs (chaffinch)	68	49	13
Parus coeruleus (blue tit)	36	12	3
Parus major (great tit)	36	13	4
Parus palustris (marsh-tit)	20	6	2
Phoenicurus phoenicurus (redstart)	52	24	7
Phylloscopus trochilus (willow-warbler)	88	67	18
Troglodytes troglodytes (wren)	48	18	5
Turdus merula (blackbird)	32	15	4
Turdus philomelos (song-thrush)	24	6	2
Columba palumbus (wood-pigeon)	44	21	6

Table 9 shows the dominant birds in thirteen ashwoods, distributed from Sussex to the West Riding. I have omitted from this list the mixed ashwoods that contain much oak or birch. It is in many respects intermediate between those for the two types of oakwood. The tree-pipit has a high score and the robin a low one, both these being perhaps connected with the absence of shrubs and poverty of the field layer. These features can, however, hardly account for the abundance of the willow-warbler, which is exceeded elsewhere only in the Scottish birchwoods. The high score of the redstart is remarkable, and is perhaps connected with the large amount of bare rock in many of the woods, for in the north of England at least the redstart nests largely in rock crevices near the ground. By contrast the coal-tit was recorded in one wood only, although other tits (including the marsh-tit) were fairly plentiful. Although its nest sites are somewhat similar to those of the redstart they tend to be rather more in cavities under tree-roots than in rocks, and these perhaps the ashwoods do not provide. In accordance with this preference for rocks the redstart, but not the coal-tit, is a characteristic frequenter of the stone walls of the north and of the ruined abbeys of Yorkshire.

Starlings were nesting in three of the Yorkshire woods, but not elsewhere. The ashwoods, even those on the hills, do not have many heath-plants in the field layer, and the only heath bird in the lists is the yellowhammer. This was seen in two of the woods, including, rather surprisingly, a large wood in the Cotswolds, which has tall trees in close canopy.

BEECHWOODS

The beech (*Fagus silvatica*) is a comparatively late forest-forming tree in these islands, for although there are a few fossil pollen-grains from about 5000 B.C. (the Boreal period—see Chapter 13) they do not become widespread until about 2000 B.C. At this time beechwoods evidently occurred over their present range, with an extension on to the chalk of Cambridgeshire. There is also some indication that in Roman times beech was present as far north as Yorkshire and as far west as Cardigan, Dartmoor, and Bodmin. Its present natural limits are given approximately by a line drawn from Gloucester to Cambridge. It is the characteristic tree of the chalk, though it also grows well on sand and has been extensively planted all over England, usually only in small blocks or as belts round parks. The probable distribution of native beechwoods is shown in Fig. 12. Although it may produce plenty of seed outside the areas shown it is seldom capable of natural regeneration, that is of maintaining an existing woodland.

The beech is a tall tree, reaching under good conditions a height

FIG. 12. Map to show where there are large or important blocks of semi-natural beechwoods.

of well over 100 feet, and casts a deep shade. This, helped by the fact that its leaves decay slowly, gives beechwoods a characteristically dark and bare appearance (Plate VI). In the typical woods of the sides of the chalk escarpments other trees are rare, though the yew, another tree which casts deep shade, is sometimes present and forms a second tree layer below the dominant. Shrubs are usually absent; the commonest, when they occur, being elder (*Sambucus nigra*) and field maple (*Acer campestris*). Ivy is often present. The field layer may be entirely absent, but sometimes, especially in older woods, where the canopy opens out, there is a low growth, seldom more than a foot high, dominated by dog's mercury, wood sanicle (*Sanicula europaea*), or ivy creeping over the ground and not climbing the trees. On plateaux, where the soil is deeper and acid even though it overlies chalk, there may be other trees, especially pedunculate oak and ash, and there is often a field layer consisting of a thick but low growth of bramble. On still more acid soils oak and birch may be present and the general appearance is rather more like that of a sessile oakwood. The field layer is usually absent, but if it is present it consists of heathy plants such as bilberry, with bracken where the shade is not too deep. Ivy is absent, but there may be some honeysuckle.

Although beechwoods are, from the botanist's point of view, somewhat complex and difficult to understand, it is likely that, as most birds see them, all beechwoods are much the same. Their chief features are the deep shade, the absence of shrubs, the absence or poor development of the field layer with its accompanying deep litter of slowly decaying leaves, and the smooth surface of the trunks of the trees.

Beechwoods make up 11 per cent. of the total high forest of England but are important chiefly in the south-eastern counties, where they are native. There are fair quantities also in Devon, Cornwall, and the West Riding. Only 31 per cent. of the beechwoods of Great Britain are 90 per cent. or more pure.

Wales has no natural or semi-natural beechwoods of any size, but Scotland has a surprising amount of planted beechwood—9 per cent. of its total area of high forest—which is concentrated in the eastern counties from Banff to Roxburgh.

My figures for beechwoods are rather slight, but the dominant birds in eight woods, mostly in Sussex, with fourteen time-quadrats, are shown in Table 10. There is some similarity to the list for pedun-

TABLE 10

Dominant birds of beechwoods: summer

8 woods, 14 quadrats, 236 contacts in 255 minutes

	Percentage frequency	*Contacts*	*Relative abundance*
Erithacus rubecula (robin)	50	12	5
Fringilla coelebs (chaffinch)	86	39	17
Garrulus glandarius (jay)	29	4	2
Parus coeruleus (blue tit)	36	10	4
P. major (great tit)	50	22	10
Phoenicurus phoenicurus (redstart)	21	4	2
Phylloscopus collybita (chiff-chaff)	36	6	3
P. trochilus (willow-warbler)	21	14	6
Sitta europaea (nuthatch)	29	4	2
Sylvia atricapilla (blackcap)	29	6	3
Troglodytes troglodytes (wren)	71	17	7
Turdus merula (blackbird)	86	24	10
T. philomelos (song-thrush)	21	3	1
Columba palumbus (wood-pigeon)	57	13	6

culate oakwoods, the jay, chiff-chaff, and blackcap being dominant in these two but in no others. Since the structures of the oakwoods and beechwoods are very different, this probably reflects the generally southern situation of the two groups. The relative scarcity of willow-warblers probably reflects the absence of shrubs, just as it does in the durmast oakwoods.

These beechwoods are an incomplete sample in that they include only one wood and one quadrat from the Chilterns, one of the most characteristic regions for this type of wood.

THE WINTER POPULATION

The only woods treated in this chapter for which I have adequate winter figures are the English and Welsh birchwoods, and the dominant species for these are shown in Table 11. It is similar to that for the durmast oakwoods in that the chief birds are tits, wrens, and thrushes, but there are very few goldcrests. The scarcity of the robin may be illustrated by the fact that 190 minutes' walking, on three separate days, in the Hillbeck birchwood in Westmorland (which contains many ashes) produced only one, although plenty were

Table 11

Dominant birds of English and Welsh birchwoods: winter

8 woods, 20 quadrats, 202 contacts in 395 minutes

	Percentage frequency	*Contacts*	*Relative abundance*
Carduelis flammea (redpoll) . .	15	12	6
Corvus corone (crow) . . .	30	8	4
Fringilla coelebs (chaffinch) . .	30	7	3
Parus ater (coal-tit) . . .	65	22	11
P. coeruleus (blue tit) . . .	70	25	11
P. major (great tit) . . .	85	36	18
Troglodytes troglodytes (wren) . .	20	5	2
Turdus merula (blackbird) . .	55	12	6
T. musicus (redwing) . . .	35	18	9
Buteo buteo (buzzard) . . .	25	5	2
Columba palumbus (wood-pigeon) .	30	22	11

present in summer. Although the robin is a visually inconspicuous bird in winter, since it lives mainly in the field layer (or shrubs if they are present), it is not likely to be overlooked if many are present, since there is a certain amount of song in all winter months, and the bird has a habit of calling 'tic-tac' if anyone comes within about 20 yards of it.

The redpoll, which was present in none of my counts as a breeding bird, now appears as a winter migrant, and the redwing is also present, greatly outnumbering the fieldfare. The chaffinch persists in the birchwoods much more than in the oakwoods, and was present at least until the end of November in two Cumberland woods and in one in Wales. At this time the Cumberland oakwoods are completely devoid of chaffinches.

My one record for a Yorkshire ashwood suggests that here too chaffinches, robins, and most thrushes leave for the winter, and my one visit to the Martindale alderwood produced no chaffinches or yellowhammers (Table 8).

I have no winter figures for beechwoods, but Lack and Venables' tables suggest that the population is much the same, except for the loss of recognized summer migrants and some reduction in the density of robins, as in summer. In particular, the chaffinch is still present and its relative abundance has gone up. It seems probable that there is a migration into the woods, whether of native or continental birds. The only part of Wyre Forest that ever contains any chaffinches in winter is a small area where there are some large planted beeches. Here they congregate to feed on the mast. Lack and Venables' correspondents also record high numbers of bramblings in the beechwoods. The brambling is of the same genus as the chaffinch, and the two birds are generally considered to be even more closely related than this implies (there are records of attempted pair-formation between them) so that their occurrence in this country side by side is interesting. A detailed investigation of their feeding habits, since both eat beech-mast, would be worth while.

I have September counts for three English birchwoods and four Scotch (all chiefly of the hairy species), for two Lake District alder-woods, and for two Yorkshire ashwoods. All of these show an almost completely winter fauna. There are a few chaffinches in the Scottish birchwoods, but the only summer migrants recorded are one willow-warbler and several redstarts in a birchwood by Loch Tummel. Visits to two Westmorland birchwoods made for me in July and August by Mr. R. W. Robson showed plenty of chaffinches and some willow-warblers, flycatchers, and redstarts. It looks therefore as if those birds which are going to leave the woods do so gradually during July and August, and are almost all gone by mid-September. The only additions in my September lists were siskins in some Scottish birchwoods. These were presumably migrants from the firwoods, where they breed.

Capercailzie

6

THE BIRDS OF CONIFEROUS WOODS

Coniferous forest is characteristic of sub-arctic climates, and Great Britain is south of the line where spruce and fir become completely dominant at sea-level. Fossil remains in the peat show that Scotch fir was formerly widespread in Britain, and some botanists believe, without any evidence, that some trees have persisted in the south of England to the present day. However that may be, it was extensively planted in the nineteenth century, for example on the Surrey heaths, on the Weald, and on the North York Moors, and as it regenerates freely it has in several places formed a scrub similar to that which exists in the Highlands of Scotland. In this latter country the 'dark wood' of Scotch fir has had a continuous history since Boreal times. The largest existing woods are those surrounding the Cairngorm mountains, including the Forests of Rothiemurchus, Glenmore, and Abernethy on the east of Strathspey, and the woods of Mar and Derry on Deeside. Smaller areas are found on the south of Loch Rannoch, and at Kinlochewe on Loch Maree in Ross-shire. There has been much felling in all these, and in places the trees are so far apart that the vegetation must be classed as tree-heath rather than woodland. Scattered firs, and a few small woods, are found in a good many Highland counties.

The Scotch fir will grow to a height of 100 feet or more, but the average in the Scottish woods is less than this. As one ascends the hills the trees become shorter, until at the upper edge (at 1,500 to 2,000 feet above sea-level in the Cairngorms) they are only 30 feet high or less. The height falls off very rapidly in the last 50 or 100 feet of altitude, a phenomenon seen also in the English hillside oakwoods. The variety of fir native to Scotland has shorter needles, of average length less than 2 inches, and a more pyramidal shape than those imported from the Continent and commonly planted. These have needles up to 4 inches long, and early lose the pyramidal shape of the young tree and acquire flat-topped crowns. There may be a good many birches and some alders in the woods, but there are few other associated trees. There are generally no shrubs, but in places there are thick growths of juniper (*Juniperus communis*). The field layer is heathy, and consists chiefly of bilberry and cowberry (*Vaccinium vitis-idaea*), with ling (*Calluna vulgaris*) in the more open places (Plate VII).

The parts of Rothiemurchus and Glenmore in which I have counted birds vary from areas which are, in the foresters' language, devastated, which means that all useful timber has been removed and only misshapen, scrub, or unwanted trees left, through open scrub at the upper edge to tracts where mature trees, largely planted in the eighteenth century, are growing in close stands; but on the whole the forests are rather open. There does not in fact seem to be much difference in the faunas of the different areas, and all my records are therefore put together (Table 12).

The general picture is very similar to that of the hillside oak and birchwoods of England and Wales, with chaffinch, tree-pipit, coal-tit, willow-warbler, and redstart as dominant species. As I

TABLE 12

Birds of Scotch firwoods: summer. Total contacts

	Speyside, 565 min. Contacts	*Speyside, 565 min.* Relative abundance	*Coille na Glas Leitir (Ross) 115 min.* Contacts
Anthus pratensis (meadow-pipit)	13	3	
A. trivialis (tree-pipit)	28	7	8
Carduelis spinus (siskin)	1		
Certhia familiaris (treecreeper)	3		1
Corvus corone (crow)	7	2	
Erithacus rubecula (robin)	7	2	8
Fringilla coelebs (chaffinch)	90	24	12
Loxia curvirostris (crossbill)	8	2	
Muscicapa striata (spotted flycatcher)			3
Parus ater (coal-tit)	27	7	4
P. cristatus (crested tit)	8	2	
Phoenicurus phoenicurus (redstart)	16	4	3
Phylloscopus trochilus (willow-warbler)	87	23	41
Regulus regulus (goldcrest)	11	3	1
Troglodytes troglodytes (wren)	8	2	3
Turdus philomelos (song-thrush)	10	3	1
Other passerines	6		6
Cuculus canorus (cuckoo)	9	3	1
Lyrurus tetrix (black grouse)	1		
Scolopax rusticola (woodcock)	2		1
Tetrao urogallus (capercailzie)	2		
Other non-passerines	30		
	375		93

pointed out in Chapter 4, the last four of these are regular or frequent ground-nesters, and the rocks and boulders of Rothiemurchus presumably provide very similar conditions to those of Birkrigg and Keskadale and the Welsh woods, especially as heather and bilberry are common in the field layer of all three. The pied flycatcher is conspicuously absent from the firwood lists, and as it breeds much further north than this on the Continent, and well into the coniferous forest zone, it is difficult to account for its absence from the Scottish woods. There are several scattered Scottish breeding records, including a few recent ones for the neighbourhood of Aviemore on

Speyside, so that it may before long be added to the list of firwood birds.

There are other notable absences or deficiencies, of which the most striking is the complete absence, with which Lack and Venables' lists agree, of all tits except the coal-tit and crested tit. There is no possibility of a geographical limitation here, for blue, great, willow and long-tailed tits are all found much further north, and have in fact been occasionally recorded from the firwoods, but their absence from all the counts summarized here must mean that they do avoid this habitat. The coal-tit, though widespread, is no more abundant than it is in many other types of wood. The situation appears to be not so much that the coal-tit is a bird of the firwoods, as that other tits are birds of deciduous woods. The relationships of the tits in the artificial conditions of the coniferous plantations described below are rather different.

There are few crows, and no jays or magpies. The Speyside woods are on the border where the ranges of the two crows, hooded and carrion, meet, so that both have been recorded. Their small numbers may be partly the result of persecution, but may also be due to the absence of sheep and scarcity of rabbits. The absence of jay and magpie is almost certainly due solely to persecution, as both were formerly widespread in Scotland but have been greatly reduced. According to Darling (1947), the jay has appeared in the firwoods on the south shore of Loch Rannoch, and with the reduction of gamekeeper-pressure both species are spreading.

The willow-warbler was almost as numerous in my counts as the chaffinch, and was well distributed in all types of woodland both in Rothiemurchus and in the neighbouring Glenmore. There seem to be no other warblers in the firwoods; the absence of the wood-warbler is striking, for the habitat, with tall trees and adequate ground cover, does not look unsuitable. The whitethroat also might be expected in the places where there are thick shrubs, but I have not seen it there; Baxter and Rintoul say that it does not reach any great altitude, and imply that their highest record is between 800 and 900 feet. The whole of the region we are considering is above this. All the other warblers are few in numbers as far north as this, so that no ecological deductions can be drawn from their absence.

The blackbird is rare in the firwoods, in spite of the fact that it occurs much farther north, and in the Highlands and Islands has even colonized treeless areas. By contrast, there are plenty of song-thrushes in those parts of the forest where there is a thick shrub layer of juniper. It happens that all of these from which I have records are near houses and penetrated by much-frequented paths, so that the thrushes might have been attracted by some of the *dejecta* of human beings; there are, however, some song-thrushes scattered through the forest in other types of situation at a rather greater density than that at which they are found in the birchwoods or sessile oakwoods. The wren and, rather less so, the robin, are also present in much smaller numbers than in the oakwoods.

There can be little doubt from the old records that the greater spotted woodpecker formerly occurred in fair numbers in the forests, but it became extinct in Scotland about the middle of last century. It has since entered the country again from England, and nested at Aviemore in 1920. In spite of this, and its continued northward spread, it does not seem to have recolonized the forests as might have been expected. Scotland is beyond the normal range of the green and lesser spotted woodpeckers.

The absence of the buzzard is likely to be due to its persecution. It was exterminated in the nineteenth century in many parts of Scotland.

The firwoods show some species which are hardly found elsewhere: these are the siskin, crossbill, goldcrest, crested tit, and capercailzie. None is present in very large numbers in my lists, and it may be that the higher numbers sometimes recorded, as for example by Lack and Venables, are not representative. These interesting birds are local in the woods, and an observer knowing in which parts of the forest they are to be found is likely to choose those for his counts without any intention of giving a bias to his results. My own record of crossbills in 1951 was biassed in this way, for I found them in the same tree as that in which I had seen them in the previous autumn. The siskin and crossbill both live in the tops of tall trees and are therefore easily overlooked, as they are difficult even to see in the dark foliage and against the light. By its method of feeding (see p. 244), the crossbill is almost bound to conifers, for although it does take other seeds to some extent it is clearly most at home in extracting seeds from fir cones. The crossbill and siskin, though rare outside the old forests, occur in suitable plantations, while the goldcrest, though for breeding purposes bound to conifers, is much more widely spread. The crested tit, by contrast, is practically confined to the natural firwood, and almost exclusively to those of Speyside. No one has ever given an adequate explanation of this.

The capercailzie formerly lived in Scotland, but became extinct, and the present birds are descended from Swedish birds put down at Taymouth in 1837–8 and later introductions. They spread fairly well, and although plantations are suitable for them, they seem to be almost confined to conifers; there can be little doubt that they were once an important natural element in the fauna of the firwoods.

An important predator in the firwoods is the long-eared owl, which does not appear in the lists because it is nocturnal. Darling records the nightjar also as a characteristic bird of the firwoods, but in spite of having been there at the appropriate time I have never heard one. Baxter and Rintoul report it as decreasing in Strathspey.

The list for the fragment of firwood in Ross-shire needs separate consideration, since Coille na Glas Leitir contains much birch, which in some places makes up more than half the trees. The list of species is very similar to that for the Strathspey woods, but includes redpoll, great and blue tits, bullfinch, and spotted flycatcher. The presence of all these probably depends on the birches. Absences based on limited observation are not so important; Darling says that the crossbill breeds in this wood, and there seems no reason why the siskin should not, since it is found on the west coast, but there seems to be no record of the crested tit from here.

One general and important thing about the breeding birds of the old firwoods is that their density is very low compared with that of many other woods. To go from the Sutherland or other birchwoods, where the willow-warblers are so numerous that they cannot be distinguished from one another, to Rothiemurchus, is like going from a garden to a wilderness. My records show 346 contacts in 565 minutes, or 37 per hour.

Lack and Venables have lists for five parts of the old firwoods in winter, and I have some scattered observations for the three forests for September and October. Very few birds are present. All but one of the specifically coniferous species, that is the crossbill, goldcrest, crested tit, and capercailzie, are present in fair numbers and in fact if, as is probable, they are completely resident and their population is not decreasing, there must be more during the early part of the winter than during the previous summer. There are also plenty of coal-tits, and some treecreepers, robins, wrens, and black grouse. The chaffinch is completely absent, just as it is from the northern oak and birchwoods, and Lack and Venables record no siskins; I have one doubtful record of this species for September. It looks as if it was, like the chaffinch, migratory, and the same is probably true of the song-thrush, which neither Lack and Venables nor I record. I have seen a greater spotted woodpecker and a willow-tit in Abernethy Forest in October; these birds probably breed in the woods although they do not appear in the published lists.

With the absence of four of the most abundant breeding species (chaffinch, willow-warbler, tree-pipit, and redstart), the firwoods are even more strikingly silent in winter than in summer. It must be remembered that all these woods are more than 700 feet above sea level, and that most of the area is above the 1,000-feet line. Further, they are in latitude 57°N, which is that of southern Sweden. They have a somewhat continental climate, and it is not surprising that most of the birds leave them.

Our other native coniferous tree, the yew (*Taxus baccata*) is widespread as an occasional inhabitant of oak or ashwoods, as in Herefordshire and Somerset respectively, or as scrub, but forms woods only in a few small areas of the Hampshire and Sussex chalk. These are nearly pure, and almost impenetrable, but in some there are numbers of whitebeam. The ground is bare, for the branches spread out only a few feet from the ground, and exclude by their shade nearly all other plants. In the older woods there is a little more space. A mature yew may reach 60 feet in height, but the trees in all our woods are less than this.

Lists of the birds seen in two of these woods are given in Table 13. Kingley Vale is a rather open scrub, consisting of islands of almost impenetrable yew in a sea of grass. The general height of the trees is 12 to 20 feet, but a few are as much as 40 feet and their girth is about 4 feet. There are several scattered whitebeams, hawthorns, Scotch firs, and pedunculate oaks, and bushes of bramble, juniper, and blackthorn. The wood extends as an east-facing strip on the hillside, a mile and a half long and two or three hundred

TABLE 13

Birds of yew-woods: summer. Total contacts

★=not recorded in timed walks but present on same day

	Kingley Vale 41 *minutes* 26.5.1954	*Butser Hill* 25 *minutes* 28.5.1954	*Total*	*Relative abundance*
Carduelis cannabina (linnet) .		1	1	1
Emberiza citrinella (yellowhammer)	1	1	2	1
Erithacus rubecula (robin) . .	7	6	13	9
Fringilla coelebs (chaffinch) .	21	6	27	19
Garrulus glandarius (jay) . .	2		2	1
Parus ater (coal-tit) . .	★	2	2	1
P. major (great tit) . .	2	1	3	2
Phylloscopus collybita (chiff-chaff) .	1		1	1
P. trochilus (willow-warbler) .	1		1	1
Pica pica (magpie) . .	7	★	7	5
Prunella modularis (hedge-sparrow)	2		2	1
Pyrrhula pyrrhula (bullfinch) .	3	1	4	3
Regulus regulus (goldcrest) .	2	7	9	6
Troglodytes troglodytes (wren) .	5	3	8	6
Turdus merula (blackbird) .	8	6	14	10
Columba palumbus (wood-pigeon) .	15	25	40	29
Picus viridis (green woodpecker) .	★	1	1	1
Streptopelia turtur (turtle-dove) .	1		1	1
Strix aluco (tawny owl) . .		1	1	1
			139	

yards wide. The Butser Hill woods from which the records come consist of two patches of almost pure yew in close canopy. There are a number of whitebeams and a few ashes, hawthorns, and hollies, but no other trees, practically no shrubs, and no field layer. The general height of the trees is about 40 feet, and their girth ranges up to 10 feet. I estimate the size of each patch at between 10 and 20 acres.

There is general similarity between the lists for the two areas, and the species which were present at Kingley Vale but not at Butser Hill—jay, willow-warbler, chiff-chaff, dunnock, and turtle-dove—are explicable by the more open and at the same time more bushy nature of the former place. The jay was in fact present in nearby yew-scrub on Butser Hill in July 1952 (Plate VIII). Too much importance must not be attached to absences from such small woods, but the low density of most tits, the almost complete absence of warblers, and the absence of the song-thrush are notable. Willow-warblers, whitethroats, and a yellowhammer were singing in the thorn scrub below the Kingley Vale wood. Bullfinches were commoner than in most woods. Coal-tits were conspicuous at Butser Hill and goldcrests in both woods. That the mere presence of conifers is not enough for the coal-tit is shown by its low density at Kingley Vale, where there are far fewer than there are in typical sessile oakwoods. The green woodpecker is perhaps present in the yews merely because the surrounding country provides plenty of ants for food, and the trees an occasional nesting site.

Most of the large estate-planting, both by private owners and by the Forestry Commission, is of conifers. The chief foreign species used are the Corsican pine (*Pinus nigra* ssp. *laricio*), distinguished from *P. silvestris* by having needles from 4 to 6 inches long and a grey, instead of red, bark; the lodge-pole pine (*Pinus contorta*), with short twisted needles; the European larch (*Larix decidua*); the Japanese larch (*Larix leptolepis*), which has leaves of a more bluish green; the Norway spruce (*Picea abies*); the Sitka spruce (*Picea sitchensis*) with leaves rhomboidal in section instead of flat, and with a longer and sharper point; and the Douglas fir (*Pseudotsuga taxifolia*); and there are small areas of several other species. These are all planted in straight lines and much closer together than they grow in natural forests, so that they cast deep shade and the field layer is thin or (especially under spruce) entirely absent. The natural spruce forests of Scandinavia, mainly on damp soils, are relatively open and have a rich flora, but our plantations have not yet reached that stage. Many of the eighteenth- and nineteenth-century larch plantations are mature or over-mature, and have a field layer consisting of plants which have come in from the surrounding fields or hills; there are no shrubs. Of the imported conifers, European larch and Sitka spruce regenerate freely in places.

As the planted species are chosen for their suitability to soil, exposure, and climate, there are marked geographical differences in their distribution. Scotch fir makes up most of the high-forest areas of the thickly wooded north-east counties of Scotland, and is common in Northumberland, the North Riding, Norfolk, Suffolk, Sussex, Surrey, Hampshire, Dorset, and Berkshire. There is some in Lincolnshire, Nottinghamshire, Staffordshire, and Bedfordshire, but little elsewhere. In all these counties it is planted chiefly on poor sands. The largest areas of Corsican pine are in Nottinghamshire and Staffordshire, where it has been planted because it resists industrial smoke better than does the Scotch fir, and in Norfolk and Suffolk. There is some in Hampshire, Dorset, Somerset, Devon, and the North Riding, but little elsewhere, and the only Scottish counties which have more than a very small area are Moray and Fife. The plantations are generally on sands similar to those used for the Scotch fir. The lodge-pole pine has only recently been planted on any large scale, chiefly in Scotland, Wales, and north-east England.

The larches are very generally distributed, with rather more in the western half of England than in the east. The spruces are practically confined to the highland counties. There are large areas in most of Scotland except for Caithness and the central lowlands, in Cumberland and Northumberland, Durham, the North Riding, and Devonshire, and in every county of Wales except Flint, Anglesey, and Pembrokeshire. They are planted chiefly on damp hillsides where the peat is too thick for any other trees to thrive; the Sitka species is preferred for the poorer of these poor soils. Douglas fir has a very scattered distribution; it is used mainly for conversion, by underplanting, of oak and other scrub to high forest.

There is no reason why mature plantations of Scotch fir on similar soil should not become very similar to the natural woods, and if they do they might be expected to have a similar avifauna. There are, however, two limitations. The climatic conditions in the south of England are very different from those of Aviemore, especially in their much longer summers and warmer winters, so that if any of the Speyside birds were limited by climate they could not colonize English woods; secondly, where man has made an area with ecological features different from those of the surrounding country, it can be colonized only if it is found by suitable species. Either birds of a wider choice of habitat must be present in adjacent regions, or those which are characteristic of the new area must find it on migration or other wanderings. We should not, therefore, expect to find crested tits or capercailzies in English fir plantations, since they have not yet had an opportunity of colonizing them. Without experiment one cannot tell if there are also climatic limitations in any particular case or not, but comparisons with other parts of the world may be helpful.

Many of the old-established plantations of Scotch fir on the sands of Surrey and the New Forest, with the sub-spontaneous regeneration to which they have given rise, do in fact resemble Rothiemurchus fairly closely. The tree is usually the continental variety of the species, but the field layer of bilberry or ling is often very similar to that in Scotland. They are seldom large enough to have a very characteristic avifauna (many were felled during 1914–18) and they often have unnatural tree or shrub species, especially rhododendron, which attract birds which are practically absent from the natural woods; but, with certain limitations, it does look as if their bird community was tending towards that of the Speyside forests. The chaffinch is the commonest species, and goldcrests and coal-tits are present in fairly high numbers. Surprisingly, the tree-pipit is not common. In some there are crossbills, but these do not come from Scotland and illustrate well the geographical limitation already mentioned. The Scottish birds, which are distinguishable by a larger bill and are known as *Loxia curvirostra scotica*, are resident and are unlikely ever to reach English plantations, but the continental form, called *L.c. curvirostra*, undergoes periodical irruptions in which it leaves its breeding places and spreads south and west. Thus, in most years, numbers appear on the east coast of England, and in some years they are found over most of the country. Some stay to breed, and nests have been recorded from most of the counties of England; in Norfolk and Suffolk the birds have become resident and are established as a breeding species.

The large plantations of the Forestry Commission are steadily making a difference to the plant cover and so to the birds of Great Britain, but they are still immature and any account of their fauna must be only an interim report. The observations that have been made on the changing bird life of the rapidly growing young plantations are described in Chapter 8, but we can at present only guess at what will be found in really mature large woods of larch and spruce. Many present plantations are much richer in species than the mature Scottish forests. The chaffinch is the most abundant bird, and the goldcrest and coal-tit are general. The jay and magpie are both present; there are blue and great tits and sometimes long-tailed tits, and the blue sometimes outnumbers the coal. The willow-warbler is the dominant warbler, but chiff-chaffs, whitethroats, garden-warblers, and blackcaps are all present in some woods. The mistle-thrush, song-thrush, blackbird, robin, dunnock, and wren are all general. Treecreepers and both green and great spotted woodpeckers occur, and the wood-pigeon is plentiful. The tree-pipit, wood-warbler, and redstart, even when they are abundant in the district, do not generally inhabit the plantations, although all three have been occasionally recorded. By contrast, the yellowhammer occurs in a number of plantations both of larch and of pine. In some districts the buzzard is present, and in central Wales the kite has begun nesting in some of the older forests of the Commission.

Reed Bunting

7

THE BIRDS OF SMALL WOODS AND SEMI-WOODLANDS

The meaning of the term ecotone has been explained in Chapter 3. Under natural conditions, where large areas of land under the same climate bear the same sort of climax vegetation, ecotones are relatively rare, and the only ones of any importance to woodland birds are the long borderlines between woodland and grassland or between woodland and swamp. In Great Britain, with its very varied topography and absence of large plains, ecotones would always have been more important than on the Continent. The action of man, in clearing woods on the one hand and planting trees on the other, has made them still more prominent, and in fact it is now difficult in many counties to find areas of uniform woodland from which the edge-effect is absent. Most of the habitats given for many song birds in the *Handbook* are natural or artificial ecotones, and it is difficult to sort out the connexions between any given species and its possible environments.

In view of the greater natural extent of pure habitats over the earth as a whole, it might at first be thought that more species would have been evolved in them than in ecotones, but this is not necessarily true, and indeed the reverse is, on the prevailing view of the method by which natural selection works, more likely. Evolution is less probable in a continuous habitat than in one which is isolated from similar areas, as is shown by the relatively large number of endemic species on islands, and many ecotones are, by their nature, comparable to islands. It is probable that some families or genera of birds, for instance the leaf-warblers (*Phylloscopi*) and the buntings (*Emberizinae*), have evolved in ecotones which are varied in nature as well as being separated geographically, but clearly this cannot apply to all the species of the present ecotones of Great Britain, since many of these habitats are of recent date and of artificial character.

There are four possible origins for a bird found in any given ecotone: it may have evolved in and for that ecotone; it may have evolved in another similar ecotone; or it may be primarily a bird of either of the constituent habitats of the ecotone. In all but the first of these cases, and especially in the third and fourth, it must have been able to change its habits to a greater or lesser degree; it must be what is sometimes called adaptable or plastic. Often the required plasticity is small, for the ecotone may be able to provide all the features of the original environment which are really important. Suitable food, a nest site and a song post are the chief things which woodland birds need, and these may all be provided by swamp on the one hand or parkland on the other, but the fact that not all woodland birds can make the change shows that some adaptation, even if it is only a psychological adjustment to the whole surroundings, is necessary as well.

Under natural conditions the most extensive ecotone in Great Britain was probably the fringe of broken and depressed woodland or scrub which must formerly have bordered the lowland woods wherever the hills rise above the timberline, usually at 1,000 to 1,500 feet above sea level. This is still represented by fragments of birch and oak, and in Scotland by Scotch fir. The birds of these high-level woods have been considered in earlier chapters, since they are not sharply marked off from those of the lowland woods of the same trees, but some further generalizations are possible. The two commonest species are the willow-warbler and the chaffinch. The first, characteristically a species of birch trees, is probably primarily a bird of the ecotone, and is only secondarily found in closed woodlands. The chaffinch is almost ubiquitous where there are trees, and is equally at home in closed woods and in scrub. I think it likely, for a reason given on page 242, that it too was evolved in fringe-woodland rather than in lowland woods. The tree-pipit, the third commonest species, is almost certainly, to judge from its relatives, a bird which has evolved in a tree-heath ecotone or woodland habitat from ancestors which were purely heath-living. Most of the other common species, such as the robin and the wren, are species which are very adaptable in their choice of habitat. The wren does not need trees, and is found in woods simply because they happen to provide what it really needs, which is a thick cover such as is given by a field layer of under-shrubs. The avoidance of these high-level woods by blue and great tits is striking, but in view of their presence in other lowland ecotones the reason may be climatic rather than ecological. The coal-tit is usually present, perhaps because the often rocky ground of the hills provides it with suitable nesting sites.

In a study of seven fell-woods in the English Lake District (Yapp 1953*a* and 1953*b*), where there is no important geographical and little climatic variation from one to the other, I found that it was possible to make some generalizations about the most constant species: they have a geographical range which extends to the far north of Europe, they feed almost entirely on insects, they are mostly hole- or ground-nesting, and some of them have a distinctly elongated tarsus when compared with related species which are not found in the fell-woods. In a general way all these features may be connected with the habitat, but they give no clue to the origin of the fauna.

In addition to the species already mentioned there are, in these woods, some which are much more typical of other habitats. The yellowhammer was present in summer in four out of seven of the Lake District woods; breeding in the woods was not proved but they were certainly used for food gathering, so that they were part of its habitat even if the nest was outside. Yellowhammers occur also in the birchwoods of the north-western Highlands and similar woods elsewhere. They are almost certainly heath birds which are in process of becoming adapted to a predominantly woodland ecotone. I have seen the ring-ouzel in the Birkrigg oakwood in Cumberland

and in one birchwood in Northumberland and two in Ross, and Dr. Bruce Campbell tells me that it comes into the scrub oakwoods of North Wales, but there is no proof of breeding in any of these. It may, like the yellowhammer, be in the process of moving in to the woods, but as most of the thrushes are woodland birds, though with a tendency to marginal habitats, it is more likely to be a species which has not quite forgotten its ancestral home.

Other heath birds which occasionally appear in the upland woods in summer are the chats. I have seen the wheatear in English and Scottish birchwoods, in a grove of rowans in the Pennines, and in Wistman's Wood on Dartmoor, while the whinchat is present in woods in all three countries, sometimes even where the trees are close together, and in 1959 a stonechat was singing well inside the Birkrigg oaks in Cumberland.

Many birds which are typically found in lowland woods where there is a thick shrub layer are found also in scrub, which resembles this without the trees. The robin, chaffinch, magpie, willow-warbler, garden-warbler, whitethroat, and blackbird are all common in this sort of habitat, and the blue, great and long-tailed tits also occur.

The other ecotone which was formerly of considerable natural extent is that of woodland/water, represented today by the alder carr of East Anglia and similar fragments elsewhere. So far as I am aware, no proper ecological study of its birds has ever been made, although there is an abundant literature on the river birds of the reed beds and water associated with it. The characteristic bird of the trees and bushes in this habitat is the reed-bunting; reeds are usually present where it is found but it is not these which attract it, and its nesting site, on the ground amongst bushes or in the bushes themselves, is not in general different from that of other scrub and woodland birds. Another small bird characteristic of some bushy fens is the grasshopper-warbler, for whom the water as such obviously has no particular attraction since it is found equally in dry young plantations. The same is true of the red-backed shrike and the nightjar, which are found on the Somerset levels.

In a small area of alder carr in Somerset, blackbirds, chaffinches, and long-tailed, blue and great tits, are present in summer, and probably breed. They are all woodland species which are satisfied by low trees which need not be very close together.

Running water in woods is not of great extent in this country and has no very well-defined fauna, but there is one very characteristic bird, the grey wagtail. Trees are perhaps not necessary for it, but I have found it most frequently where fast rocky streams of depth enough to make fording difficult run through woods or are bordered by trees. The association alleged in the books between the pied flycatcher and water I have not been able to confirm. Few of the fell-woods which are its normal habitat are without some running water, but it occurs also in those which are quite dry.

A bird of peculiar mixed habitat is the heron, which generally uses tall trees for nesting, but feeds in shallow water, which may be a small stream, the edge of a lake or a tidal estuary. Like the typical birds of parkland (p. 103) it nests socially and ranges widely for food.

Tree-heath was probably never of great extent in this country, but it still exists in parts of the old firwoods of Scotland, and more artificially in places such as the Surrey heaths and the North York Moors where firs, as well as birches and oaks, seed themselves and spread from planted areas amongst the heather. There are also many hillsides where gorse becomes a large enough shrub to produce a partially woodland appearance. The fauna of this type of ecotone shows a considerable overlap with that of the fell-woods. The tree-pipit, chaffinch, and willow-warbler are all present and common and can all be satisfied by relatively low bushes of 10 feet or less in height. My impression is that the tree-pipit needs higher trees when they are isolated than when they are growing in close canopy; it is found in birchwoods in Sutherland where the trees are only 20 feet in height, but I have no records of it on tree-heaths where the trees are as low as this. It is present in some plantations where the trees are only 3 feet high. The yellowhammer, whinchat, and stonechat are all characteristic, and all seem to need song posts which rise a foot or two above the general level of the vegetation. The grasshopper-warbler, though much more local in its distribution, lives in the same type of habitat.

All these are birds which probably evolved in and for the ecotone, but some which come from the woods may also be present. The magpie in particular strays far out into tree-heath, though it often, but not always, likes to be able to get back to thicker cover when disturbed. In some parts of the country it occurs in almost treeless areas, although this is usually where there are hedges, as will be discussed below. The crepuscular nightjar is frequent in some districts on tree-heaths, although it seems to need a fair density of trees. It is characteristic of that rather open type of woodland sometimes called by botanists oak-birch-heath, which develops on many sandy soils. Even when the trees are close together there is generally much space below them where it can catch moths on the wing.

The isolated or scattered trees, chiefly rowans, that grow by the sides of becks to 2,000 feet or more in the Lake District, attract a number of woodland species to them. Carrion-crows and willow-warblers especially follow them to the limit. At lower levels the pied flycatcher, redstart, and even the wood-warbler are satisfied by the irregular double lines of trees that border the gills.

Parkland, or grass with scattered trees, must formerly have been of very small extent in this country, as it could have existed only as a band joining the woodland to the few areas of grass without heath plants found on some of the chalk downs and some of the northern hills. It is now, if it is taken in a broad sense, the commonest English habitat, for it includes not only the planted areas round country houses from which it takes its name, but the whole pattern of Midland England with grass meadows, hedgerow trees, the woods of small size, lines, belts, clumps, and groves in the sense in which these woods have been defined in Chapter 3. The extent of this is shown by the Forestry Commission's sample survey of hedgerow and park timber and woods under five acres. It was estimated that in 1951 the total number of trees in these situations in Great Britain was 73 million, of which 56 million were in England.

Ecologically the birds of parkland can be put in three groups. There are those such as the skylark and stone-curlew (*Burhinus oedicnemus*), which are steppe birds that make no use of the trees, so that we are not concerned with them; there are the birds which seldom leave the hedges, which they probably regard as peculiar pieces of woodland; and there are the true parkland birds which make use of both trees and grass. I shall say something about the hedgerow birds below, and shall consider now the third group. They do not make a well-marked community, but include some characteristic species.

Most important of them is the rook. It nests in tall trees but feeds almost entirely on grassland or on cornfields, which are a sort of artificial grassland. Its method of feeding is to dig by inserting the bill into soft turf. This is clearly suitable only to ground of a medium degree of firmness, neither soft enough to be brushed aside as the blackbird does the leaves on the floor of a wood, nor firm enough to damage the bill as might happen in rocky country. The rook does not normally nest in large woods, and its present predilection for lines of trees must be a recently acquired taste, since none of these are more than a few hundred years old. It frequently nests in clumps and groves, and these are likely to have been its original home. The fact that there were few of these is possibly the origin of its colonial nesting habit, and this in its turn probably led to the bird's wide ranging for food.

The jackdaw and starling have similar feeding habits to the rook, but though probably primarily dependent on trees for nesting are more adaptable in their choice of site. The starling still nests in holes in trees, but probably oftener in holes in buildings, so that it is very largely a parasite on man; the jackdaw also may use buildings, though usually only large ones, and also makes much use of cliffs, which might possibly be considered its chief habitat in this country. The jackdaw and starling, like the rook, nest communally, and probably for the same reason. All three species congregate in very large numbers in winter roosts. The biological value of this habit is difficult to see, since the birds scatter at dawn to feed, and it is inconceivable that suitable roosting sites were even less widely distributed than suitable nesting sites. At the present time the birds fly over and ignore spinneys and groves which appear every bit as suitable as those to which they often cling so tenaciously.

The four birds of prey, barn owl, little owl, kestrel, and the rare hobby, all nest largely in trees but take their food outside. The hobby takes mainly birds and insects on the wing, and so can feed in any suitably open country where it can pursue its prey, but the other three take mainly mice and voles which are typical of grassland, over which most of their searching for food is done. The tawny owl, also feeding on small rodents, takes some of its food over grass, but is more typically a bird of dense woodland.

The vanishing wryneck, now limited to a few pairs in the south-east of England, is a bird of parkland. Its habitat is perhaps connected with its food, which consists largely of ants. Many species of these are found in woods, but others live in the open, and nearly all live chiefly on the ground. The green woodpecker, which has probably taken to feeding on ants more recently, has also become, in some parts of England, predominantly a bird of parkland.

All the species so far considered are birds which need large trees mixed with grassland, but there are others which are satisfied with small trees or even bushes. The linnet, goldfinch, greenfinch, hedge-sparrow, and whitethroat are examples, and the house-sparrow is largely a grass feeder in autumn, so that this was probably its normal habitat before it became domesticated. The woodlark, cirl bunting, yellowhammer, and tree-sparrow also are birds of bushes with grass, but they prefer, and perhaps the cirl bunting requires, some trees as well. All these, except for the woodlark and the migratory white-throat, are chiefly, and in winter almost entirely, seed eaters. Grasses, and the associated plants of open spaces which botanists call ruderals, tend to have large seeds, so areas bearing them can presumably support a denser population of birds than some other habitats. With the spread of cultivation there has been an increase in the supply of such seeds, partly through the increased size of ear of the plants bred for food for man and animals, and partly through the disturbance of the land which gives the opportunity for a wider and more rapid distribution of ruderals.

In autumn and winter, chaffinches are added to the seed-eating parkland birds, and do not differ greatly in habit from the others, but the chief winter additions are the completely migratory red-wing, fieldfare, and brambling. The first two of these feed mainly on grassland in this country, but they feed also on berries of trees such as the hawthorn, and roost in shrubs or even well inside tall woods, so that they are truly birds of the ecotone. This is in line with their habit in the breeding season, for although they are found in dense woods, their nesting habitat includes also the sort of ecotone which I have described here as fell-woodland.

The second-order ecotone is the actual wood-edge. In a general way it is known that many birds, such as the willow-warbler and spotted flycatcher, are found in higher numbers along the edges than inside a wood, but no numerical studies seem to have been made of this. Such studies could only be carried out on large woods, and would too often be complicated by hedges, cattle, and houses standing just outside. Since a sharp edge to a habitat is an uncommon thing in nature, it is likely that the birds of the wood-edge really belong to one or other of the communities of the first-order ecotones which I have discussed. Carpenter (1935), working on the much longer edges which can be studied in North America, has shown that there is a preferential occupation of the lee side of a wood. This is in spite of the fact that the insect distribution is uniform along all the edges. This suggests that the birds avoid high winds, another example of what must in some sense be a psychological preference.

Besides the plantations made for forestry, there are a number of types of man-made habitat which have many features in common with woodlands and so have attracted woodland birds. The most important of these, which make an artificial ecotone, are the hedgerows, which give a spurious well-wooded appearance to southern England when it is seen from near the ground, as, for example, from the window of a railway train. Hedgerows probably existed in the Middle Ages and enclosures are frequently mentioned by Leland, but it was in the eighteenth and early nineteenth centuries that they became the dominant feature of most of the countryside. No proper study of them from the botanical or any other point of view has ever been made, and what follows is based on my own superficial and incomplete observation.

The commonest type is a well-grown hedge of hawthorn, with fairly frequent standard trees. The hedgerow was one of the traditional places in which to plant oaks to give the 'knees' referred to above (p. 47), and the value of hedgrow timber was often great enough to be taken into account in assessing the price of the land. Oaks are still common as hedgerow trees in some counties; they are the most frequent tree in Cheshire and there are many in Warwickshire. Also common are the elms, of which the species *Ulmus procera* is found throughout England; it is a large tree, reaching 100 feet in height. A number of other species, mostly rather shorter, have been distinguished chiefly on small characters of the leaves, and the process of splitting is still going on; they are all restricted in distribution. In parts of Cumberland the ash is the commonest hedgerow tree, and has been since the eighteenth century, for it was commented on by Coleridge and William Gilpin. Many other trees occur occasionally, mostly planted, but as the thorns give protection from grazing animals there is also natural growth of any trees that may be in the neighbourhood. The Forestry Commission's sample survey of 1951 did not distinguish between trees in hedgerows or in parks, and woods of under 5 acres. Taking all these together it was found that half the total number of trees in England occurred in the southern counties of Kent, Surrey, Sussex, Hampshire, Berkshire, Wiltshire, Gloucestershire, Herefordshire, Dorset, Somerset, Devonshire, and Cornwall. Oak is the chief species in Wales and all parts of England, with ash common in the north, on the belt of oolite that runs across the middle of England, in the south-west and in Wales. Elm is commonest in the east, especially in Huntingdonshire, Lincolnshire, and Bedfordshire. In Scotland, beech, oak, ash, sycamore, and Scotch fir are all plentiful. These figures are obviously weighted by the small woods (groves in my nomenclature) which greatly raise the proportion of oak.

The thorn trees that make up the main part of the hedge are, in the best farming practice, regularly 'laid' every fifteen years or so; the straightest-growing branches are cut three-quarters of the way through near their base and bent over to make an angle of about 30° with the horizontal, and at the same time much thinning is carried out. The result is a thin, low hedge from which lateral branches grow in three directions—to right and left and upwards—to make the characteristic thick hedge. Old neglected hedges become thin at the bottom and, as individual boles die, gradually change into a line of hawthorn trees.

Many other shrubs are associated with hedges, and in some counties are dominant. On the clays of the south Midlands, as seen for instance from the railway which separates rather than connects Oxford and Cambridge, the hedges are almost pure blackthorn and there are very few trees. In parts of west Somerset and east Devon there are many hedges of beech, which are seldom seen elsewhere except as the boundaries of gardens, and were introduced here when Exmoor Forest was reclaimed in the early nineteenth century; they make a thin but nearly windproof screen and the leaves stay on long into the autumn or even right through the winter. The plants are not allowed to develop into trees. In other parts of Devonshire there are hedges of hazel. In

TA

Birds of three stages of W

Area 1. *Birch*

	1950–53 111 *min.*			1954–59 74 *min.*		
	No./ hr.	*To- tal*	*R.A.*	*No./ hr.*	*To- tal*	*R.A.*
Aegithalos caudatus (long-tailed tit)	3	5	8	2	2	2
Anthus trivialis (tree-pipit)	1	1	2			
Corvus corone (crow)						
Emberiza citrinella (yellowhammer)						
Erithacus rubecula (robin)	3	5	8	3	3	4
Fringilla coelebs (chaffinch)	1	2	3			
Garrulus glandarius (jay)	1	2	3			
Parus ater (coal-tit)				2	3	4
P. coeruleus (blue tit)	2	3	5	3	4	5
P. major (great tit)	1	2	3	5	6	7
Phoenicurus phoenicurus (redstart)	1	1	2	2	3	4
Phylloscopus collybita (chiff-chaff)	1	1	2	2	3	4
P. sibilatrix (wood-warbler)						
P. trochilus (willow-warbler)	14	26	44	26	32	38
Sylvia atricapilla (blackcap)						
S. borin (garden-warbler)	1	2	3	2	3	4
S. communis (whitethroat)					1	1
Troglodytes troglodytes (wren)	1	1	2	3	4	5
Turdus merula (blackbird)	3	6	10	6	8	10
T. philomelos (song-thrush)	1	1	2			
Other passerines		1		2	2	
Columba palumbus (wood-pigeon)				3	4	5
Cuculus canorus (cuckoo)						
Dendrocopus major (great spotted woodpecker)					1	
Phasianus colchicus (pheasant)						
Picus viridis (green woodpecker)						
Other non-passerines					5	
	32	59		68	84	

14

orest: summer. Total contacts

Area 2. Oak and Birch						Area 3. High Oak and Beech					
1950–53 204 min.			1954–59 264 min.			1950–53 474 min.			1954–59 722 min.		
No./hr.	Total	R.A.	No./hr.	Total	R.A.	No./hr.	Total	R.A.	No./hr.	Total	R.A.
				1			3	1		8	
3	10	11	8	36	11	5	41	10	4	44	5
				6	2	2	12	3	2	19	2
				5	1		1		1	14	2
4	15	11	6	26	8	5	39	9	4	47	5
1	5	4	9	38	11	7	58	14	10	118	14
2	7	6	1	4	1	1	6	1	1	15	2
3	9	8	3	11	3	1	9	2	2	21	2
3	9	8	3	14	4	3	27	6	3	31	4
3	9	8	2	10	3	1	8	2	2	19	2
	1	1	2	8	2		2		1	16	2
1	2	2		2		2	14	3	3	36	4
1	2	2	1	4	1	4	34	8	2	25	3
6	21	19	21	93	28	4	29	7	14	167	19
						1	5	1		1	
				2		1	9	2	3	35	4
1	2	2	2	9	3	1	10	2	1	13	2
3	10	9	4	18	5	4	31	7	3	34	4
1	3	3	3	15	4	3	22	5	3	40	5
				2		1	9	2	2	20	2
	5			1			9			9	
			2	10	3		2		4	43	5
				3			3	1		8	
				3		1	10	2	2	26	3
1	2	2	3	11	3	2	17	4		31	4
				2		1	4	1	1	16	2
							4			7	
3	113		77	338		54	431		72	864	

some exposed districts, such as Cornwall, parts of north Wales, and the Isle of Man, hedges are of gorse (*Ulex europaeus*). In East Anglia and to some extent in Lancashire and Cheshire the hedges, though of hawthorn, are little more than boundary lines, being thin and cut to 2 or 3 feet in height. At the other extreme, surrounding the hop-yards of Herefordshire and Worcestershire are tall thin screens of thorn 15 or more feet high.

It is obvious that the smaller the fields the greater the length of hedge on a given area. An inspection of a random collection of the 2½-inch Ordnance Survey maps showed that in the regions free from villages, motor roads, and open country, the length of hedge per square mile ranged from 4 miles in Oxfordshire to 12·5 miles in Devonshire, and there may well be parts of the country that go outside these limits. The average would appear to be about 8 or 9.

Nowhere in nature do shrubs grow in straight lines intersecting at right angles with often a single species extending for miles in the network; as a bird looks at them, hedges probably appear much like the edge of a wood—or rather two edges separated by only a few feet—or like the mixture of trees and field layer that constitutes parkland or tree-heath. Botanists have long recognized that the flora of a well-grown hedge is a modification of that of the woods, and the same is to a great extent true of the avifauna. No proper study of the distribution of birds in hedges can be made until a botanical survey is first done. A number of observers have made surveys of farm birds, but a farm is a mixture of ecological types rather than a unit, and it is impossible to extract from the published papers the information that we need. Yellowhammer, robin, chaffinch, dunnock, whitethroat, blackbird, throstle, and wren are probably the chief species, with the thrushes tending to be dominant. Most of these I have already mentioned as found in one or more of the natural woodland ecotones. In winter the tits should be added, but owing to the absence of nest sites they do not commonly breed in hedges.

I have no doubt that careful examination would demonstrate both regional differences and those due to the varying composition of the hedges. Thus a short series of transects made from the train between Birmingham and London in 1949–51 showed rather higher numbers of magpies near Leamington and Coventry than further south. Their abundance in south Warwickshire is connected with the large and neglected whitethorn hedges of this region, in which they nest. By contrast, in the Isle of Man they are common on farms where the only hedges are of gorse and only 5 or 6 feet high. These two situations, which to human eyes are rather different, presumably provide the bird with its two important requirements of grass for feeding and dense cover for nesting.

On the chalk near Cambridge the nightingale is a hedgerow rather than a woodland bird, presumably because thick hedges are more suitable for it than the woods, which are mostly of beech and have little or no shrub or field layer. It was also the hedges that were occupied when it extended its range into the lower part of the Vale of Berkeley in Gloucestershire in the early 1940s. The chiff-chaff, which, according to my observations and the published lists, is rare in woods, is common in some areas where there are fairly frequent trees along the hedges. It is perhaps a bird of line plus hedge, rather than of either by itself.

How hedges or a few trees can bring together birds of diverse habitats is shown by some observations made on Exmoor in May 1952. Here, in a few hawthorns at 1,250 feet above sea level, were a redstart, a pair of whitethroats, and a whinchat. A little higher up, at 1,320 feet, one of the characteristic overgrown beech hedges held a bullfinch and a cock ring-ouzel. The latter flew along and in and out of the hedge just like a blackbird. All these were far from any woods except a small patch of thin and damp alderwood a quarter of a mile away, and were on grassland probably reclaimed from the open moor in the early years of last century. The extension of such typically woodland birds as the redstart and bullfinch into such an unpromising region, and their association with the heath-dwelling whinchat and ring-ouzel, suggest either a pressure of population in the lowland areas, or a greater breadth of taste than birds are sometimes credited with.

The same thing is shown with artificial hedges. Post-and-wire fences and stone walls might seem to have nothing in common with hedges except their function of demarcating field boundaries, but in fact they have features which enable them to act as substitutes for woods, or at least for trees. The tree-pipit and many of the tree-heath birds, such as yellowhammer, whinchat, and cuckoo, make use of the posts as stations from which to sing. Old stone walls, especially those built without mortar of the stones lying ready to hand, are characteristic of the hill districts from Somerset to the far north, and are full of holes which make suitable nesting sites for birds. The redstart, which in woods may nest in holes in trees or in cracks between rocks and the ground, is at least as common in the Lake District on enclosed farm land as it is anywhere else. Presumably the holes in the walls appear to it as holes in rocks; where there are cattle there are plenty of flies; and if there is any real need at all for trees it is met by the occasional ash or rowan along the field's edge. Less often the nuthatch and great, blue, coal- and marsh-tits nest in walls, and near farms the pied flycatcher also does so. Since it is not now common in the valley woods, their clearance and replacement by walled pasture may even have enabled the birds' numbers to increase.

An artificial woodland ecotone of a peculiar nature is the orchard. Most farms have a small field with a few apple or pear trees, but in some counties, notably Kent, Somerset, and Worcestershire, fruit is one of the chief crops and orchards are continuous over fairly large areas. As with hedges, no study of their birds has ever been made, which is especially surprising in view of the potential economic importance of birds, on the one hand as destroyers of bud, bloom, and fruit, and on the other as a protection against harmful insects. The bullfinch is notoriously a pest of fruit trees because of its habit of feeding on buds. It is one of the few woodland birds, as I shall show in Chapter 9, which is largely vegetarian, and as fruit trees have been unconsciously selected for large, and perhaps succulent, buds, it has not surprisingly transferred its attention to them from the smaller and less tender buds of forest trees. Many other woodland birds, especially perhaps the tits, are common in orchards. In a restricted area of south Shropshire the pied flycatcher nests in old and decayed orchards, where the apple trees have plenty of holes, in preference to the adjacent sessile oakwoods which are its more natural habitat.

In autumn the fruit itself attracts many birds. Blackbirds are notoriously fond of cherries, and blue tits of apples. Starlings glut themselves on pears. While blackcurrants seem to be neglected by almost all birds, the red and white sorts are taken before they are ripe by thrushes and many warblers.

Finally, gardens, especially the larger sorts with many trees and shrubs, are no doubt to a bird's eyes a sort of woodland, but as they provide unusual and excessive food they are too artificial a habitat for the scope of this book.

Blackbird

8

SUCCESSION IN DEVELOPING WOODS

When man carries out a scheme of afforestation, he converts, over a period of years, an area which was formerly grass or heath into a closed woodland. There is a gradual change in the appearance of the land as the trees grow and come into contact with each other, and associated changes are impressed on the plants of the field layer and on the fauna. These natural or semi-natural changes constitute what the ecologist calls succession, and are a special case of a phenomenon which is widespread wherever climatic changes, the activities of man, or the actions of the plants and animals themselves, bring about gradual changes in their environment, so that it becomes suitable for different species as time goes on. The growth of a plantation produces what is in effect an ecotone in time as well as space. At first the steppe or heath birds are little affected by the young trees; then the birds which really need open country have to leave, and others, which need low song posts or bushes for nesting, come in; and finally with increasing height of the trees the land becomes a wood, and only those birds which can live under a closed canopy can survive.

It is rare for any extensive areas to be planted in this country with pure stands of natural hardwoods, but there are several places where forests which were clear-felled in or after 1914 have regenerated with oak or birch, with forestry treatment in the later stages. So far as I know there has been no long-term study of the succession of birds in these conditions, which is a pity, as the changes would probably be similar to those which would occur in nature after forest fires, or where the woodland is spreading northwards under climatic amelioration. Since oak grows slowly it would be a lifetime's work or more to trace through the succession on one area, but much could be done by a comparison of the birds of nearby areas of different ages since felling, if such could be found. Natural regeneration of this sort differs from the growth of a plantation in that there is a succession of the species of shrubs and timber trees as well as of the field layer. Birch is nearly always associated with oak and keeps ahead of it both in density and height for some years, and hawthorn similarly leads ash on the limestone soils.

Table 14 shows the results of counts made by the line-transect method in three portions of Wyre Forest, the natural vegetation of which is sessile oak, in the three months of April to June in the years 1950–3. All contacts (except those with juveniles) are summed, so that late migrants will be slightly underestimated, and passage migrants, notably the willow-warbler and chiff-chaff, may be slightly overestimated, but the detailed figures suggest that these errors would not affect the general picture. Area 1 was clear-felled in 1939 and has regenerated with a thick tangle of birch except for a few rides that have been cut through it; it was much thinned in the spring of 1951. During the period of the counts the general height increased from about 6 feet to about 10. Oaks are present but are not conspicuous. The area consists of two blocks of 1,300×450 feet and 900×300 feet, separated by a grass roadway with some well-grown oaks. Birds in these were omitted from the counts, but as the total area is only about 16 acres some of the more casual birds may have been wanderers from outside. Area 2 was formerly maintained as coppice and was last cut between 1931 and 1935 and, when the counts were made, consisted of oak and birch in the proportion of about 1 : 2 and about 25 feet high (Plate IX). There is no shrub layer, but for the most part the field layer is fairly thick, with bracken and bramble. These plants, according to Salisbury (1925), become abundant as the result of the increased light intensity following the cutting of the trees. There has been some thinning in places during the course of the observation. The area in which the records were made is 165 acres, but another 180 acres of very similar coppice adjoins it.

Area 3 consists of well-grown oaks about 40 feet high, with occasional birches, mostly reaching into the oak canopy (Plate X). Except in one small part where there is hazel there are no shrubs, but the whole area has been underplanted, from 1936 to 1942, with beech. The youngest beeches were only about a foot high when the counts were made and did not show above the field layer, but in the older compartments they were 10 feet or a little more and quite dense. The field layer is mostly of bilberry or heather with bracken in the lighter parts. Selective felling of the oaks continued throughout the time of the survey. The total area is 214 acres. In areas 2 and 3 there are occasional old yews. The three areas represent fairly good stages in the natural regeneration from clear-felled land to mature high forest.

The number of species present clearly increases with age, but the total number of individuals does not alter so much. In the young birch the total contacts were 31 per hour, in the oak-and-birch 33, and in the mature oak 52. This is, however, a big enough difference in density to make the relative abundance misleading if taken by itself. The greatest specific density is given by the willow-warbler in young birch, with 14 contacts per hour; in the oak-and-birch this has dropped to 6 per hour and in the mature oak to 4 per hour. In spite of the greater total number of birds in this third area, the commonest bird, the chaffinch, scores only 7 per hour.

When I began the study the birches on area 1 were already 5 or 6 feet high and almost impenetrable. Probably for this reason no true heath birds were present, although they occur in other open parts of the forest. The dominance of the willow-warbler is very marked. It is possible that the blackbirds fly out into the nearby oaks for singing, although I have not seen them do this. The chiff-chaff was probably a wanderer from the oaks. The grasshopper-warbler, heard in one year only, was singing on the edge where the birches were more open and there was much thick heather. The absence of the wren may be connected with the density of the birch, which prevents the development of a thick field layer.

In area 2 the willow-warbler is still the commonest bird but has lost its dominance, a condition which is in contrast to its position in the Ross and Sutherland birchwoods described in Chapter 5. The robin rather more than holds its own, but the blackbird has almost disappeared. A number of woodland birds are beginning to be important, especially the tree-pipit and, collectively, the tits. The coal-tit is as common as either the blue or the great. The chaffinch rather surprisingly is still hardly present, although in the fell-woods that appear comparable in many ways it is abundant. The requirements of the wren now appear to be satisfied by the thick field layer.

There is rather a big jump in age from area 2 to area 3 so that there is little indication of how the other woodland birds come in to give the full lists characteristic of durmast oakwoods. The high numbers for the pheasant are certainly misleading, as it scores thus because the crowing of the cock is heard over a wide area. While the number of blue tits per hour is about the same as in the oak-and-birch, those of great tits and coal-tits have fallen to one-third their former density. Some of the birds, such as the whitethroat and jay, are confined to those parts of the area where the underplanted beech is well grown, and are dependent on this rather than on the maturity of the oaks. The wren has maintained or slightly improved its position, perhaps because the field layer is here for the most part slightly thicker than in area 2. The robin is the most consistent bird throughout the three stages, both in its rank and in the number of contacts per hour; this fits with its well-known plasticity in choice of nesting site. The chaffinch is a clear dominant in the oaks, fairly closely followed by the tree-pipit, robin, and wood-warbler. The presence of a number of tree-pipits and two wood-warblers in the oak-and-birch suggests that this area has just about reached a critical point in the transition from scrub to woodland.

Since 1953 there have been further changes in the birds, although the vegetational changes that have determined them have been man-made rather than natural. It is convenient to begin with the high oaks, where the underplanted beech has developed considerably. By 1956 most of it was about 10 feet high and had begun to form a significant shrub layer which in places was difficult to walk through, but some of it was still less than 6 feet. By 1959 there was little beech less than 10 feet, and some was as high as 24 feet, while for the most part walking was difficult or impossible except along the rides and in a few open spaces where, for some reason, the growth of the birch had been checked.

Table 14 shows also the birds recorded in the years 1954–9. The total density of birds is high, and it is obvious that there has been a marked fall in the relative abundance of the tree-pipit, wood-warbler, robin, and wren; there has also been some fall in the densities of all these, especially of the wood-warbler. Until I worked out the figures I had not been aware of any change in robin and wren, but the fall in tree-pipit and wood-warbler was even more noticeable in the field than it is in the table, since these species were entirely absent from areas where they had previously been common. As the beech grew they became confined to the parts of the forest where it is shortest and thinnest. At a height of 6 to 8 feet it seems to exclude them completely.

The chaffinch has increased its density and maintained its relative abundance, but there are signs that in the last two years its numbers have fallen again. If this is not a population-fluctuation caused by extraneous factors it suggests that the high and closed layer of beech is less favourable to the species than a lower shrub layer.

The chief increases are shown by the warblers (other than the wood-warbler). There has been a slight increase in the chiff-chaff, and a big jump in density and relative abundance of the willow-warbler, which is now as dominant an element in the avifauna as it is anywhere except for the Sutherland birchwoods. The whitethroat has maintained its numbers and the garden-warbler has increased considerably. These two first appeared under the oaks where the beeches were thickest, and then gradually spread. The blackcap, which appeared about the same time as the garden-warbler, has not increased.

The vegetation of the two younger areas has changed little. The young birch has grown so that by 1959 the general height was about 16 to 20 feet. The oak-and-birch has undergone some thinning, but otherwise is much as it was in the earlier years.

Table 14 shows that in both areas the density of birds has more than doubled but that otherwise there have been few important changes, the increases being generally spread over many species. The tree-pipit has improved its position in the oak-and-birch, both relatively and absolutely, but the wood-warbler, contrary to my expectations, has barely held its own. Perhaps this is because there has been a big increase in the willow-warbler, which has raised its relative abundance from 19 to 28 per cent. The chaffinch also has increased both relatively and absolutely.

Niebuhr (1948) in Germany made some comparisons of the birds of woods of pedunculate oak of different ages. He found that in a mature wood 200 years old 86 per cent. of the birds nested in trees or shrubs (many of them in holes) and only 12 per cent. on the ground. Where the trees were only 19 to 22 feet high, 75 per cent. nested on the ground, and of the remainder none nested in holes. There is some similarity here to the Lake District woods, where the trees are mostly about 24 feet high and most species nest on the ground, although some breed in holes in trees as well. Niebuhr's figures must be taken with some caution, as in the young stage only three species—chaffinch, wood-warbler, and willow-warbler—were present, and the numbers were very small.

Morley (1940) made a brief survey of the succession of birds on a Sussex oakwood after burning, and the observations, so far as they go, agree fairly well with mine in Wyre. At four years, tree-pipit, robin, and willow-wren had begun to nest, but chaffinch and white-throat occupied only portions of the burnt area that overlapped with the unburnt forest. In the forest as a whole, before it was burnt, thirty-six species were recorded in the breeding season.

The plant succession in conifer plantations differs from that in nature in three main ways, in addition to the presence of a new, and often foreign, dominant species. The trees are planted so close together that at an early stage in their growth a dense canopy is formed, light is excluded, and the field and ground layers are killed; any gaps which do occur through death are filled, at least where the Forestry Commission is in charge, by the systematic process of 'beating up'; and at about fifteen years the trees are 'brashed'. This last means that the lower branches are cut off some years before they would naturally die and fall; they are generally left lying on the ground so that to some extent they provide the cover which would normally be given by the missing field layer (Plate XI).

Duffey (1947) described the birds of an area in Leicestershire where a mixed oak–ash–birch wood was clear-felled and planted with 99 per cent. conifers. He found that in the second year the plantation was colonized by tree-pipit, willow-warbler, hedge-sparrow, whitethroat, and wren, with occasional grasshopper-warblers and whinchats, which were both new to the district. The most interesting point of this is the early appearance of woodland birds, especially the tree-pipit, for the trees were only 3 feet high. In view of the Lacks' observations on the Breckland plantations, to be discussed below, it is possible that this is due to the absence of competition from heath birds. If this is so, it appears that some woodland birds can tolerate non-woodland conditions if the species proper to the habitat are absent. This sort of thing is well known in plants and in other groups of the animal kingdom, and several ornithologists have described examples of some extension of habitat-range of birds in the absence of congeneric competitors. I do not know of any examples where it has been claimed that a bird's habitat may be greatly extended in the absence of species of different genera and families. Morley (1940) has remarked that the tree-pipit can give full song from a perch only 18 inches high and I have found it present in a number of coniferous plantations less than 3 feet high, in association with meadow-pipits but always where chats were absent.

The early appearance of woodland birds continued; the robin appeared in the third and fourth years, and jay, blackbird, song-thrush, and wood-pigeon between the eighth and eleventh. Before this there was a decrease in the willow-warblers and whitethroats.

Lack and Lack (1951) studied plantations of Scotch and Corsican pine on Breckland, and obtained rather different results. They recorded the age of the trees, but not the height, and as there is much variation in the rate of growth their results must be treated with some caution. Moreover, their counts were made in April, which is too early to give a proper picture of the breeding fauna. Most summer migrants have not then settled down to breed, and even the chaffinch may still be in the process of taking up territory. These plantations were made on bare heath, much of which still surrounds the forests, and has a characteristic avifauna of skylark, meadow-pipit, whinchat, and stonechat, with some wheatears and yellow wagtails. As the trees grow, the heath birds decline and are replaced by two communities in succession. The heath birds persist until the eighth year, and willow-warbler and whitethroat, which are present in small numbers on the unplanted heath, reach a maximum in the seventh to twelfth years. The other woodland birds appear in two groups: chaffinch, hedge-sparrow, thrushes, and wren from about the seventh to the tenth years, with a few earlier occurrences, and the robin, jay, tits, and goldcrest at about fifteen years.

The disappearance of the warblers, thrushes, and hedge-sparrows when the trees are brashed at fifteen years is very sudden. This by itself does not justify the classification of all these as scrub species, for a woodland without either shrub or field layer, which is the condition which the forester achieves by his operations, is something known in this country only to a very limited extent in some beech and yew woods and on very steep slopes. There is every reason to suppose that if the lower branches were left, or if shrubs were allowed to develop, some of these birds, and especially the thrushes, would persist until the trees were very much larger and perhaps indefinitely. The late arrival of the tits and of the robin is noticeable. The former have probably to wait until the trees are large enough to provide nesting sites, and the latter looks as if in the early stages it might be in competition with the two chats. The absence of these from the land on which Duffey's observations were made would account for its much earlier arrival on his plantations. The wren extends fairly uniformly through the series. After the trees are brashed it makes use of the dead branches lying on the ground for shelter. Presumably it would not continue after these decay, which must be soon after these counts cease. There is a striking absence of the tree-pipit, which may be for geographical rather than ecological reasons for the bird seems to be inexplicably scarce in the Cambridge region, but may be due simply to the early dates of the counts.

Since 1955 I have made a number of counts in the Forestry Commission's plantations, chiefly in the counties of Cumberland, Montgomery, Radnor, and Devon, and mostly at altitudes of 1,000 feet or more. Most of these plantations were made on grass moor—mat-grass (*Nardus stricta*) or purple moor-grass (*Molinia coerulea*)—but a few on heather moor. The chief trees are Sitka and Norway spruce.

Three stages can be distinguished. In the first, though the trees rise a little above the original vegetation, this persists between them and the effect is that of a moor or heath with frequent bushes, or a rather dense ecotone. Next, when the trees are about 6 feet high, their branches touch and the original field layer is killed. In this, the foresters' thicket stage, the trees, especially if Sitka, are quite impenetrable and one can only observe the birds from the rides and rackways. Occasional trees are by this time 8 feet high, but there are also often patches where growth has been poor and some grass or heather persists. Finally, as the trees grow, their lower branches die so that it becomes possible to stoop underneath them, but before this process has gone far brashing is usually carried out.

I have grouped my observations according to these three stages, and Table 15 shows all the birds that at any time in the succession are dominant by the criteria used in Chapters 4 and 5. For the youngest plantations all tree species are grouped together, but for the older trees the birds of Sitka and Norway spruce are shown separately. At these altitudes in the forests where I have chiefly worked there are few stands of Scotch fir or larch, and my figures for these, which are necessarily slight, do not suggest any important differences.

It is clear that there are no sudden changes. A few individuals of almost all the woodland and scrub birds are present before the thicket stage is reached, the exceptions being coal-tit, hedge-sparrow, chiff-chaff, and song-thrush. Conversely, all the moor and heath birds persist into the thicket stage, though in reduced numbers. They are found in fact only where patches of the original field layer persist. By the time that brashing has taken place they have been eliminated altogether, not because of any direct effect of the brashing itself, but because by this time there are no open spaces left. If, indeed, brashing has any effect at all, it is on the shrub birds, for after it has been carried out there are no linnets, redpolls, yellowhammers, or hedge-sparrows, and a reduced number of willow-warblers and thrushes.

While the fauna of the thicket stage is relatively rich, with a total of 39 species observed, of which 18 are dominant in at least one type of wood, that of the brashed trees is poor, for although 31 species were recorded, only 9 were dominant, and 2 (the chaffinch and goldcrest) made up 60 per cent. of the total contacts. Twenty-one species were common to the two stages.

The tree-pipit is commonest when the trees are less than 6 feet high, and is scarcely present after brashing. This is presumably because in these closed spruce forests with no field layer there are no nest sites, for in the older larch plantations of Wyre Forest, where bracken grows under the trees, a few are regularly present.

The most important species that are more or less restricted to the thicket stage are the linnet, redpoll, yellowhammer, hedge-sparrow, and whitethroat, with the grasshopper-warbler (not shown in the table) also important in some forests. The fact that all of these were commoner in Norway spruce than in Sitka may be significant, but other possible factors must be investigated before we can be sure of this.

The relatively low numbers of coal-tits compared with goldcrests in the brashed woods is perhaps caused by the smaller number of suitable nest sites. Only four blue tits and two great tits were recorded, and the scarcity of these is not surprising, as hardly any tree-holes in which they could nest are present. It may, however, be partly because blue and great tits have never found these woods, as they are equally uncommon in winter, although plenty of coal-tits are then present.

There is much less difference between the three stages in winter. I have very few counts for the areas under 6 feet, but what I have suggest that the usual heath and moorland birds are present, but in small numbers. In the same way the scrub birds (linnet, yellowhammer, hedge-sparrow, and thrushes) are at low density in the thicket stage. There are, however, many more coal-tits and goldcrests than in summer, and these two species together make up nearly half the total daytime contacts. One of my counts in a Cumberland forest was distorted by a flock of finches coming in to roost. These included at least 200 chaffinches, as well as bramblings, linnets, redpolls, and perhaps other species. In the brashed plantations coal-tit and goldcrest make up over 60 per cent. of the total contacts and the only other numerically important bird is the crossbill, which occurred in flocks in two of the winters in which I was counting. It is naturally confined to trees of cone-bearing age. A

TA

Succession in coniferous plantatio

	Not brashed, less than 6 ft. Percent-age freq-uency	Rela-tive abund-ance
Alauda arvensis (skylark) . . .	52	23
Anthus pratensis (meadow-pipit) . .	72	35
A. trivialis (tree-pipit)	22	6
Carduelis cannabina (linnet) . . .	8	3
C. flammea (redpoll)	3	
Corvus corone (crow)	6	
Emberiza citrinella (yellowhammer) . .	6	
Erithacus rubecula (robin) . . .	14	2
Fringilla coelebs (chaffinch) . . .	19	2
Parus ater (coal-tit)		
Phylloscopus collybita (chiff-chaff) . .		
P. trochilus (willow-warbler) . . .	25	7
Prunella modularis (hedge-sparrow) . .		
Regulus regulus (goldcrest) . . .	6	
Saxicola rubetra (whinchat) . . .	33	6
Sylvia communis (whitethroat) . . .	13	1
Troglodytes troglodytes (wren) . . .	6	2
Turdus merula (blackbird) . . .	6	
T. philomelos (song-thrush) . . .		
Columba palumbus (wood-pigeon) . .	6	1
	Quadrats	*Total contac*
	36	606

5

mmer. Dominant species only

Not brashed, more than 6 ft.				*Brashed*			
Sitka		*Norway*		*Sitka*		*Norway*	
ercent-age freq-uency	*Rela-tive abund-ance*	*Percent-age freq-uency*	*Rela-tive abund-ance*	*Percent-age freq-uency*	*Rela-tive abund-ance*	*Percent-age freq-uency*	*Rela-tive abund-ance*
11		6					
11	3	22	3				
13	2			6		8	
8		28	1			3	
13	2	39	10				
24	2	6		16	1	10	
5		44	3				
57	6	67	6	53	6	80	11
75	20	78	12	81	30	90	28
27	4	55	4	56	9	67	8
16	1	22	2	31	3		
75	21	72	18	16	2	26	4
27	2	50	3	15	1	5	
62	14	78	12	81	30	90	31
13	1	22	1				
19	2	33	2	3			
49	5	55	4	56	10	59	6
30	2	55	4	13	2	10	
24	2	44	3	22	2	15	
35	6	55	6	13		28	3
uadrats	*Total contacts*	*Quadrats*	*Total contacts*	*Quadrats*	*Total contacts*	*Quadrats*	*Total contacts*
37	658	18	473	32	462	39	693

total of 23 species was recorded against 26 in the unbrashed areas, with 17 species common to the two. The relative lack of distinction between the faunas of the two stages presumably reflects the fact that a bird is much less demanding in its habitat requirements in the winter than when it is breeding.

Magpie

9

THE INTER-RELATIONS OF THE COMMUNITY: (1) Food

It is interesting, but difficult, to try to work out the ecological relationships of the community. These have three aspects. First, there is the dependence of each species, directly or indirectly, on the vegetational background for many of the things that make life possible; secondly, there is the complementary exploitation of this background by various species, so that they are not in complete competition with each other and the resources of the habitat are used to their fullest extent; and thirdly, there is some degree of direct dependence of one species on another. Fundamental to all these is the food relationship, for without an adequate supply of food suitable to the beaks, gizzards, and other digestive organs of the particular bird, life of the individual will stop after a few hours or days. For the successful completion of the life-cycle, that is for the production of young and their growth to maturity, birds are closely dependent on the right material background, for the nest of each species can vary in its site and design only within somewhat narrow limits. Lastly, birds, more obviously than any but the highest mammals, have a rich psychic life which, though full of individual variations, runs for each species always on a constant theme; if the physical conditions to make this possible are not provided, breeding cannot occur, and there is likely to be at most a temporary and limited population.

Quite apart from the ordinary classification based on structure and supposed ancestral relationships, animals may be divided according to the type of food that they eat. The simplest and fundamental division is into those that feed on plants (herbivores), those that feed on other animals (carnivores), and those that feed on both animals and plants (omnivores). Since all primary production of organic matter on the earth is by plants, the carnivores must feed, either directly or at one or more removes, on herbivores, so that a series of food-chains exist all of which start with the plant and then proceed to a herbivore and to one or a series of carnivores, each feeding on the one before it, and ending only with an animal that has no enemies at all.

For practical purposes the simple triple division is not enough, but there is no agreed and consistent system of subdivision. Herbivores (or phytophagans or vegetarians) may be divided into graminivores (which feed on grain), frugivores (which feed on fruit), and xylophagans (which feed on wood), but although the word phyllophagan, for an animal which feeds on leaves, is in the dictionary, it has never become usual. Carnivore is often restricted to animals that feed chiefly on the flesh of warm-blooded animals (mammals and birds) and will be so used in this book. No animals, at least in this country, feed predominantly on reptiles and amphibians, and an animal that feeds on fish is a piscivore. There remain the animals that feed chiefly on invertebrates, and here there is some difficulty in nomenclature. The old word for an animal that feeds on a mixed collection of invertebrates—earthworms, snails, woodlice, grubs and so on—is insectivore, and I shall use the term only in this sense, so that it does not mean 'an animal feeding on insects' if by insects we mean the creatures now so-called by zoologists, that is, members of the group Hexapoda. The difficulty arose because the word insect, which derives from Pliny, originally included all animals, such as earthworms, with a segmented body ('insect' means literally 'cut into') and was early extended to include such animals as snails, and this usage has persisted in popular speech. The continuation of the use of 'insectivore' in this sense is justified by the persistence of the name Insectivora for a group of mammals, the shrews, hedgehogs, and moles, which feed on insects in the old sense not the new. For an animal which feeds chiefly on members of the group Hexapoda, insects in the strict or zoological sense, I shall use the term entomophagan, derived from the Greek.

Some of the lower animals are strictly limited in the food that they eat and may be confined to a single animal or plant, but birds are much more catholic in their choice, usually taking anything that comes within a broad range of size and nature. Many of the carnivorous birds, for example, such as owls and the kestrel, take a good many of the larger invertebrates in addition to the small mammals that are their staple food. Moreover, many species change the type of food they take according to the season, and in some the food of the young is different from that of the parents. An exact classification of birds according to their food is therefore difficult, and is made more so because for many species we have only relatively casual and incomplete information. On the basis of the summaries in *The Handbook of British Birds*, themselves based largely on a series of rather crude analyses of gut-contents by W. E. Collinge, supplemented by some other published information, it is possible to make a tentative subdivision of the chief woodland birds according to their food. This is shown in Table 16, with the dominant birds on the left, and any other species of special interest or importance on the right.

This classification must be regarded as provisional. I have ignored, in making it, any foods conspicuously provided by man, since I am concerned with birds in woods, and in gardens the same birds may take different foods and become greatly modified in habit. The true position of the blue and great tits is doubtful. The stomach analyses of Betts (1955) made chiefly on birds in oakwoods in the Forest of Dean, suggest that they take much vegetable matter for most of the year, much more than the coal-tit, and on these results I have placed them as omnivores, but I have myself seldom seen either species feeding other than by searching for insects and such-like. It is always

TABLE 16

Woodland birds classified according to their food

	Dominant species	*Others*
Herbivores	Yellowhammer	Bullfinch
	Wood-pigeon	Black grouse
		Capercailzie
Omnivores	Crow	Magpie
	Jackdaw	Great spotted woodpecker
	Chaffinch	
	Jay	
	Blue tit?	
	Great tit?	
	Marsh-tit	
	Nuthatch	
	Starling	
	Blackcap	
	Garden-warbler	
	Blackbird	
	Song-thrush	
	Mistle-thrush	
	Pheasant	
Carnivores	Buzzard	Sparrow-hawk
		Tawny owl
Insectivores	Robin	The young of Magpie
	Starling (in spring)	
Entomophagans	Tree-pipit	Long-tailed tit
	Chaffinch (in spring)	Treecreeper
	Pied flycatcher	Whitethroat
	Spotted flycatcher	Green woodpecker
	Coal-tit	
	Redstart	
	Chiff-chaff	
	Wood-warbler	
	Willow-warbler	
	Wren	
	Cuckoo	
	and the young of	and the young of
	Jay	Bullfinch
	Blue tit	
	Great tit	
	Nuthatch	

possible that feeding habits differ in different parts of the country. It is possible that the greater spotted woodpecker would be better placed as entomophagous rather than omnivorous.

The most remarkable thing about this list is that very few birds feed almost exclusively on vegetable matter, and that even of these the bullfinch feeds its young on insects while the yellowhammer is a heath bird that only occasionally invades the woods. In spite of the huge annual production of organic matter by the plants of the wood, the common birds, with the exception of the wood-pigeon, seem to be unable to make more than partial use of it. This is in great contrast to the insects on the one hand and the mammals on the other, many of which are exclusively vegetarian. No bird eats wood, and, more surprisingly, none eats leaves, at least as a regular habit. Colquhoun (1951), in his study of the food of the wood-pigeon in the Oxford area, twice found leaves of elder in a bird's crop, and more frequently leaves of herbaceous weeds. His birds were shot over a wide area which was not extensively wooded, and probably most or all of the birds were on farm land. (His classification of the feeding grounds on which wood-pigeons were seen does not include woods, so that his total picture, from the ecological as distinct from the agricultural point of view, is somewhat misleading.) The bullfinch when adult eats largely buds, and these are also eaten to some extent by coal-, blue, great, and marsh-tits, but otherwise the only parts of the plant which are eaten by birds that have become dominant in the woods, are the seeds and fruits. These are necessarily seasonal in abundance, although there is a succession of species throughout the year which to some extent smooths out the supply. Colquhoun's figures suggest that the wood-pigeon takes advantage of this, switching from one species to another as each becomes available, and the same is obviously true of thrushes, and no doubt of other species.

The two game-birds that are chiefly vegetarian (though both take some animal food) have not been very successful. The capercailzie, which feeds mainly on the shoots of coniferous trees, became extinct perhaps because it was unable to transfer to other foods when the native firwoods shrank in size. No doubt its large size made it easy to kill and vulnerable to firearms, but it has thriven and spread in coniferous plantations since it was re-introduced. The black grouse, which takes a wider range of shoots, both of trees and of herbaceous plants, has survived, but in small numbers.

Many birds in the omnivorous group switch from vegetable to animal matter according to the season. In autumn, for example, there is some temporary soft fruit—bramble, raspberry (*Rubus idaeus*), elder, bird cherry, privet (*Ligastrum vulgare*)—which is taken by the thrushes, the robin, and of the warblers the whitethroat and blackcap, and perhaps to some extent the willow-warbler. The berries of hawthorn, holly, rowan, and other trees, which stay on the branches for months without decay, are not largely used until much later; by this time the warblers have gone and the thrushes and the robin have this food to themselves. Hartley (1954) has claimed that the three resident woodland thrushes (and the redwing and fieldfare which are winter visitors) have different preferences for the various fruits that are available, but his figures need to be taken with some caution since there were differences in different parts of the country, and the lumped figures may represent geographical differences in distribution. It does appear, however, that the song-thrush and mistle-thrush take a much higher proportion of yew-berries than does the blackbird.

Hard seeds, especially the acorns and hazel nuts which fall to the ground, are taken in autumn in very large numbers by those birds such as the jay and wood-pigeon whose gullets are large enough, and by smaller birds such as the woodpeckers, nuthatch, and great tit, whose bills are strong enough to split or pierce them open.

The only carnivorous woodland birds which are at all plentiful are the tawny or brown owl and, in some districts, the buzzard. The owl feeds chiefly on a variety of small rodents and other mammals. In woods the three chief species are the long-tailed field mouse or wood mouse (*Apodemus silvaticus*), the bank vole (*Clethrionomys glareolus*), and the short-tailed vole (*Microtus agrestis*). Since these rodents feed to a considerable extent on the seeds and fruits which form part of the winter food of many small birds, it is possible that the presence of tawny owls in a wood is beneficial to the latter. On the other hand the owls occasionally take birds for their own food, and have been recorded as killing those as large as jays or even pheasants. Southern (1954) found that in Wytham Wood near Oxford the small mammals were taken in rough proportion to their abundance, and that in summer, when the vegetation was thick and the small mammals were presumably difficult to find, there was a switch to the larger mammals—mole (*Talpa europaea*), rabbit (*Oryctolagus caniculus*), and rat (*Rattus norvegicus*).

The buzzard takes most of its food outside the woods, and in some areas before myxomatosis fed largely or entirely on rabbits, but in

V. Ashwood in July, Berkshire. The trees, 55 years old and 68 feet high, are much better grown than is usual; there are few shrubs, probably because the trees have been planted close together, but the thin field layer, largely dog's mercury, is characteristic of many ashwoods.

VI. Beechwood in September, Sussex. The trees are 170 years old and 100 feet high; there are no shrubs and no field layer except for a little dog's mercury.

wilder places, where rabbits were always few or absent, it must have fed chiefly on small rodents. These have been shown to be its main food in some continental surveys, and as the rabbit is an introduced animal in Britain and northern Europe, it could not be the buzzard's natural prey.

The exact position of the sparrow-hawk is difficult to determine. It is now so rare in most woods that it can have little influence on the bird population, but before it was shot on sight—or perhaps before guns were so accurate, for Newton in Yarrell describes it as 'common throughout the whole of Great Britain'—it was much more frequent and may possibly have kept some of the smaller species in check. The list of prey-species, with their frequency, given by Owen (1932) suggests that birds are taken roughly in proportion to their abundance, and birds such as the chaffinch and yellowhammer that have a habit of sitting on outstanding twigs are the chief victims. The common habit of the sparrow-hawk of flying rapidly down rides or open spaces in woods is one which is hardly appropriate to natural woodlands, and is possibly a late acquisition. The other method described in the *Handbook* in which the bird 'threads its way with astonishing dexterity through the secondary growth of a wood' is more likely to be its natural mode of hunting.

In addition to the regular carnivores, other woodland birds sometimes kill and eat small birds. This is a normal habit with the crow, jay, and magpie, which also take eggs, and one that occurs occasionally in the great tit, mistle-thrush and greater spotted woodpecker. It is possible that any of these species is an incipient carnivore, and whether the habit will or will not develop will presumably depend on the success which it brings the birds in rearing their young. Flesh-eating is a specialized habit, for clearly it could not have come into existence until the mammals and birds were well-established, and must have arisen in the existing hawks and owls as a development from a more generalized mode of feeding. The jay which, although still largely vegetarian, sometimes takes mice as well as birds, has gone quite a long way on a road which its relatives the ravens and crows have followed even further. Since the direction of evolution is seldom reversed the Corvidae may quite possibly progress still more in the direction of flesh-eating. The other species have only just begun on the road and may or may not continue to follow it.

I have placed only the starling (in spring) and the robin in the insectivorous group, and I am not sure that both would not be as well or better placed as omnivores. It seems in general that if a bird takes invertebrate food other than insects and their relatives, it also eats at least some vegetable matter. Just as there are few birds which are exclusively vegetarian, so there are few which feed exclusively on worms, molluscs, and arthropods. This suggests a lack of specialization in the digestive organs of birds, in comparison with those of mammals, which would be well worth physiological investigation.

The true insect-eaters, or entomophagous species, are rather more specialized, as there are several which take very little other food and more which, though the adults have a wider choice, feed their young almost exclusively on insects. Presumably foods which are entirely surrounded, as are the bodies of arthropods, by a layer, however thin, of insoluble chitin, is not readily digested; so far as is known no vertebrate possesses an enzyme capable of breaking it down, nor have birds been described as possessing any symbiotic bacteria in the gut which might deal with it. The ejection of pellets of undigested insect remains has been recorded for a wide variety of birds, not only for hawks and owls which regularly produce pellets and feed on the larger and tougher insects such as cockchafers and grasshoppers, but for very many smaller insect-eaters such as warblers and flycatchers, and a list is given by Tucker (1944). In view of the small size of any pellets likely to be ejected by such birds and the difficulty of observation, it is at least possible that they are produced regularly by all birds that eat animals with indigestible parts. Perhaps there is no real digestion of chitin and the food is merely broken mechanically, but if this is so it is surprising that finches are almost the only passerines with a gizzard. It may be that the reason why the young of so many entomophagous and other birds (blue tits, great tits, leaf-warblers, bullfinch, nuthatch, whitethroat, and wren) are fed on larvae is that these are softer and easier for the nestlings to squash in order to extract the digestible material. Whether during life there is any change in the digestive organs of birds such as the bullfinch and chaffinch which change as they grow up from a purely entomophagous to a largely vegetarian diet is unknown. On the analogy of the frog, which at metamorphosis changes in the reverse direction from being herbivorous to being insectivorous and undergoes profound alterations in the gut, one would expect that there would be.

There is some obvious specialization amongst the entomophagous forms. The treecreeper finds its food almost exclusively on the trunks of trees and feeds on those insects and spiders which live in the bark. How far this specialization of habit in the bird leads to specialization of its food will depend on how far the invertebrates of the bark are different from those of the twigs and leaves. The difference is presumably great, but there must be some overlap. The eggs of the winter-moth (*Operophthera brumata*) and mottled umber (*Erannis defoliaria*), for example, are laid indiscriminately on small twigs and on the main trunk, although the caterpillars feed exclusively on leaves. Unless the treecreeper ignores these eggs and the young larvae while they are ascending to the leaves, it must to some extent be in competition with the great and blue tits which feed their young on the older caterpillars of these moths. The nuthatch, especially when it is feeding its young, presumably also takes bark-dwelling insects, but it keeps much more to the medium-sized branches than does the treecreeper. The woodpeckers, although they are trunk-feeding species, exploit a different type of food, the larvae of the relatively large wood-boring insects, such as long-horn beetles (*Cerambycidae*) and the goat moth (*Cossus cossus*); to obtain these they excavate holes with their beaks. The green woodpecker has also developed the very specialized habit of myrmecophily or ant-eating, and in some districts seems to get most of its food in this way; where the large wood-ant (*Formica rufa*) is present, the distribution of this insect largely determines the distribution of the bird.

Some birds, and a relatively high proportion of the woodland community, have developed the habit of feeding the young by regurgitation; food swallowed by the adult is partially digested (or at least softened in the crop; precise physiological information is lacking) and vomited for the use of the young, who take it from the parent's beak. This happens in the bullfinch and green woodpecker; in the latter the regurgitated food is described as 'a milky paste'. The wood-pigeon, like all pigeons, has gone one stage further, and feeds the young in a way comparable to the suckling of mammals. 'Pigeon's milk', produced in the crop, is partly a secretion but contains also many broken down epithelial cells which are sloughed off from the tissues. It contains a protein similar to or identical with the casein of the milk of mammals.

In summary, it appears from what we know of the food of birds in woodlands, that there is fairly full exploitation of the available food supply except that the vegetative parts of plants are eaten very little, and that there are varying degrees of specialization in food so that while no two birds have exactly the same diet, there is for most species a good deal of overlap with one or more others. It does not follow that conditions are the same in all types of wood, and it might be expected that in botanically simple woodlands, with a narrower range of insects, there would be greater overlap and more interspecific competition than in the natural woods with more than one species of tree and very many species of insect.

Food is, from the practical point of view, even more important than oxygen, for while all except diving birds have no difficulty in getting all the air they need, there is a limited supply of food, for shares in which many individuals and species must compete, and at some seasons, and especially in severe weather, there may be a real all-round difficulty in obtaining any food at all. The temperate regions of the earth, in which Great Britain is included, are a marginal environment in which occasional hard winters may greatly reduce the population of many species of animal, and not least of the birds.

All animals are, in the last resort, dependent on plants for their food, but few woodland birds feed directly on plants except when seeds and fruits are plentiful in autumn, and probably only the game-birds and wood-pigeons can survive the year round without animal food. The other species are links in food chains; for most woodland birds the chain is short, of three links only; the tits, for instance, feed on aphides which suck the sap of plants, or on moth caterpillars which eat the leaves. For others, the chain is lengthened, either at the middle or at one or other end. We really know very little of the exact species of small insect taken by tits and warblers, but there can be little doubt that some of their prey are predatory on other insects, and the birds certainly take spiders (and their eggs) which also feed on insects. We have then the possible (and almost certain) chain:

Bird→spider→predatory insect→vegetarian insect→plant

There are many species of insect, especially Hymenoptera, which are free-living as adults but spend their larval stages as parasites in the larvae of other insects, and there are even hyperparasites, whose larvae are parasitic on grubs already parasitic on others. These give the possibility of two further links in the chain. A full series of this sort has been worked out for some American woodpeckers, and here there is an addition at the plant end, for the vegetarian wood-boring insects on which the predators feed are living not on the tree itself but on the fungi which are living on its tissues. There can be no doubt that similar chains could be found in British woods. Finally, the birds of prey such as the sparrow-hawk add a link at the other end. The theoretical maximum would then appear to be:

Bird of prey→insectivorous bird→spider→hyperparasitic insect →parasitic insect→predatory insect→fungal-feeding insect→fungi →green plant

The possible existence of such complicated chains makes it difficult to say whether a given species of bird is beneficial or injurious to forestry or agriculture. Only when observation shows that there is such a heavy direct predation by birds on insects injurious to plant crops that the other possible links can be ignored, can one say with any safety that a bird does more good than harm. Even then there is the possibility that a small amount of feeding by the bird on predatory insects at a particular time of the year may do more to allow the increase of an injurious species than can ever be overcome by heavy attacks on it when it is numerous. The addition of man as an extra predator at the beginning of the series has results which may sometimes be reasonably guessed but which cannot with any confidence be predicted.

In recent years there has been much discussion of what has been called Gause's principle, which has been alleged to state: 'when closely related species occur in one habitat they are separated ecologically, or else one species, being better adapted for occupying the habitat, supplants the other'; and ingenious attempts have been made to prove the principle for woodland birds. In fact Gause (1934) enunciated no such principle, and was careful to say, 'Among animals the processes of the struggle for existence are much more complex [than in plants] and as yet one cannot speak of any general principles', and to point out that no two species were likely to have the same habits in nature. One might go further and say that if two animals have exactly the same habits, they would be of the same species.

What Gause did deduce mathematically, as others had done before him, was that if two species living together *in a microcosm* used exactly the same food, if they had different reproductive rates, and if the microcosm could support different total numbers of the two species, then one would disappear; he claimed to have shown by experiments on animals living in test-tubes that this was what happened in practice, but his figures do not entirely support his claim. Even if they did, they would have no direct relevance for birds, which do not live in a microcosm.

I should not have introduced this theoretical and tedious argument if Gause's alleged principle had not coloured much of the recent work on the food-habits of birds, and even more the conclusions that have been drawn from the observations.

Five minutes' observation in the woods will show that the different species of tit, even in a mixed flock, often occupy different positions; the great tits move predominantly in the shrubs and undergrowth, the blue tits in the canopy, while the coal-tit clings to the bark of the larger branches and trunk much more than the others. A series of papers from Oxford has given some degree of precision to observations of this sort, and has shown that the separation in feeding niches varies from one time of year to another, and that it is associated with differences between the foods eaten.

Hartley (1953) found that for most of the year the vertical zonation of the blue and great tits is quite distinct, the latter being found much lower down, and that the two species feed together only when there is a superabundance of a particular type of food. His observations on feeding stations were paralleled by those of Betts (1955) on stomach analyses. She found that the great tit took largely adult insects, especially weevils, while the blue tit fed mainly on scale insects (*Coccidae*) and small larvae and pupae on twigs and leaves. In the breeding season there was rather more overlap, for both fed their young largely on the larvae and pupae of moths, but even then the great tit took many adult insects which the blue tit ignored, while the blue tit alone took many pupae of the oak roller moths (*Tortrix biridana*) which get their name from the larva's habit of rolling itself up in a leaf. Gibb (1954) found a greater difference between the feeding stations of blue and great tits in summer than did Hartley, but drew the same general picture of their relationships.

The conclusion that has been drawn from these observations (I quote Betts), that 'there is no competition for food between these species', is not justified. Her own analyses show that two species do at times take the same food, and Gibb (1958) showed in detail that both eat larvae of the moth *Ernarmonia conicolana* from fir-cones, the two together taking 50 per cent. or more of the total population. If there is any overlap there must be some competition. The human analogy is apt: the inhabitants of Britain and the United States live 3,000 miles apart and have measurably different preferences in food, clothes, and furnishings, but they compete with each other for a wide variety of products, from whisky to uranium, and an excessive acquisition or consumption of any of these by the population of one country leads to a change in the pattern of life in the other. The effect of competition of this sort is greatest when the supply of a product is reduced, as that of whisky was during the war; in times of stress, when substitutes are impossible to obtain, even survival may be affected, as perhaps happened in Germany as a result of the blockade during both World Wars. Similarly, when the birds find it difficult to get food, as during frosts, the effect of overlap in food will be increased. If conditions are such that many individuals are going to die anyway, competition may determine that a higher proportion of one species than of another survives.

Even if it were true, as has been claimed against the weight of the evidence, that two species of tit feed on the same food only when it is superabundant, there might still be competition between them, for a mass attack on it by two species might cause serious diminution in the supply of the same food in future years, which might affect detrimentally the species which favoured this food when it was not abundant.

Two or more birds feeding in different niches at different times of the year may be in clear competition with each other; the winter-moth might be attacked when it was an egg in a crevice of bark, a caterpillar feeding on leaves, a pupa buried in the soil, or a flying adult. There would be ecological separation in habit of four birds feeding in these ways, but as much interspecific competition between them for food as if they were all feeding on the same stage of the insect in the same time and place. A mere knowledge of feeding niches is clearly not enough; we need to know the exact species of insect taken by birds, and their proportions and stages. Things are further complicated by the existence of food chains, for while a bird which feeds on a parasite or a predatory insect assists others which feed on the prey or host of these, one which feeds on a hyperparasite, or on a parasite of the predator, would be in competition with them. The winter-moths, for instance, are attacked by predatory beetles and parasitized by Hymenoptera, and I have no doubt that these in their turn have further parasites which could be the food of birds. There is no conclusive evidence that such slight separation of feeding habit as exists in closely related species in any way eliminates competition for food, or even reduces it to any great extent, and the more nearly related the species the greater this competition would appear to be. This is, indeed, just what we should expect. If two species are derived from a common ancestor their divergence in habits, as in structure, will be gradual, and the more recent that divergence and the greater their similarity in structure, the greater will be their similarity in feeding and other habits.

Large predators are rare in British woodlands, chiefly through the action of man, but some indication that they could never be very plentiful is given by a consideration of their requirements in food. A rough average density of the breeding birds of woodland is two pairs per acre, and most of these are small. If a sparrow-hawk needs only one small bird per day, a pair will consume 730 in a year, exclusive of any more that will be needed (and they will be many) when young are being reared. This is the entire population of 180 acres, or about a quarter of a square mile. If, as Owen (1932) estimates, the total prey of a pair of sparrow-hawks, including what they take for their young, is 2,000 small birds a year, and if each pair of small birds rears, on the average, four young, sparrow-hawks at two pairs per square mile would therefore account for nearly half the total mortality of small birds with a stable population. What the average number of young reared by the small birds of a wood may be is not known; it is about ten in the blue and great tits (Gibb

1950) and must be much less for birds such as thrushes and finches with their smaller broods; in addition the migratory warblers and others are removed from the environment for most of the year and so are not available as food for the hawk. Tinbergen (1946) estimated for Dutch woods that sparrow-hawks accounted for half the total summer mortality of house-sparrows, one quarter of that for chaffinches, and very much less for all other species. It looks as if a density of the order of one pair of predatory birds per square mile is the maximum that the woods could stand under the best possible conditions, and on the whole it would probably have to be very much less to meet exceptional mortality of the prey from other causes. Hawks do in fact range widely in their search for food and it is in their interests not to reduce the population of their prey too much over a small area. This low density of carnivorous birds is one case of the Eltonian pyramid, the principle that each species of animal in a food chain is present in smaller numbers, and makes up a much smaller biomass, or total weight of living matter, than that of the next lower link of the chain, the greatest biomass being given by the green plant at the base.

Predators that live on small mammals may reach a rather higher density, because the mammals themselves, feeding largely on the vegetative parts of plants, are nearer the base of the Eltonian pyramid and so themselves present in greater biomass than the entomophagous or omnivorous small birds. Southern (1959) found that on the 1,000 acres of the Wytham estate near Oxford there were from 16 to 30 pairs of brown owls, each keeping strictly to its own territory throughout the year. At this density the food-supply appeared to be controlling the numbers of the owls, for in years when the density was high the proportion of pairs that actually bred, the clutch size, the proportion of laid eggs that hatched, and the proportion of fledged young obtained from the hatched eggs, were all lower on average than when the density was low. In years when the mouse-population was abnormally low not a single pair of owls even attempted to breed. These variations in mortality have not, however, prevented the owl population from rising steadily over the twelve years of Southern's study.

The effect that birds may have on the numbers of their prey has been much debated but, as mentioned above, because of the existence of food-chains it is usually impossible to make any certain statements. It seems from Tinbergen's figures quoted on page 141 that under natural conditions the sparrow-hawk does control the number of small birds in the woods, but even so it does not follow that their density would necessarily be any higher if sparrow-hawks were absent, for then more of the small birds might die of starvation or from other causes. It has in fact been shown that a high predation on the young stages of fish does, in certain circumstances, increase the density of the adult population, since it reduces the competition and so allows more individuals to reach maturity. It is generally believed that a high population of jays and magpies, which may take whole clutches of eggs or nestlings, reduces the numbers of small birds present in a wood, and this may very well be true.

While Southern's owls were steadily increasing, the mouse-population of the wood was undergoing the usual cyclic fluctuations, with three or four peaks in the twelve years, but there is no indication that predation by the owls had any important effect on the numbers of mice.

A number of authors have drawn attention to the way in which birds such as tits concentrate on eating particular species of insect when these are so abundant as to be a plague in woodlands, but, as Turček (1954) has pointed out, under these conditions, when the rate of multiplication of the insects has got out of hand, the effect of the birds is likely to be least. Betts (1955) tried to study the effect of tits on the population of the winter-moth in normal years, by comparing the predation in one area of the Forest of Dean with nest-boxes and a high density of tits with that of another area without nest-boxes. She concluded that there was greater predation where the density of tits was higher, and that it might be enough to exert some control. But she found also that the density of winter-moths was higher in the nest-box area than the other, which suggests the opposite.

Turček (1949 and 1954) has recorded an interesting example of the possible complications. In an oak-hornbeam woodland in Czechoslovakia there was an outbreak of gypsy-moth (*Liparis dispar*), preceded by a peak in the population of the beetle *Calasoma sycophanta* which preys on the larvae of the moth. Birds fed heavily on the beetles, so presumably reducing their effect on the moths. In the next year the density of moths was low and that of the beetles moderate. In this year too birds greatly reduced the numbers of the beetles, so enabling those that survived to make better use of the small amount of food available to them. The peak year of the gypsy-moth doubled the number of birds, but there was a lowering of the nesting success because the defoliation of the trees by the caterpillars led to greater exposure of the nests to weather and predators.

Turček (1954) has also suggested many ways in which birds may by their feeding habits help in the natural maintenance of the woodland community. Although birds may strip a tree of its whole crop of fruits, the *seeds* are not always destroyed—thrushes, for example, feeding on haws, eat the fleshy part and scatter the stones on the ground—and there is sometimes distribution of seeds taken away for food. Jays bury acorns, and over large areas of the Continent appear to be the chief agents in the spread of oak, even into coniferous plantations, for some of these have been converted into mixed woodlands in this way. The spread of oakwoods uphill can probably not go on at all unless the acorns are carried by jays or other animals. The distribution of the jay is almost the same as that of the oak, and the plant and the bird may be closely linked to their mutual advantage; the jay feeds largely on acorns, and the oakwoods cannot spread or be renewed to any extent without the jay. Since acorns cannot survive either severe drying or long frost (Jones 1959) it is likely that burying is necessary for successful regeneration, and the lack of this in many English woods may be due in part to the absence or low density of jays.

The jay also distributes other seeds such as beech-mast and hazel nuts, and some seeds are scattered by tits, finches, thrushes, nuthatches, and woodpeckers. Some of these, such as the finches and the redwing and fieldfare, feed mostly outside the wood but enter it to roost, where they may drop seeds of shrubs such as hawthorn, which may be able to germinate and survive in the forest.

Woodpeckers are probably important in spreading the spores of fungi from one dead tree to another. Some authors have claimed that woodpeckers attack preferentially what have been called 'mixed-in' trees, that is those foreign to the community, for example pines in oak–hornbeam woods and hornbeams in pinewoods in

Czechoslovakia. Certainly in Wyre Forest the greater spotted woodpecker attacks chiefly the birches amongst the oaks, but this may be only because the foresters remove rotten oaks but leave the dead birches, so that only the latter provide nesting sites.

All birds have good eyesight, and most woodland birds find their food by sight. Gibb (1958) has described how blue and coal-tits find larvae of the moth *Ernarmonia conicolana* in fir-cones. While both species find the cones by sight the coal-tits carry out a more minute inspection to see which scales are infected, but the blue tit taps the scales with its bill and decides in that way which to attack.

Owls find their prey by sound. The asymmetrical arrangement of their ears gives them a high ability to determine the direction from which sounds, particularly high-pitched ones, are coming, and so they can tell the position of mice by their squeaks. Their approach to their prey is facilitated by their soft feathers and noiseless flight.

The total population of birds that a wood can hold is ultimately determined by the photosynthesis of the trees and other plants, and we are now beginning to get a little information on this. The maximum rate of production of dry matter (i.e. all substances, except water, in the trees' tissues) of Scotch fir plantations in East Anglia is about 22,000 kilograms (22 tons) per hectare[1] per annum (Ovington 1958). On older plantations the rate falls, but is made up, at least to some extent, by production by the increased shrub and field layers. Of this 22,000 kilograms, only 5,000 kilograms consists of leaves, cones, and seeds which, as is said on page 131, are the only parts of the plant that are directly used by birds. Even the invertebrates on which they feed are living chiefly on the same materials, not on the bole, roots, and branches that make up the bulk of the trees' production. The foresters' tables for annual increment (Laurie 1958) show that, in terms of the rate of growth of the bole, the Scotch fir is rather poor amongst conifers, but better than the beech and nearly twice as good as pedunculate oak, the comparisons being made for second-class sites for each species.

Turček (1956) estimated the biomass of birds in Czechoslovakian spruce as less than half a kilogram per hectare, and has given figures for other types of forest ranging up to 2 kilograms per hectare.

[1] One hectare is 1/100 of a square kilometre, or about 2·5 acres.

Gibb (1957) showed that blue tits daily consumed in dry weight of food about 20 per cent. of their own body-weight, and great tits rather less. Larger birds would need a smaller proportion, but if we take the average as 20 per cent., the woodland birds would be using only at the most about 200 kilograms of material per hectare per annum, which is negligible in comparison with the productivity of the plants.

If the populations of birds were limited by the ultimate food supply one would expect that the densities of population in different types of woodland would bear some direct relation to the productivity of the trees. Laurie's figures for the ratio of production of volume of trunk, which we may take as roughly proportional to total production, are shown in Table 17. The superiority of the

TABLE 17

Relative productivity (annual increment of volumes of timber) of trees on second-class sites, and densities of birds

Woodland	*Relative productivity (adapted from Laurie)*	*Density of birds, summer Contacts/hr.*	*Based on total contacts of*
Pedunculate oak	5·1	82	579
Sessile oak		56	1,033
English and Welsh birch		51	253
Scottish birch		42	739
Ash		57	366
Beech	8·4	56	236
European larch	8·6		
Scotch fir	10·7	41	468
Japanese larch	12·3		
Norway spruce	16·0	63 (brashed) 74 (thicket)	472 658
Corsican pine	16·0		
Sitka spruce	27·8	57 (brashed) 98 (thicket)	693 473

conifers is due partly to the fact that, as evergreens, they have a longer growing-season, but even allowing for this they have a higher productivity than the hardwoods. These figures do not necessarily apply to any particular woodlands, but as many of our existing hardwoods are on poor sites, the table probably underestimates the difference between the productivity of our native woodlands and the Forestry Commission's plantations. If the hypothesis were correct, there should be a lower density of birds in oaks than in beech, and a much lower density in these than in spruce. What little information we have does not prove this. My line-transects show that there is very little difference in density in different types of woodland, the range being from 30 to 76 contacts per hour (Table 17). Since the highest density for mature trees is given by pedunculate oak and the lowest by the Scotch birchwoods and fir-woods, the differences may be caused as much by the climate as by the type of tree. Climate may itself affect the growth-rate of the trees, but there seem to be no figures for this effect within Britain. The decrease in temperature and length of growing-season as one goes north is to some extent counterbalanced by the increased length of day.

Marsh-Tit

10

THE INTER-RELATIONS OF THE COMMUNITY: (2) The breeding cycle

In finding food a bird is often in competition with other species of bird, and in the food that it eats it has profound effects on many other members of the community, both plant and animal. In its reproductive relationships it is much more strongly confined to competition with members of its own species, but even here it is sometimes in competition with others, and the breeding cycle can only take place in the correct environment, or an adequate substitute, the factors of which are largely determined by the vegetation.

The first element in the cycle is finding a mate. Here there is no interspecific competition and all that is necessary is some sort of advertisement by which one sex can find the other. It is generally the male who advertises himself, whether by sight or sound, and the female who seeks him out, and almost all British woodland birds have a more or less well-marked song. The only exceptions seem to be the bullfinch, the hawks, and the crows. The first has a loud call note and is exceptionally brightly coloured for a British bird, while the hawks are wide-ranging and so likely to encounter each other without any special auditory signal. The songs of the crow family are weak and seldom heard, and probably of no value in mate-finding. This is clearly no problem in the social rooks and jackdaws, and the jay and magpie both have communal gatherings in spring during which presumably pairs are formed; moreover they are brightly or conspicuously coloured. The carrion-crow, though solitary, is like the hawks wide-ranging. It looks as if, in this country, song is essential to success as a woodland bird unless special circumstances enable it to be dispensed with.

If the function of a song is to bring and hold together cock and hen of the same species, one would expect that there would be a high degree of specific distinctness, and also that songs of individuals would be recognizable. The first of these expectations is generally true, the second doubtfully so. It is obvious that, as we can recognize most species of birds by their song, the birds, whose ears are at least as good as ours, are likely to be able to do so also. But there are exceptions. I find it impossible always to distinguish the songs of the blackcap from those of the garden-warbler, and even if this be due to a deficiency on my part it shows that the difference is less than the regional and individual differences between chaffinch-songs, which are discussed below and which I have no difficulty in recognizing. I have been deceived into thinking that a pied flycatcher with an exceptionally elaborate song was a redstart, and that a redstart was a nightingale. A bird which normally sings a chiff-chaff song will sometimes give a nearly perfect willow-warbler song, and vice versa. As the only means of identifying these two species in the field is by their songs, the possibility of confusion is great.

Some birds are mimics. The starling is probably the best in this country, but though it may introduce phrases from many birds (and other extraneous sounds) into its song, the resulting medley is unlikely to be mistaken for anything but what it is. The Swedish Broadcasting Company's record of the red-backed shrike includes a version of the chaffinch's song that has deceived everyone to whom I have played it.

The learning and inheritance of the songs of some birds, particularly the chaffinch, have been studied intensively in recent years. Thorpe (1958) has reared birds in various degrees of isolation and recorded the songs by means of an instrument called the sound spectrograph, which produces on paper a record of the pitch, duration, and amplitude of the notes. These records, although admirable for

VII. Firwood in June, Rothiemurchus, Inverness-shire. There are no shrubs, and the field layer, on block scree, is chiefly bilberry and cowberry.

VIII. Yew scrub in July, Hampshire. The combe in the chalk is being rapidly colonized by yew (which shows dark in the photograph) and various other trees and shrubs. The yew will in time, if not checked, form a nearly pure wood in close canopy, as it does in other combes on this hillside.

the comparison of individual songs, direct attention rather too much to the detail, and in what follows I shall use a more general description which anyone with an attentive ear can check against the actual songs.

The normal song of the chaffinch consists, in musical language, of a single subject and a cadence which are put together in several different ways. In the commonest, the subject, of about five quavers on the same note, is announced and then repeated once at a lower pitch, and the cadence has three to five notes, the whole being done *accelerando* and *crescendo*. One common variant is for the subject to be stated three times in descending sequence, followed by the cadence; another is for the subject to be stated twice, descending as before, and the cadence twice. Sometimes the notes of the subject descend slightly and they may be preceded by grace-notes. There may be variations in the form both of subject and of cadence from one bird to another, and in the repetitions. Marler (1952) has listed 14 types of variation in the subject pattern and 45 types of cadence, including repetitions and phrases of up to seven notes. As he did not consider differences in length, absolute pitch, or timbre of the notes themselves, of which there are many, it is obvious that the number of songs is, for practical purposes, infinite. It has often been remarked, and is obvious to anyone who listens and is not tone- and timbre-deaf, that there are geographical variations in the song; this has been laboriously confirmed by transcriptions in a sort of shorthand of some thousands of songs; but to say, as one author does, that what has been known for years 'can only be detected by statistical analysis', is to exalt mathematics to a position which no mathematician would give it. To travel by night in spring to the Rhineland or to Sutherland and to wake up to German or Scottish chaffinches will show them talking a different language as clearly as are the human beings around them. In Finnish songs there is a pause after the cadence, and then a single unmusical note very similar to the call of the greater spotted woodpecker, for which some ornithologists at the International Ornithological Congress at Helsinki in 1958 mistook it.

If these geographical dialects were consistent, if they were inherited, and if the birds that sing them were isolated, they could represent the incipient break-up of the chaffinch species into a number of subspecies. The consistency is there to some extent, and is most marked when European and British populations (which are in fact regarded as separate subspecies) or English and remote Highland populations are compared. There is also some degree of isolation, for birds tend to return to their birthplace to breed, and even more strongly to return to their first breeding place in subsequent years. The inheritance of the song has been shown by Thorpe to be complex.

When birds are taken from the nest at the age of about five days and then reared in isolation so that they hear no other birds, they start singing at about the proper time in the following spring. The subject of their song consists of notes of about the right timbre, but usually at a lower pitch than the normal song, with little trace of the change of pitch that indicates the repetition of the subject. The cadence is absent, or consists of a single unmusical note. Such a song must depend on inheritance, and differences between individuals must depend either on this or on chance variations in the structure of the voice-box.

If juvenile birds are caught in the wild in September and then reared in isolation, they produce in the following spring a song which is more or less normal. If a group of such birds are kept together they learn from each other and all come to sing alike. After they are about thirteen months old there is little subsequent change in their songs.

It thus appears that while the ability to sing, the length of the song, the timbre and pitch of the notes, and the general form of the subject, are inherited, the details of the song are learnt by imitation, largely while the birds are juveniles and before they ever sing themselves, but partly in the following spring when they sing and practise and develop their individual songs. Experiments with a 'song-tutor', in which notes from chaffinch songs were arranged on tape in the wrong order, showed that these abnormal songs also could be learnt, but that other bird songs, except to a limited extent that of the tree-pipit, which in tonal quality is similar to that of the chaffinch, could not.

It seems, then, that there is a hereditary element in the chaffinch's song but that the dialects are learnt, and some ornithologists have concluded from this that they are of no great importance and certainly do not indicate incipient subspecies. But this is by no means certain. Since much of the song is learnt in the bird's first summer, it will be learnt from the bird's own parents and neighbours, and there will therefore be a tendency to build up a dialect, which will be more marked the more consistently young birds return to the district where they were born. Moreover, we do not know how far, if at all, young birds that have the opportunity to learn different types of song choose to imitate those that are like their parents'. The experiment of rearing in isolation birds from parents of known song-dialects, and then exposing them to two types of song, their parents' and another, has not been performed. The human parallel is apt. It is obvious that children pick up their accents with the greatest of ease from whatever adults and other children may be near them, yet it has been shown that the central European's inability to pronounce 'th' is correlated with genetic characters and probably has a genetic base itself, and the same is probably true of other such difficulties in speech. As Darlington and Mather (1949) say: 'This genetic control must limit, not so much the ability, as the ease with which races and individuals are capable of uttering the various sounds within the range of the human voice.' The same must apply to the chaffinch.

The linnet and the yellowhammer, like the chaffinch, inherit the general pattern of their songs but learn the details. Other birds are different, deviating in one way or another. The bullfinch and greenfinch are much more imitative, being able to learn songs quite foreign to them, while the reed-bunting and corn-bunting (*Emberiza colandra*), the blackcap, whitethroat, and blackbird, all inherit perfect songs; but even in these there may be some copying of other members of the species, as, for instance, by the blackbird.

In addition to the geographical variation, there is some individual variation in chaffinch song. Most individuals probably have more than one form of song, and some have as many as six; the different songs tend to be sung in groups, and one usually predominates. In Wales in 1952 I heard a chaffinch with a song quite unlike the normal, and reminiscent of the redstart's 'wee-choo-choo, wee-chu-wee'. This was on the 15th of May, when the bird should have been in full song. Other birds with a more or less stereotyped song, such as the yellowhammer and willow-warbler, have more than one variant of it. The wood-warbler has two quite different stereotypes, and the coal-tit sometimes sings its two-note song in iambics and sometimes in trochees; I have heard two birds disputing their territories and singing against each other, the first in the one measure, the second in the other. In a few species geographical dialects have been noticed, and sometimes individual songs are recognizable. In birds with more complex songs, such as the blackbird and nightingale, the number of phrases permits an almost infinite number of songs, and individual preferences for one set of patterns rather than another become much easier. It seems likely that many hen birds recognize their mates in part by their songs and that this is most important in those species that pair for life.

That the same theme can be expressed in different forms is an everyday musical experience. We may recognize 'Greensleeves' if it is sung by the human voice, picked out with one finger on the piano, played on a flute, or played by an orchestra in the form of Vaughan Williams's *Fantasia*; yet all these are different. In the same way specific constancy and individual differences can be combined in bird song, the theme being always the same but with enough changes of detail, pitch, or timbre to make the performer identifiable.

When the members of a pair have met, whether through song or any other form of advertisement, there must be courtship to establish the bond between them, and in many species this takes the form of mutual wooing. Further, before each act of coition there must be some special stimulation of one or both sexes—foreplay, in the language of the psychologists.

Foreplay may be vocal, as for instance in the tawny owl, where a pair give duets in the spring, the hen calling 'ke-wick' and the cock hooting, often rather faintly, in reply. After one of these which I observed, in which the hoots were of two syllables only and quite distinct from the normal song, the cock flew to the hen and mounted her. Coition took place on a main branch near the trunk of the tree, and was accompanied by much wing-flapping. When it was over the cock moved to a perch a few feet away and sat silent, while the hen continued to call as before. This occurred at dusk in April before the birds had left their roosts for the night's hunting.

More often both courtship and foreplay are primarily visual, taking the form of the special posturing and movement which are collectively known as display. The male displays to impress or woo or stimulate the female, while she may crouch, as does the hen chaffinch, to invite him to copulate. Display is generally speaking best developed in those birds where the cock has different colours from the hen, and he is then usually brighter than her, with some parts of special brilliance that he can show off. The chief woodland examples are the chaffinch, bullfinch, and pied flycatcher. I have no evidence that there is any systematic difference in either courtship or foreplay between woodland birds and others.

After display and pairing comes egg-laying and the rearing of the young. All woodland birds except the cuckoo make nests, and for each species there is a more or less limited type of situation in which they can be built. A classification of the more important woodland birds by their nest sites is given in Table 18.

No doubt finer subdivision is possible, particularly in distinguishing tree-nests from shrub-nests, but most birds show considerable variation in the height at which they build and in the sort of tree that they choose, so that in the absence of numerical records no very precise distinction can be made.

It is obvious that the tree- and shrub-nesting species exploit a good many different situations, and that there is not much overlap. The wood-pigeon is the only one which regularly nests in or near the canopy, all the others preferring to be away from the crown of the tree or in shrubs. They range from the garden-warbler and blackbird, which seldom nest more than a few feet up, to the long-tailed tit, which usually makes its nest in thorns and such-like at not more than 20 feet, but has been recorded as doing so in trees 50 feet above the ground. I have placed the robin and the wren in brackets because although they sometimes nest in shrubs the typical site is elsewhere.

The hole-nesting species can be at once divided into those which make their own hole and those which do not or cannot do so. Of the birds in the list only the two woodpeckers normally excavate, but the blue tit, marsh-tit, and starling occasionally enlarge an existing hole. Conversely, the nuthatch usually reduces the entrance of a natural hole with mud. The treecreeper nests in a hole not in a tree but on a tree, if the expression may be allowed—behind a piece of bark or between ivy and the trunk. Pied flycatchers and great and blue tits readily use nest-boxes, and the nuthatch and starling sometimes do so.

The ground-nesting birds are few, and the wood- and willow-warbler are the only ones that regularly nest strictly *on* the ground.

TABLE 18

Nest sites of woodland birds

Branches of trees and shrubs	
Crow	Long-tailed tit
Jackdaw	Jay
(Robin)	Magpie
Chaffinch	
Spotted flycatcher	
Blackcap	
(Wren)	
Blackbird	
Song-thrush	
Mistle-thrush	
Buzzard	
Wood-pigeon	
Holes	
Jackdaw	Treecreeper
Pied flycatcher	Tawny owl
Blue tit	Great spotted woodpecker
Great tit	Green woodpecker
Marsh-tit	
Redstart	
Nuthatch	
Starling	
(Wren)	
Near ground	
Yellowhammer	
Chiff-chaff	
Garden-warbler	
On ground	
Tree-pipit	
Robin	
Coal-tit	
(Redstart)	
Wood-warbler	
Willow-warbler	
Wren	
(Blackbird)	
Game birds	

The coal-tit generally nests near it but in a hole or crack under a rock, and its relative scarcity in southern oakwoods may be in part due to the absence of suitable nest sites. It occasionally uses nest-boxes. It seems possible that the ground was the original nest site for both robin and wren, but they frequently use other places.

Five of the birds in the list (long-tailed tit, chiff-chaff, wood-warbler, willow-warbler, and wren) build domed nests with the entrance at the side. Since the situations of these vary widely it is difficult to see any common use in this form of construction. Its value as a protection from the weather seems obvious, but the closely related willow-warbler and chiff-chaff build very similar nests in quite different places, so that it is difficult to see how both can be appropriate to their situations. Since nearly all the members of the genus *Phylloscopus* build domed nests it appears that they are descended from a common ancestor which also did so. Where this hypothetical bird built it is impossible to say, but in view of the habits and distribution of the genus it may well have been on the ground. There is then some slight suggestion that domed nests are primarily designed for ground sites, where they possibly give more protection against both weather and predators than is needed amongst the foliage of shrubs. The nest of the long-tailed tit, of a type found only in the genus *Aegithalos* which is now considered to contain but one species, is an artistic *tour de force* for which an evolutionary explanation is difficult. Most other species that make comparable nests are tropical and it has been suggested that they are a defence against snakes.

In the selection of a nest site there may be much competition, both between members of a species and between species. In the woods this is most noticeable in the hole-nesting species, perhaps because suitable holes are much harder to find than suitable bushes, especially in well-looked-after woods, in which trees are not allowed to reach old age and decay. Great and blue tits compete with each other, and to a lesser extent with marsh-tits. Hinde (1952) found that in interspecific skirmishes in these species there was a much higher proportion of actual combat than in similar skirmishes between members of the same species. It is not clear how far this is because members of the same species quarrel over territory as well, while those of different species fight only over nest sites, where the emotional tension is much greater, and how far it is because in fights between different species the habit of submitting in order to save bloodshed, which is common in intraspecific fights, has not been developed. Titmice also compete with pied flycatchers, and here they have an advantage in being able to take possession before the migratory flycatchers arrive, although they are unable, according to Blezard (1943), to dislodge them once they are in possession. Redstarts and starlings have also been described as competing with the pied flycatcher.

The liking of starlings for woodpeckers' holes is well known, and here their behaviour has gone beyond mere competition and become a form of parasitism, for the woodpeckers excavate the holes for themselves and are then ejected by the starlings. This forces the woodpeckers to move elsewhere, and even if they can find another suitable tree they may be unable to breed until June, when the starlings are well established. Fortunately starlings are absent from many woods which the woodpeckers frequent.

The material of which nests are made could be a factor which would limit distribution, but as there is so much variation within a species, in spite of a common basic pattern, and as the commonly used materials are ubiquitous, it is unlikely that they impose any important restrictions. If they do so at all it will be in woods of simple botanical composition such as those of beech and fir. Twigs, as used by jay, bullfinch, treecreeper, dunnock, and wood-pigeon, are obviously easy to obtain, and there is likely to be no difficulty with the moss used by the chaffinch, treecreeper, tits, leaf-warblers, thrushes, robin, dunnock, and wren, or the dead leaves used by the nuthatch, chiff-chaff, song-thrush, blackbird, robin, and wren. Some birds, such as the chaffinch, wood- and willow-warblers, blackcap, whitethroat, thrushes, and wren, make much use of grass, and this might be absent from many woods, so that it could be restricting if it were an essential material and not merely used when it is available. The books say that the chief nest material of the starling is straw, which is clearly an artificial material, although it could be carried into the woods by the birds, which have a wide feeding range. There is great scope for careful record of the nesting material used by the same species of birds under different ecological conditions. I suspect that most birds are more adaptable in choosing the materials that are available than is sometimes thought.

Some birds line their nests with feathers, and although it would be possible for a woodland bird to pluck these from its own body, as does the eider-duck, I can find no evidence that this is ever done. The feathers are collected from elsewhere and brought to the nest, many of the older writers particularly mentioning collection from farmyards, where, before the days of deep-litter and batteries and specialized farming, there would always have been plenty from the flocks of hens. Several people have taken long-tailed tits' nests to pieces and carefully counted the feathers that they contain, obtaining totals from 835 to 2,457, with a mean for 18 nests of 1,493. A cock house-sparrow that I plucked in June 1960 had 3,005 small feathers, plus 46 quills, but about half were so small that they could be plucked only under a lens and were probably too tiny to be of any significance in nest-lining. It seems therefore that a long-tailed tit's nest contains as many feathers as can be got from the body of a sparrow-sized bird. This number is not likely to be achieved by casual collecting at a time of the year when moulting is not taking place, even though, as Wetmore (1936) has shown, resident birds lose many feathers between winter and summer. But in the absence of man and his poultry there is one prolific source of feathers in the woods—the carcases of birds killed by sparrow-hawks. These birds scatter the feathers of their prey as they eat, and leave the backbone, especially of larger birds, on the ground with skin and feathers still attached. It is possible that under natural conditions the long-tailed tit, in whose nests feathers seem to be a necessity, is dependent on the presence of sparrow-hawks. Where there is a shortage of feathers there could be strong competition between different pairs of tits.

When a male bird starts singing in anticipation of a mate, he is usually in possession of a territory, that is to say, of a tract of land which he will defend against other males of the same species, and into which he will welcome a hen. His song serves both purposes; it is a warning to other cocks to keep out and an invitation to hens to come in. It has often been claimed that the song changes after he is mated, but except that it may not be so loud and may be uttered less frequently, there seems no certain evidence of this.

The territory must be suitable to hold a nest and other features are often necessary as well, particularly suitable song posts, from which the male can give his song or start his song-flight, near its perimeter. These may be very variable; the tree-pipit usually chooses trees at least 30 feet high, but is satisfied on young plantations by little trees of 2 feet or so, that barely project above the surrounding vegetation. We know little of the size of territory held by most species, but there is evidence that the territory is an elastic area, which contracts and expands according to the ecological conditions and the pressure of neighbours. Lack found that the territories of his robins in Devonshire varied from about 2 acres down to 0·4 acre, and there was no evidence that this was in any sense a minimum; the birds occupying the smallest territories successfully reared broods of normal size. May (1949) found that the territories of willow-warblers on the mixed oak and birch scrub of a Surrey common had an even greater range, from 1·2 to 0·16 acre, and here again the birds on the smallest territories were quite successful in rearing young. The mean size of territory was 0·35 acre in 1945 and 0·48 in 1946, so that there is no evidence that the area could not, on territorial grounds, have held more pairs. The territories of tits also vary widely, Hinde and other authors having recorded 0·4, 0·6 and 2·0 acres for the blue tit, 0·6 to 4·2 with a mean of 2·0 for 14 territories of the great tit, up to 65 acres for the willow-tit, and 1 to 16 acres for the marsh-tit.

It is obvious that many species of bird may simultaneously choose the same major habitat, and that there is, in any given wood, a great deal of overlap in their feeding ranges. It is generally believed that while the immediate vicinity of the nest is defended against most birds, nesting territory is only held against members of the same species. There are certainly exceptions to this; according to Durango (1956) the red-backed shrike drives away almost every sort of bird up to the size of magpies, and Mountfort (1956) describes the hawfinch also as defending its territory against a wide range of species. I think it possible that this wider form of exclusiveness may be relatively common. I once heard a song-thrush and a chaffinch singing in the same garden; every time that the chaffinch sang, the thrush stopped abruptly, and resumed only when the chaffinch's song was over. Any general effect of this sort would clearly lead to territory being less effectively advertised, however firmly it was held. I have seen a coal-tit chasing a cock chaffinch in and out through an oakwood, with the hen chaffinch following and another coal-tit taking no part. The chase ranged over 100 yards or so, and was resumed after a pause; it was much more than a mere driving away of the chaffinch from the vicinity of the nest site, and indeed was unsuccessful in this. There was no physical contact between the birds. I have also seen a cock chaffinch chasing a nightingale, a willow-warbler chasing a coal-tit and on another occasion a great tit, a blue tit chasing a chiff-chaff, and a wood-warbler chasing a hen chaffinch, in places which may have been near but which did not appear to be in the immediate vicinity of the nest. On the other hand I have seen pied and spotted flycatchers apparently happily in the same tree, and similarly a willow-warbler and a pair of stonechats in the same bush.

Some birds, especially those that are more or less sedentary, form their pairs in a way different from that just described. Blue and great tits, for example, gradually form pairs within the winter flocks, and there is inspection of possible nest sites by both sexes. Gradually the flocks break up, one nest site is chosen, and a defended territory is established round it. It is possible that a pair once established holds together throughout the following winters and summers until one member dies, and Southern and Morley (1950) showed that this is certainly true for the marsh-tit. These birds not only pair for life but hold their territories all the year round, attaching themselves only temporarily to the tit-flocks that pass through them in travelling through the wood.

Rook

11

THE INTER-RELATIONS OF THE COMMUNITY: (3) General

Elton (1939) has discussed the concept of 'cover', which is of some importance to woodland birds. Like many biological terms it is difficult of definition but it includes such things as shelter from inclement weather, protection from predators, and concealment of predators in approaching their prey. The trees, shrubs, and field layer of a wood may all provide cover even when they are not essential for giving food or nesting sites, although the cover aspect of the latter is itself of importance. Many woodland birds feed, at least at times, in the open, the jay and green woodpecker being good examples; when disturbed they at once fly to the trees, the jay to the thickness of large shrubs or the lower branches of big trees, and the woodpecker usually to the trunk or big limbs, where its colour and shape give it some degree of cryptic protection. Even the woodpecker, although in some districts it feeds mostly on the ground, remains essentially an arboreal bird because of the cover which the tree can give. It is not dependent on the woods as such, for the sort of cover that it wants, as well as nesting and roosting sites, can be given by scattered trees, and so it is also a characteristic bird of parkland (Chapter 7). The cover that the jay uses, on the other hand, cannot be adequately provided by isolated trees, and it is therefore a strictly woodland bird.[1]

Lower down in the wood the wren takes shelter in a thick field layer of herbs or small bushes or brambles. Such a habitat is most frequently provided in this country in woods and it is there that wrens are chiefly found, but where, as on the fells of the north and the Scottish islands, similar cover is present in districts with no trees, wrens manage to live quite successfully without them. The same is true to a lesser extent of the robin, blackbird, and song-thrush. These seem to be able to obtain cover from quite low under-shrubs, but mostly demand higher vegetation for nest sites or for song posts. It is noticeable that a disturbed blackbird often flies upward, a disturbed wren hardly ever. In the treeless Shetland, which it has colonized within the last eighty years, the blackbird nests chiefly in or near buildings or walls, and so, according to Venables and Venables (1952), is largely dependent on man.

The function of woodland cover in protecting from extremes of weather is obscured in this country by the greater provision of food in the vicinity of farms and gardens, so that it is a common observation of bird-ringers that tits, for example, leave the woods and come for their bait chiefly in frost or snow, but under natural conditions the woods provide a much more sheltered and equable environment than open grassland. One has only to enter a wood on a day of high wind to realize how true this is, and both high and low temperatures are less extreme amongst the trees. The infrequency of frost-bound soil under the carpet of ground vegetation and dead leaves must often enable the omnivorous birds to survive when their food would be quite unobtainable on open grassland.

Roosting is a subject about which we know little except for the spectacular massed roosts of starlings, rooks, and a few other birds, but clearly it could have some effect on winter distribution. Most small passerines roost in bushes, and under garden conditions several

[1] But see page 199.

species often congregate in fairly large numbers in such places as thick shrubberies. The same sort of communal roosting occurs in woods but little is known of it. All the hole-nesting species also roost in holes, the woodpeckers excavating special ones for the purpose if necessary. Some at least of the tits are less exacting; the blue tit fairly commonly uses evergreens, ivy, and thick bushes, and although records are few the coal- and marsh-tits appear to be similar; tits use also brambles and other thick vegetation near the ground. The three native thrushes, although they usually feed singly in winter, generally but not invariably roost in shrubs in small parties of half a dozen or so, often containing more than one species, and sometimes with redwings. Fieldfares sometimes roost in quite large flocks in the oak canopy. The robin and hedge-sparrow roost singly in bushes; the wren is as catholic in its choice of roosting sites as in its choice of nest sites, using shrubs, ivy, holes, or old nests; generally it is solitary, but sometimes, especially in cold weather, a number occupy the same hole. The tawny owl roosts in holes, on the larger branches of well-grown trees, or low down in birch or yew, and in larch plantations and durmast oakwoods quite commonly on the ground. It uses the same spot for a few weeks at a time.

In most of the relationships which I have described so far one bird hinders another, but there are others in which there appears to be some mutual advantage. Many woodland birds are, at least at some seasons of the year, social, and it is presumed, on the principle of natural selection, that this habit would not have evolved unless it had some advantages for the species.

There are in this country no woodland birds which are strictly colonial nesters, but the rook and heron, which are birds of the ecotone, nearly always nest in this way. I have already suggested that the habit may be the result of a scarcity of suitable nesting sites under natural conditions. Certainly with such large birds protection cannot now be important, and even if large birds of prey were once much commoner than they are now, the value of association for defence against them is doubtful. The starling, which often nests in loose colonies, is also a bird which feeds largely outside the wood and has perhaps become partly social for the same reasons as the rook and the heron. As it does not require such large trees as they do, it must always have been easier for it to find suitable nesting sites. The only other fairly common woodland bird of which numbers nest together is the redpoll. It is a bird of the scrub birchwood or birchwood ecotone, and largely a seed-eater. I can suggest no reason for its sociable habit, as the sort of surroundings which it likes are still fairly extensive and must formerly have been more so. It not only nests in loose colonies but feeds in small flocks even in the breeding season, both in trees and on the ground.

The habit of communal roosting is even more difficult to explain than colonial nesting. The association of solitary thrushes and other birds in hollies and other evergreens may be taken as merely accidental, birds from the surrounding district crowding into the most suitable bushes available, but the way in which large numbers of rooks, jackdaws, and starlings come together from an area of many square miles is something quite different. It cannot be for protection, for once in their roost the birds are seldom disturbed, and the assembly of starlings before the roost settles down for the night is a well-known attraction for sparrow-hawks. Rook-roosts are said usually to be on the site of a present or former rookery, so that it is tempting to suggest that the winter assembly is a return to the ancestral home, those birds which have founded new colonies going back for the winter to that in which they were bred, and showing their young the way there by example and imitation. This is a rather far-fetched explanation and it is not applicable to the starling, whose roosts are for the most part in quite different situations from their nests and may be occupied only for a few years, or even for a few months or days.

There remain the very common associations of birds for feeding outside the breeding season. These tend to form as soon as nesting is over and to last until the pairs break away and take up territory again in the spring, so that the term 'winter flock', though convenient, is not wholly accurate. The majority of the birds seen in the woods in winter are in flocks; robin, jay, magpie, marsh-tit, wren, blackbird, sparrow-hawk, greater spotted and green woodpeckers, and pheasant are solitary or in pairs, and almost all the others in more or less firmly held flocks. These are of two sorts: those which are of one species only, and those looser aggregations in which several species associate together.

The most conspicuous of the former type are the large flocks of wood-pigeons which come into the woods especially when there is a rich crop of acorns. The usual size is some hundred or so birds, but flocks running into thousands have been recorded. These flocks are generally thought to be migrants from overseas, but Colquhoun (1951) has given reasons for thinking that they are composed of birds of the year and that migration is of limited extent and almost all within this country. The small number of ringing returns do not show any considerable overseas migration. Pigeons are opportunist feeders, moving from place to place and switching from one form of vegetable food to another as each in turn becomes abundant, and the flocks may have had no other origin than the association of birds on a favourite and readily available food supply. This would no doubt be helped by their poor territorial sense, for although nests are normally well spaced out, where nesting sites are few a number of nests may occur close together. The winter flocks are certainly very loosely integrated, for when one is disturbed the birds often, perhaps usually, split into two or three parties which fly off in different directions.

The much smaller winter flocks of redpolls probably have a similar origin, though it is possible that these consist also of birds which have nested together. Twenty or thirty is perhaps an average number, and the flocks appear in woods where the birds do not breed. They may associate temporarily with other species, especially tits, but remain aloof from them. While a disturbed tit-flock at most moves a little faster through the trees and seldom splits into component parts, the redpolls rise into the air together and fly over the tops of the trees some hundreds of yards into another part of the wood. When chaffinches flock in winter they cease for the most part to be woodland birds, but remain so where there are beech trees. Other finches, especially bramblings which come as winter migrants, may be associated with them.

The most characteristic winter flocks of English woods are those of the tits. With them are often associated other small birds: goldcrests, nuthatches, treecreepers, and greater and lesser spotted woodpeckers, and in autumn leaf-warblers may attach themselves, and more rarely other warblers and pied and spotted flycatchers. Of the regular associates, only goldcrests ever form any important part of the flock. I have once seen three treecreepers in a tit-flock, but otherwise have never seen more than a single bird or, more usually, a pair. The nuthatch, woodpeckers, and creeper, though sometimes associating with the tits, appear not to form flocks themselves.

In spite of their ubiquity, tit-flocks have been little studied, the most important work in this country being that of Hinde (1952); he worked primarily on the great tit but paid some attention to the other species present. The area of Wytham Woods, near Oxford, in which his observations were made, was rather small—about 55 acres—and the vegetation is mixed and highly unnatural. It is possible that these features affected the behaviour of the flocks, although they are unlikely to have had any effect on their formation.

He found that within a week of leaving the nest broods of young great tits began to mix, and within a further ten days they mixed with the young of other species. Blue tits were much the same, but the mixing of young marsh-tits was delayed, probably because of the larger nesting territory in this species. These early flocks were very loosely integrated, but by autumn most flocks were stable and kept to one part of the wood. The flock area was not defended but might be held for months, even though the individuals which composed it were gradually changing. The degree of integration varied, both with the flock and with the time of day. It tended to be greatest in the morning, the flocks breaking up as the day went on. Hinde describes two sorts of movements: a slow drifting while the birds are feeding, and a more definite translation of the whole flock, in which the birds cease feeding and fly for up to 200 yards in one hop. In the first type the birds keep together by the indefinite 'tsit' call; the second is initiated by one bird flying upwards, and calling 'twink'; others do likewise, and after a few minutes the whole flock moves off. Second-year and older birds seemed to remain paired in the flocks throughout the winter, and birds of the year formed pairs at any time from autumn onwards. The flocks broke up in the spring when the pairs scattered and gradually established breeding territory.

Hinde found that the flocks were almost entirely local, with only some wandering by first-year birds, and that the drifting movements were slow, with a maximum speed of about 200 yards per hour.

My own observations, made in Wyre Forest, do not entirely agree with these. The two areas in which I have chiefly studied tit-flocks are the oak underplanted with beech, previously described, with an area of about a third of a square mile (*c.* 214 acres) and larch plantations from nineteen to twenty-eight years old, of 200 acres. These comprise only a portion of the forest. The birds were not colour-marked, so that individual birds could not be recognized, but I have no doubt that there was in fact a considerable autumn and winter influx and much movement. The number of tits present in the winter is very much higher than in the breeding season, and the composition and distribution of the flocks do not remain as steady as they do at Wytham. As I have also found that in the isolated fell-woods of the Lake District the composition of the winter flocks by no means corresponds to the breeding population, I suspect that in the Midlands and north, or perhaps under more natural woodland conditions, there is much more movement, or perhaps southward migration, than under the semi-domestic conditions where most ringing studies have been carried out. Gilbert and Walker (1954) report the coal-tit as being distinctly rare in Herefordshire in the breeding season but common in winter, so that there too it must migrate or wander.

Hinde records about a dozen as the usual number of great tits in a flock, with sometimes as many as fifty, and other species up to over 100. The usual flocks in Wyre are certainly much smaller than this; it is impossible, except under very favourable circumstances, to be sure of the true size of the flock, but on the whole the Wyre flocks seldom have more than half a dozen of any one species. There is an indication of some difference between the flocks in oak and those in larch, although a given flock often goes from one type of woodland to another without a check. In oaks the blue tit is the commonest, with the coal-tit not far behind. No flock that I have recorded failed to contain one or other of these species, and most contained both. Great tits were present in about two-thirds of the flocks, and were in rather smaller total numbers than coal-tits. Long-tailed tits were present in only one-third of the flocks, but a few large parties brought their total numbers up to something between those of the coal-tits and great tits. Marsh-tits, goldcrests, and treecreepers were each present in about a third of the flocks; of the first of these I never saw more than a pair together. Willow-tits, nuthatches, and lesser and greater spotted woodpeckers were occasional and confined to particular parts of the forest.

In larches the pattern was rather different. The flocks were on the whole larger, the biggest recorded being 155, of which about nine-tenths were coal-tits. Blue and coal-tits again predominated and one or the other species was present in every flock, but this time they were in about equal numbers, with the coal-tit perhaps a little ahead. Great tits, marsh-tits, and long-tailed tits were each present in less than a third of the flocks, the first two in very small numbers. Some of the parties of long-tailed tits were of the order of a dozen, and in one flock there were four marsh-tits. Goldcrests were present in about half the flocks. There were a few treecreepers, but no other associated birds.

The drifting movement of flocks described by Hinde is of two kinds. Sometimes a flock remains practically stationary for several minutes. I do not know what the maximum period of time is, as with other things to do I have usually had to move on before the birds did, but I have recorded as much as twenty-five minutes. During these periods there is considerable movement of individuals within the flock, and there may be some slight movement of its edges, but some portion, and usually most, of the area originally covered by the flock remains so covered throughout the time. Presumably the birds have discovered an abundant food supply and are making good use of it. At other times, though the birds are feeding, each individual stays only a short time in a tree and the centre of gravity of the flock moves pretty steadily. The course followed is generally some sort of open loop, and there is nothing that the observer can see to suggest why a change of direction, which is sometimes a complete reversal, is made. A number of tracks of tit-flocks, drawn approximately to scale, are shown in Fig. 13. Sometimes a flock passes a boundary from one type of woodland to another, for example oak to larch or larch to spruce, without changing either direction or speed. Some of the speeds that I recorded are much higher than any that Hinde found: the highest for oak is about 1,000 yards per hour, and for larch 1,650 yards per hour. There is some indication that the speeds in larch are generally higher than in oak. Győry (1956-57) has recorded speeds of up to 2,200

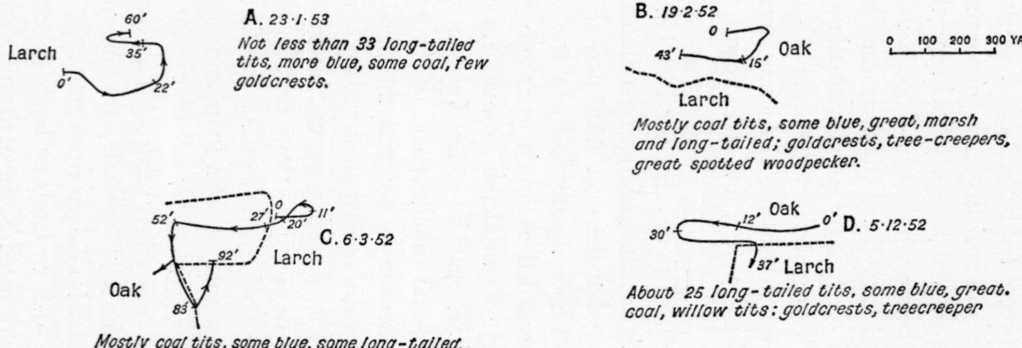

FIG. 13. Tracks of tit-flocks. The dotted line shows the boundary of the type of woodland.

yards per hour in Hungary, with an average of half this. Gibb (1960) found that in pine plantations in Breckland the larger flocks, with more species, tended to move faster than the others, long-tailed tits especially having an accelerating effect. The highest speed that he recorded was 1,320 yards per hour.

Tit-flocks often fragment into smaller flocks, and when this happens it is often the birds of one species that go off together. Long-tailed tits and great tits probably detach themselves from a mixed flock more often than do the other two common species; this is perhaps connected with their somewhat different feeding habits. Long-tailed tits often outpace the rest of the mixed flock, and simply leave the other species behind.

The general picture that comes out of this is of individuals and species associating together at the first opportunity after breeding is over, and of their liking each other's company. Though always willing to divide into smaller parties, tits, except for marsh- and willow-tits, are only rarely in pairs and practically never solitary during the winter. Even when species are using different foodstuffs they may keep together, so that it is common to see a mixed party of coal-tits and blue tits moving together through the canopy while great tits follow the same track in the brambles and brushwood below, and the treecreepers in a mixed flock follow their normal habit of spiralling up a tree trunk from its base and then flying to another to treat it in the same way.

The strict Darwinian must try to find a reason for the flocking habit in terms of its survival value. Protection against predators is, as I have said above, unlikely. It has been suggested that the flock disturbs the insects on which the birds feed and so makes them easier to find. This is ingenious but not very likely, and there is certainly no evidence that such disturbance really does take place. It certainly cannot account for the association of great and blue tits in the form in which I have just described it. Psychological explanations of biological phenomena are unfashionable, but birds do certainly have a rich psychic life, in many ways comparable to that of man. Their rituals of display and courtship show this, and it seems fairly clear that the presence of numbers is necessary for the successful breeding of some sea birds. It is possible that flocking in some sense makes the birds happy, so that they are better able to withstand severities of climate and food supply. It is to be noted that it is the smaller birds, on whom the rigours of winter fall most heavily, which flock, and that flocks tend to increase in size in hard weather. The importance of stress in reducing survival-rate under severe conditions is now well established for small mammals, and is likely to apply to birds also.

Several observers have described for tit-flocks the phenomenon of dominance, which is much better known in farmyard hens and in monkeys. There is a hierarchy, or order of precedence, such that any individual gives way when threatened by another above it, but supplants one below it. It has been seen in tit-flocks chiefly when the birds are feeding on large objects, such as nuts and beech-mast, or at a bird table. One individual flies down and supplants another already engaged in eating the food. It has been said that in both the great tit and the blue tit the order of dominance depends on the nearness of established territories, the bird being higher in the list the nearer it is to its home, but the order is changeable and does not remain fixed for so long as it does in the more highly organized social animals. It does not seem as if dominance is of any great importance in the titmice. Most of their feeding is on small particles which are swallowed at once, and apart from sexual chases when pairs are being formed the flocks live a very harmonious life.

A peculiar form of temporary flocking occurs when many small birds combine to mob predators or supposed predators; it is of doubtful biological value. It could be argued that it is in their interests to combine and chase away a sparrow-hawk, but many observers have described the hawk on such occasions seizing and going off with one of the flock. Tawny owls, which seldom take birds, and cuckoos, which never do, are also mobbed, and no explanation for this behaviour seems possible. The cuckoo's egg, once in the nest, is accepted quite happily, although natural selection might, if the opportunity had arisen, have chosen behaviour that would lead to the ejection of the egg, an action which would be much more effective than mobbing the parent.

It is generally stated that mobbing is induced by the sight of the owl or whatever it may be, but things are more complicated than this. Last summer a blackbird regularly sang from my rooftop in a position where he could not possibly see a tawny owl that roosted in a thick horse-chestnut. Equally regularly, as the light began to fail but before the owl called, the blackbird stopped singing, flew to the tree and started mobbing, being joined by several other birds. After ten minutes or so of this he gave up, sang once or twice more, and himself went to roost.

Besides the song, which is generally sexual and territorial in character, woodland birds make other sounds which to some extent constitute a language; that is, they convey information to the mate, the young, or other birds. The voice of the chaffinch has been very fully studied by Marler (1956) who has distinguished thirteen calls in addition to the song, and has suggested what each of them means to other chaffinches. The flight-call, a low 'tsup', given when the bird is flying or about to fly, may be heard at all times of the year but is commonest when the birds are settling into the woods in spring. If it is given by a female flying over a territory already occupied by a male, it may induce courtship behaviour in him and so lead to pair-formation. Its meaning may be summed up as 'chaffinch here in friendly mood'. The meanings of the 'pink', called by Marler the social call, and of the 'wheet' (the rain call or *regenrauf* of continental authors), are not so clear. Both are sometimes danger-signals, 'pink' for example being given when a hawk flies over, and both are sometimes used by males with adjacent territories apparently with aggressive intent. Both calls have variants which possibly have different meanings.

All thirteen calls, except sometimes the social and rain calls, are fully inherited and do not need to be learnt.

Calls, like songs, if they are to convey the information that they come from a particular species, must obviously be distinct, and this is generally so. There are, however, exceptions. The brambling's song is indistinguishable both by the human ear and by the sound spectrograph from the call (which may also be the first note of the song) of the greenfinch. These two species overlap in range in southern Scandinavia but whether they ever occur in the same habitats I do not know. One of the great tit's calls may be mistaken for the chaffinch's 'pink', and many of the social calls of tits and finches are nearly or quite indistinguishable in two or three species.

When the information to be conveyed is the presence of danger, not the identity of the caller, there is less need for specific distinctiveness. The calls that several birds, such as blackbirds, robins, wrens, and chaffinches, use in mobbing owls are all more or less alike, and the information that they convey is given to several different species. Even more clearly similar are the 'tseep' calls which several species of thrush, robins, chaffinches, and spotted flycatchers use to announce the near presence of a predator. These are also very difficult to locate, and so do not tell the predator where the caller is. Their similarity in several species may be an auditory example of what in butterflies is called Mullerian mimicry, where natural selection has been more intense where it can act on several species simultaneously.

The effect of competition and of anything, whether the action of man or a change in climate, that alters the conditions under which a bird lives, will be less if the bird is adaptable or plastic and can change either its habits or its habitat, or both. Woodpeckers suffer much from the attacks of starlings because they are bound to a particular kind of hole excavated by themselves in trees which have begun to decay. Starlings, even if not aggressive by nature, would be much less vulnerable, for they can nest in a hole of almost any size above a minimum in almost any situation, even in the ground, and occasionally not even in a hole at all, but in thick evergreens. It looks in fact as if the only condition that they need is some degree of darkness.

Adaptable birds may, like the starling, be able to spread over a number of different habitats simultaneously without any obvious preference, or they may move to a second habitat when conditions require it, while retaining a preference for the first. A number of examples of the second group are given by the large birds which have been much persecuted by man. The common buzzard is on the Continent a bird of wooded areas where there is also open country over which it hunts, and in Britain it was formerly common in this type of habitat, being found all over England, Wales, and the mainland of Scotland. Persecution in the nineteenth century confined it, or more probably drove it, to the hills; that it is basically a bird of trees is shown by its nest, which is made of twigs and leaves. With this change in habit there has possibly gone a change in diet, for while on the Continent its chief food is apparently voles, here, until 1954, it took largely rabbits. The rabbit is not a native of this country but has for long been one of our commonest mammals and is certainly the most conspicuous. As a result of a natural increase in numbers and a relaxation of the attacks of gamekeepers, the buzzard has recently begun to move back into the lowlands, where it is once more characteristically a bird of the woods.

When it went to the hills the buzzard was able to change its nesting site to cliffs or the ground and to use heather or other material for its nest where twigs were not available. It was possibly this adaptability that saved it. The kite, a bird of similar general habits and living like the buzzard in woods with adjacent open space, has not been so fortunate. It seems seldom to nest on cliffs, and perhaps for this reason has become restricted as a result of persecution to a few pairs in a limited part of central Wales. An inspection of the map will show that this is almost the only part of England and Wales which has woods of any extent which are remote from populated areas or sporting estates.

The raven is in much the same state as the buzzard. It was formerly found over most of England and nested in tall trees, and then became confined to the mountains and sea coast, where it nested on cliffs. It has recently begun to come back into the lowlands, though not to the same extent as the buzzard, and in some of its new situations, as in Worcestershire, it is living in woods and nesting in trees.

Birds of an ecotone, such as were discussed in Chapter 7, may be stably adapted to the mixed habitat, as is probably true for the willow-warbler and yellowhammer, or they may be in process of passing from one pure habitat to another. The redstart with its tendency to nest in walls and ruins may be an example of this. The genus to which it belongs consists mostly of birds which live in mountain woodlands, and there is a strong tendency for them to frequent rocky places. Some of the species, including the black redstart (*Phoenicurus ochrurus*) whose range just reaches this country, are by nature wholly birds of the rocks. The common redstart looks as if it were moving in the same direction. It would certainly be able to survive even if all the woods were destroyed. The jackdaw is probably another example which is also in process of moving from trees to cliffs. The crows as a whole are tree-dwellers, although creatures of parkland or scrub rather than woods. The jackdaw does still nest in trees but so far as my observation goes is numerous only where there are cliffs, preferably with woods near by. A further step commonly taken by cliff-nesting birds is to houses and buildings, which make artificial cliffs. Both the jackdaw and the redstarts show this and in some parts of the Continent the black redstart has become domestic, breeding entirely on or in houses. In its recent invasion of this country it has nested chiefly on bombed buildings in the centre of towns.

The factors which we have been considering in this and the two preceding chapters decide, together with the fecundity of the birds and the action of climatic conditions in determining the death-rate, whether the population will increase or decrease, or whether it will remain constant. Within limits it generally does the last. There are fluctuations, especially decreases caused by severe weather, but the total seldom goes outside characteristic limits. This has led to the conception of density-dependent factors; that is, of factors which vary with the density of the birds on the ground. It is thought, for instance, that when after a severe winter the population is reduced, some other factor, perhaps competition for food, becomes less severe, so that a rapid increase, such as is generally observed, can take place in the next year or so. Gibb (1960) has claimed to show that the numbers of coal-tits in pine plantations are controlled by the food supply, but his figures do not support his conclusion. The simplest interpretation of them, and so the one that the scientist must provisionally accept, is that the mortality (or emigration) depends in a non-density-dependent way on winter temperature.

The classical example of a density-dependent factor is the predator-prey relationship. There can be little doubt that the lower the density of the prey the harder it will be for the predator to find its food. But there are probably no birds in this country which are kept in check by natural predators, and while density-dependent factors are perhaps sometimes important, it is probably more likely that the population of a species is generally determined by a series of limiting factors. Under normal conditions increase is prevented because some one factor, such as food or the supply of nesting sites, is taken up to the limit. A fall in population can be almost immediately restored because each pair of survivors produce several young, and now there is no longer any difficulty in all of them finding enough food or nesting sites or whatever it was that was limiting before. This would account for the spectacular increase in pied flycatchers in the Forest of Dean which followed the provision of nesting boxes, an increase which clearly has nothing to do with density-dependent factors.

The frontiers of the area of distribution of a species are presumably determined by such things as climate or habitat-type which prevent colonization. The fact that slight improvements in climate, such as have gone on in north-west Europe in the past century (see page 219), are accompanied by the extension of range of many species, suggests that there is a surplus population waiting to take up new areas as they become available. Creation of new suitable habitats by man will have the same effect. The planting of the Forestry Commission has greatly increased the number of woodland birds, and the ploughing that took place during the war increased the number of rooks.

The same thing must happen when a bird alters its habits and extends the range of habitat in which it will breed, as has happened with the redstart in the north of England, where it nests in walls and ruins, and the pied flycatcher in Scandinavia, where it has become a bird of towns and gardens. In all these cases there will be an increase, the rate of which is determined chiefly by the birth-rate, until the old factor again becomes limiting or is replaced by another one. In this conception it is the absolute numbers of the birds in a geographical area that matter rather than their density at a point, for while there is a maximum population which cannot be exceeded, below this maximum the density has no importance. The distinction between the two types of factor was clearly made for man by Malthus many years ago when he wrote of ultimate and immediate checks to population. He thought that the first, which was always the limiting food supply, never operated except in conditions of actual famine; many of the second he recognized as peculiar to man, and in fact the only three that are of general application are predation, parasitism leading to disease, and the action of weather. The first of these is unimportant for woodland birds, and the evidence suggests that it is rare for disease to cause great mortality. We are then, in this country, probably left with a balance between weather and the upper limiting factors of food and suitable habitat.

Woodlark

12

PROBLEMS OF DISTRIBUTION

The distribution of birds, as of all animals and plants, is determined by two groups of factors which are called broadly geographical and ecological. It is necessary in the first place that the species or its ancestors should have been able to arrive in the area under discussion, and, having arrived there, they must have been able to survive and produce descendants which could also survive. The absence of European birds such as thrushes and finches from New Zealand was due to a geographical limitation; the land was so remote and separated by such a wide band of sea from the birds' natural homes that they never arrived there, but when introduced by man they throve and multiplied, showing that there were no ecological limitations. Birds, by their powers of flight and consequent great mobility, are less bound by geographical conditions than most other animals, and it must usually be an ecological factor which determines whether a given European species is found in Great Britain or not. The absence from, or rarity in, this country of many species common in France clearly depends on the fact that conditions here are not suitable for them, for they would have no difficulty in crossing the Channel. The golden oriole (*Oriolus oriolus*), for instance, turns up here often enough, but has never been able to establish itself as a breeder. Exceptionally, there are some species of eastern Europe which could possibly persist in our climate but which live too far away to reach here in large enough numbers for breeding to be successful. The difference between geographical and ecological factors is shown very clearly by migratory birds, which visit a country but do not breed in it. Redwings and fieldfares, for instance, are present in England in large numbers every winter, but have never been known to breed here.

Some writers have argued that because the distribution of animals is determined by both ecological and geographical factors at the same time, it is impossible or pointless to try to distinguish between them. This is like falling into the philosophical fallacy of thinking that an object can have only one property; a lemon is both yellow and bitter, but this does not mean that colour and taste are the same thing. Although there are cases where distinction is difficult, it is usually possible to decide whether geographical or ecological factors have had the main influence on distribution; what is more difficult is to decide which of the many possible ecological factors is of most importance.

The most general ecological factor is climate, and this acts on birds both directly in determining their ability to survive under the available conditions of food-supply and so on, and indirectly in determining both the vegetation which gives them shelter and the invertebrates which are available as food. It is itself determined in general terms by latitude and proximity to the sea, and locally by a number of special topographical features such as altitude and slope. Both all-the-year-round climate and the extremes in the hottest and coldest or driest and wettest months affect animals, but the mobility of birds makes them less affected by the adverse extremes than are most animals, since they can, and do, go away to avoid these and return when conditions are better. There are only slight variations from month to month in the rainfall of this country, so that temperature is the most important climatic variable. With our Atlantic type of climate, with relatively mild winters and cool summers, even this has less effect than on the Continent, and it is noteworthy that many birds, such as the chaffinch, which are fully migratory at the same latitudes in Europe, are here largely sedentary.

Special ecological factors are many: the ones which are most likely to affect birds are the vegetation, with which the earlier chapters of this book have largely dealt; the altitude, acting mainly through climate and vegetation; the soil, acting chiefly through the vegetation and the invertebrate fauna; and the other animals, whether serving as food or entering into the life of the bird community as predators or commensals. It is obvious that different factors interact on each other so that their effects on the birds are often indirect, and further, the effect of any given factor is influenced by the intensity of others. Thus low temperature may not be important if plenty of food is present, and low density of food may be counteracted in summer by high latitude, which means a long day and more time in which to collect what food there is.

The starling, one of our commonest birds, illustrates well the difficulty of deciding the factors which determine distribution. It is a bird of trees, but its chief feeding ground is grassland, so that it may be classed as a bird of the park-ecotone. It is, however, very adaptable, and is found in many different situations. Its geographical distribution in Great Britain is not now remarkable, but a hundred or even fifty years ago it was very different. In the middle of the last century the bird was found on the mainland of Scotland only in the south-west lowlands, and at the same period it was chiefly a winter visitor to Wales and to Devon and Cornwall. It first bred in Devonshire about 1830 and in Cornwall in 1855. Since then the position has changed and it is now resident in every county, although as recently as 1923 I noted in a schoolboy diary that it was absent from West Pembrokeshire in July, and it is still a rare breeding species in Cardiganshire. There has thus been both a westward and a northward spread which makes climatic change an unlikely cause. Moreover, the summer temperatures of Scotland and Cornwall are well within the extremes at which the bird successfully breeds on the Continent, in Finland and northern Italy. The change seems to be a geographical spread, based on increasing numbers, into districts which have long been ecologically suitable.

The starling, as well as being a resident in this country, is a winter visitor, and the birds come from the east, not the north (Fig. 14).

It looks as if its centre of evolution was eastern Europe or beyond, and this view is supported by the fact that the combination of trees and grassland which seems proper to it is characteristic of a continental not an Atlantic climate. It is only in historic times, with the clearance of woodland, that open country in which starlings can feed has occurred to any extent in western Europe. Even in glacial and immediate post-glacial times (see next chapter) there was little

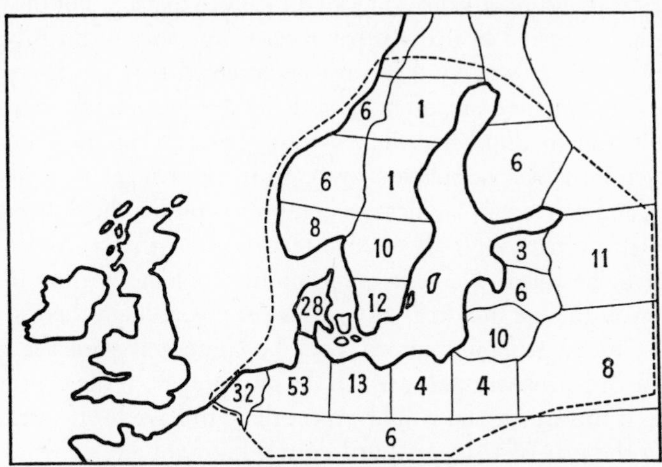

FIG. 14. Origin of starlings that winter in Britain. The figures show the numbers of starlings recovered during the breeding season (May to August) that had previously been ringed in the British Isles during December, January, or February. From M. J. Goodacre, *Bird Study*, 6:181, Fig. 1 (1959).

or no steppe in Great Britain. As the numbers of the birds have increased it has spread westward, partly by occupying new and suitable niches created by man, and partly by changing its habits to live in new environments. This spread would have taken place in part by the failure of some of the winter visitors to return home.

There seem to be only two facts which do not fit easily into this hypothesis: that starlings have been present from time immemorial on the Outer Hebrides, Orkneys and Shetlands, and that there is some very slight evidence that the spread of the bird over Scotland in the nineteenth century was a re-advance following a previous retreat. The continued presence of starlings on the islands is explicable by a winter arrival of a few birds followed by a failure to return home. Whatever the proximate factor which initiates eastward migration in spring—rise in temperature or increase in sunlight—it might well fail to work in these northern and cloudy latitudes. The starlings of the Shetlands and the Hebrides (but not of the Orkneys) are ranked as a different subspecies from those of the mainland, which suggests a relatively long isolation from the main stock.

A retreat and re-advance is more difficult to explain, but the same thing has occurred in many other species, not only of birds but of other animals as well, and it must be accepted that species on the edge of their range are often subject to these periodic fluctuations. A reduction in numbers, whatever the cause, seems to lead to a contraction of the population away from the fringes towards the centre, and conversely an increase in numbers pushes the distribution outwards even though all suitable territories in the centre do not appear to be filled. The increase in numbers of the starling in this country in the last hundred years, which seems, though there are no figures, to be generally agreed, may be connected with the great increase of permanent grass, which the bird prefers, at the expense of arable. If this be so, one would expect there to have been a decrease during the war of 1939–45, but I do not know of any evidence for this.

The crossbill has undoubtedly extended its range in much the same way as I have postulated for the starling. It occupies large areas of the coniferous forests of northern Europe where it feeds on the seeds of the trees, and though it does not migrate it moves away completely from its normal haunts in years when, as sometimes happens, the cone-crops fail. In such years it may reach Britain, and these irruptions have been known since the Middle Ages. There is a small population of crossbills in the native firwoods of Scotland which was first recorded in the 1830s, and this may be descended from birds which failed to return to Europe after one of these irruptions. As the Scotch birds are of a different subspecies from those of Europe, they form a strong parallel to the starlings in the Hebrides and Shetlands (but see page 243). The rest of Britain for long provided no suitable habitats so that the visitors either moved on elsewhere or returned home, but as a result of the extensive plantations of conifers colonies became established in East Anglia after a great invasion in 1909, and there has been less regular breeding in many counties. After the large invasion of 1956 birds remained in various parts of England until the following June, and breeding was proved in several counties and suspected in others.

The distribution of the greater spotted woodpecker is in some ways similar to that of the starling. In the middle of the nineteenth century it was unknown in Scotland and rare in Northumberland, and when Macpherson wrote his *Vertebrate Fauna of Lakeland* in 1892 only one or two breeding pairs were known in Cumberland and Westmorland. It began spreading north and west at the end of last century and is now found fairly regularly up to the Great Glen and sporadically beyond, and is reasonably common in the Lake District. Even so, it is absent from many apparently suitable districts in both Scotland and Cumberland, and it does not breed in west Cornwall. Old records show that it was formerly numerous on Speyside and Deeside and occurred north of the Great Glen. Its retreat is generally said to have been due to the destruction of the old pine forests in the eighteenth century, and its re-advance to the development of plantations, but this is too simple an explanation. Although much timber was cut on Speyside there is no evidence that it was ever cleared of trees, and the bird persisted until the middle of last century, by which time the eighteenth-century plantations should have provided it with shelter, for it does not need very large timber and decayed trees occur in woods of all ages. Moreover, it is quite at home in woods of oak and birch.

Like the starling, the species is to some extent a migrant, and the nineteenth-century writers agree on its being much commoner in both Northumberland and Cumberland in winter than in summer. Like the starling, then, it may be a continental bird on the edge of its range. The case is made more difficult by the fact that the British breeding birds are considered to be a separate subspecies from that of northern Europe, to which the winter visitors are presumed to belong. But the differences are small, and as the British form is not found elsewhere it must have been derived, possibly quite recently, from one of the many continental forms. There is a tendency amongst ornithologists to think that subspecies are immutable, whereas the real probability is that the slight differences in colour and statistical differences in wing or beak length on which most

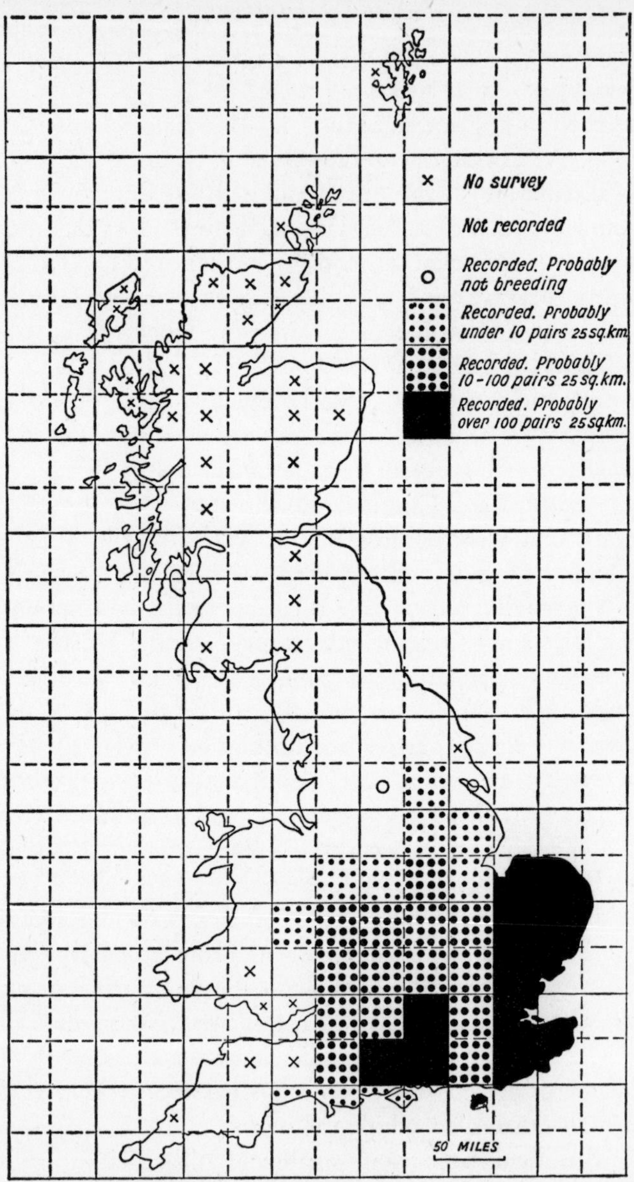

FIG. 15. Breeding distribution of the nightingale. The map shows the highest density estimated by experienced observers in any one 5 × 5 km. square within each 50 × 50 km. square of the national grid. From C. A. Norris, *Bird Study*, 7:134, Fig. 3 (1960). The West Gloucestershire and Somerset squares would probably have scored under 10 or 10–100 pairs had there been any observers.

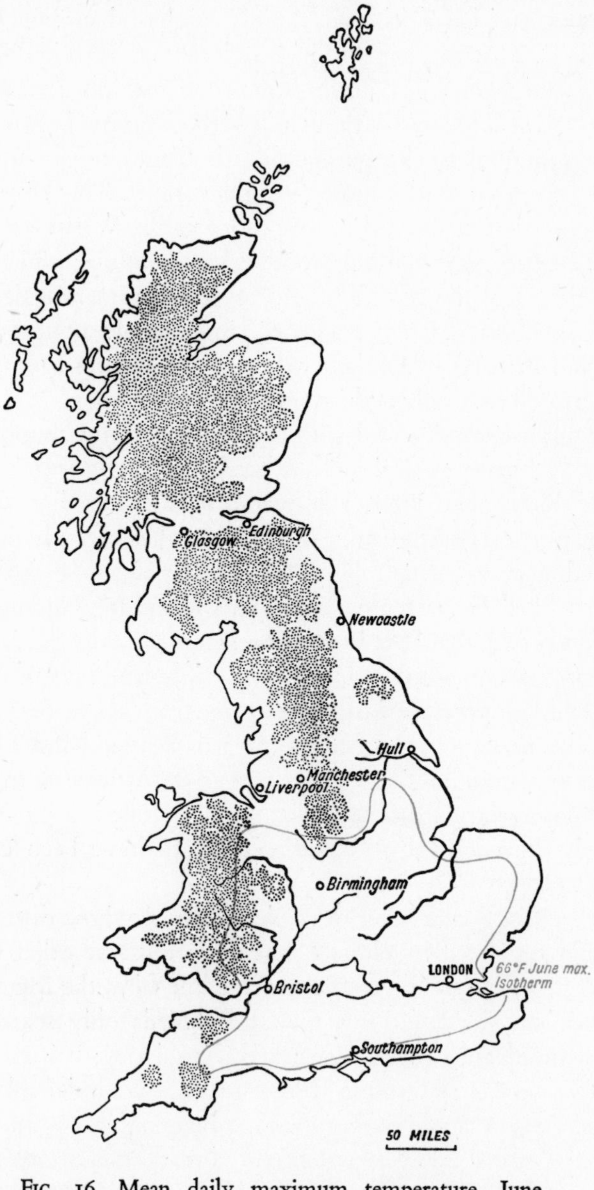

FIG. 16. Mean daily maximum temperature, June. 66 deg. F. isotherm. The cooler east and south-east coasts, the only parts outside the isotherm that have high densities of nightingales, have high minimum temperatures in June.

subspecies are based change rapidly under changing ecological conditions. That this happens in Lepidoptera is well known: Dowdeswell and Ford (1953) have shown, for example, that an isolated population of some tens of thousands of the meadow brown butterfly (*Maniola jurtina*) can change significantly from one year to the next, that is in one or at the most two generations. There is no reason to suppose that birds need be any more stable. Whatever the status of the British great spotted woodpecker, anything which reduced the numbers of the species would cause a contraction of the peripheral distribution. There is a general impression amongst naturalists that even in parts of England where it has always been present it has increased in numbers during this century.

The nightingale is a bird with a well-marked distribution in both habitat and geographical area. It needs woods or semi-woodlands with a thick shrub layer, but overall it is confined to the south-eastern portion of England. Norris (1960) has recently shown that its breeding distribution follows very closely the 66° F. (19° C.) June isotherm (line of equal temperature) (Figs. 15 and 16). This suggests, but does not prove, that it is limited by summer temperatures, and its recent increase in numbers in the west of England may be due to the increase in temperature which took place from about 1925 onwards. It has also made some expansion towards Scotland and a bird sang at Stirling throughout the summer of 1952. A decrease in numbers in Lower Saxony from 1890–1935, and a following increase, are similarly considered by Niebuhr (1952) to have been caused by temperature changes.

The nuthatch is another example of a bird whose distribution is probably restricted by climate, but there must be other factors as well. It is present in all counties up to a line from the Mersey to the Humber, but further north than this breeds only sparsely. This general statement conceals a marked irregularity; it is common in Oxford, very rare around Birmingham in similar places, and common again at Shrewsbury. Since Birmingham is intermediate between Oxford and Shrewsbury in climatic conditions and since there is no lack of apparently suitable habitats, it looks as if the bird is restricted by some ecological factor which we do not know. The only other explanation would be that the bird is in such a state of balance with its environment that any increase in numbers is impossible, and that it just happens to have become well established in Oxford and Shrewsbury because one or two pairs which were already there were able to increase during a few exceptionally favourable seasons. As it also lives in the Backs at Cambridge, another explanation would be that it has a respect for classical learning. That zoologists would all agree in saying that this is impossible illustrates the danger of saying that because two things frequently occur together one is the cause of the other.

The nuthatch has been introduced into Scotland, but all the birds have disappeared.

Two birds with peculiar distributions which seem at first sight quite inexplicable are the cirl bunting and the woodlark. The former breeds south of a line from the Bristol Channel to the Thames, with a wide northern extension up the Severn valley and an outpost on the coast of North Wales, and the latter has a very similar distribution except that it is found over most of Wales, is present in Norfolk and Suffolk, and is absent from Kent and East Sussex (Figs. 17 and 19). These do not match very well any of the well-known meteorological features, though they approximate to the isotherms for the May minima. A better fit can be got by taking the line which indicates an average mean of daily duration of bright sunshine of 4 hours. This runs in a wide curve from the south side of the Humber approximately through Bedford and Gloucester to Cardigan Bay, and then continues to cut off the Lleyn Peninsula, Anglesey, and the coast of North Wales. Everything south of or outside this curve has more than 4 hours of sunshine per day, or approximately 1,500 hours per year. This is fairly close to the distribution maps for the cirl bunting and woodlark, but there are still differences. If on the sunshine map are superimposed the January isotherms, it will be seen that the distribution of the woodlark is very nearly that part of England and Wales which has either 1,500 hours sunshine a year or a mean January temperature of more than 41° F. (5° C.), but excluding that part of the East Midlands which has an average January minimum temperature of less than 34° F. (1° C.) (Fig. 18). The only exceptions are that the bird is absent from some districts near coasts and estuaries—East Anglia, Kent and Sussex, the Severn Vale, Glamorgan, the Lleyn Peninsula, Snowdonia, and Cheshire. To some extent this may be because there are no suitable habitats, but

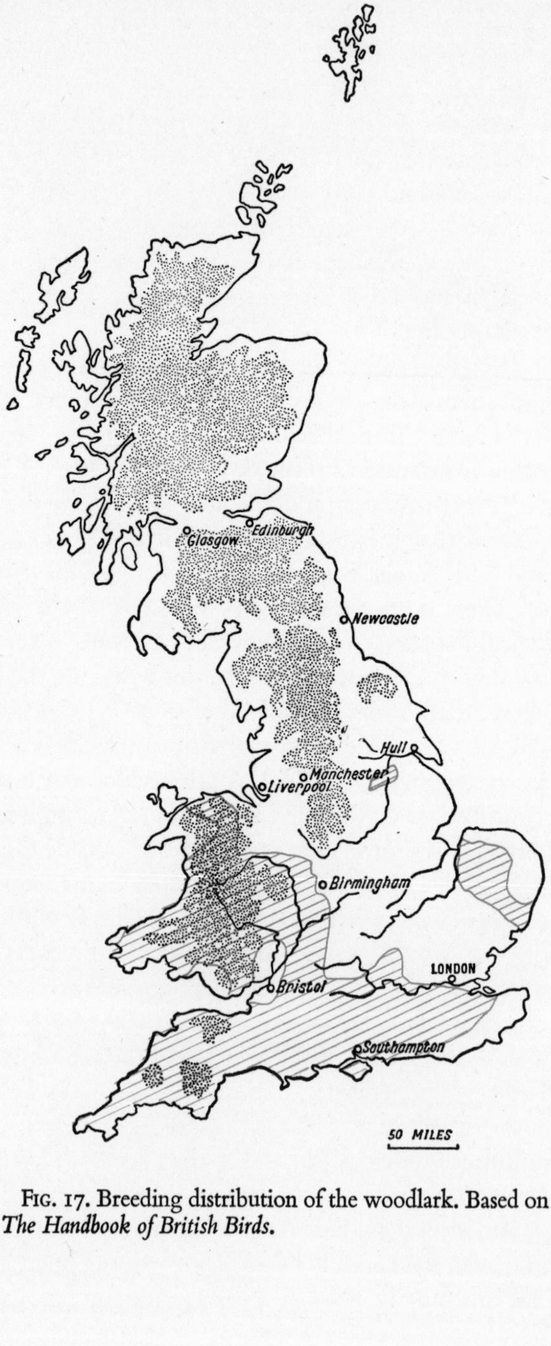

FIG. 17. Breeding distribution of the woodlark. Based on *The Handbook of British Birds.*

FIG. 18. Possible meteorological factors influencing the distribution of the woodlark.

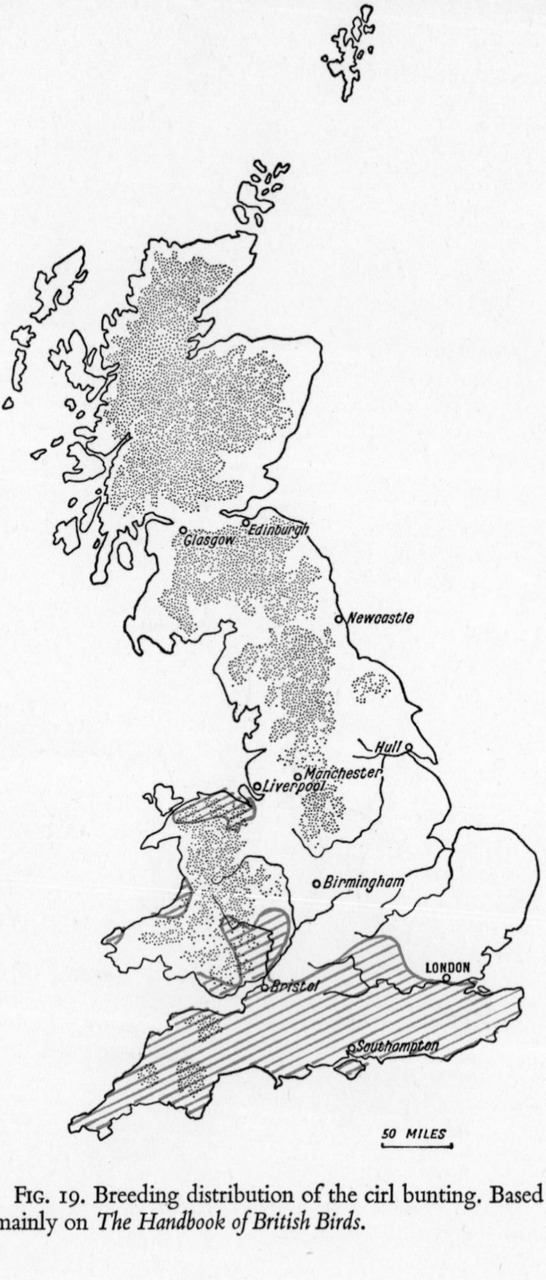

FIG. 19. Breeding distribution of the cirl bunting. Based mainly on *The Handbook of British Birds*.

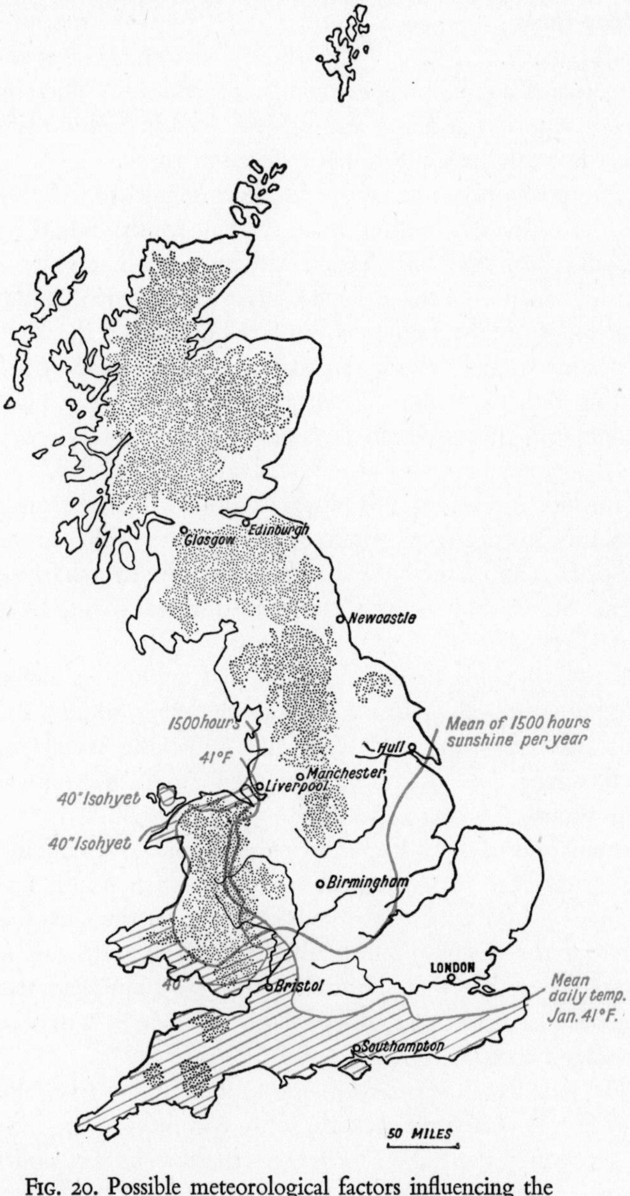

FIG. 20. Possible meteorological factors influencing the distribution of the cirl bunting. The distribution of the bird is approximately that part of England and Wales which has a mean January temperature of not less than 41° F. and either 1,500 hours of sunshine a year *or* less than 40 inches of rain.

other climatic factors such as wind may be important. It is not surprising that a bird which is hardly known to migrate at all should be partly limited in its range by winter temperatures. Gilbert and Walker (1954) report it as being almost destroyed in Herefordshire by the great frost of 1929, and much reduced in 1947.

The position of the winter isotherms will similarly explain the absence of the cirl bunting from the East Midlands and East Anglia, but this bird may also be affected by rainfall. Fig. 20 shows the sunshine map with the 40-inch isohyet (line of equal rainfall) as well. The bulge in the range of the cirl bunting in the Severn valley corresponds fairly closely to that part of the map which, though getting rather less than 1,500 hours sunshine, has a mean January temperature of more than 41° F. (5° C.) and has a yearly rainfall of less than 40 inches (102 cm.); that is, it is mild and dry. The presence of the bird on the coast of North Wales fits the high sunshine there, while its absence from Anglesey may be due simply to the fact that the place is an island, for even such a narrow stretch of water as the Menai Straits may act as a barrier to dispersal owing to its psychological effect.

E. M. Nicholson has observed that within its range the cirl bunting is especially common on south-facing hillsides and near the health resorts such as Malvern and Worthing which are affected by men retired from warmer climates. Both these empirical observations fit into the suggestion that the bird is distributed according to a combination of sunshine, mild winters, and low rainfall, for these are exactly the meterological assets on which health resorts pride themselves and which those who have spent their lives in warmer parts of the Empire presumably seek. The birds are not found elsewhere within their climatic range for they need their proper vegetational cover, which for both of them is a special type of woodland ecotone.

The pied flycatcher has a distribution of an entirely different kind (Fig. 21). It was, until recently, only common in the hilly parts of Wales and in the Lake District, northern Pennines, and Cheviots, but there were small outlying colonies in Devon and Somerset, the border counties, and north Yorkshire. This is very close to the area over which the durmast oak is the chief native tree, but omits the southern Pennines and a tract of upland country along the Welsh

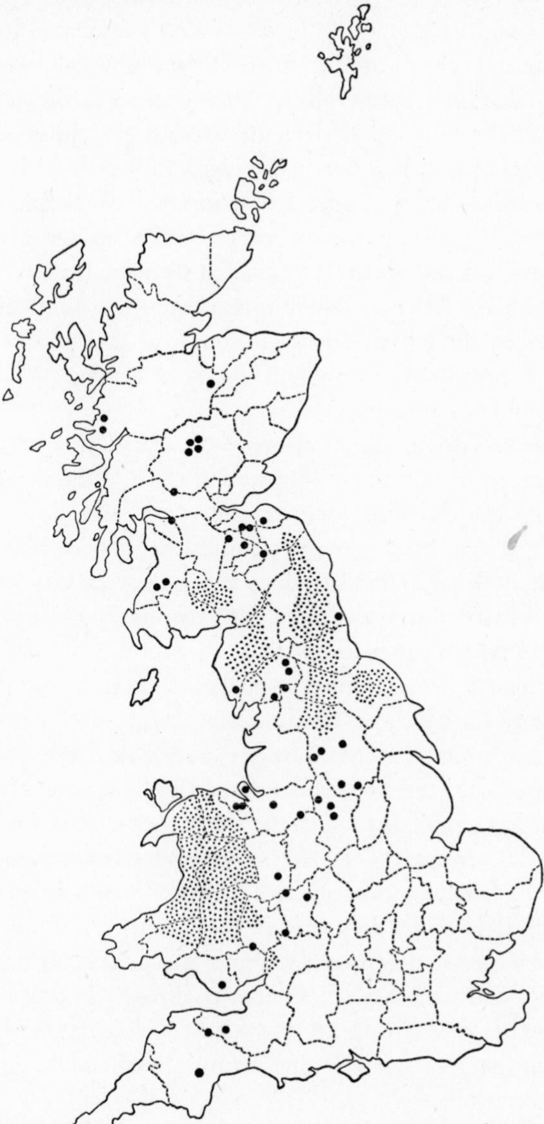

FIG. 21. Breeding distribution of the pied flycatcher. Small dots show areas of general distribution in suitable habitats; large dots indicate a few breeding pairs. From B. Campbell, *Bird Study*, 1:87, Fig. 2 (1954).

border. Within its range the bird is by no means confined to oakwoods, though commoner in them than elsewhere. The southern Pennines, although their valleys were probably formerly covered with oak, have few woods left and are largely industrialized. The introduction of nest-boxes into the oakwoods of the Forest of Dean in the late 1940s led to a spectacular increase of the pied flycatcher in that area. While then it may sometimes be limited by absence of nesting sites, it is not entirely restricted to oaks. It prefers hills, and even in the Lake District, where it is common, is rarer on the valley floors than in the fell-woods. Campbell was able to find some fifty records of breeding in lowland England during the nineteenth century, but only two for the twentieth.

The reasons for the distribution of the durmast oak, which have been discussed in Chapter 4, are obscure. The pied flycatcher may simply like the durmast type of oakwood, with few shrubs, or, since it is absent from somewhat similar open oakwoods in the south, it may be restricted by some of the same factors which determine the distribution of the oak. The most likely of these is rainfall. The area in which the pied flycatcher is found is in fact fairly close to that which has more than 40 inches of rain a year (Fig. 4). Its absence from the southern Pennines has already been explained, and the Craven Pennines and Mendips are unsuitable for it as they consist of limestone and have no woodlands of the right sort. There is even a patch of high rainfall to account for its occurrence on the North York Moors. Its rarity in the otherwise suitable south-western counties of England and its absence from most of Scotland, where it breeds regularly only in some of the border counties, I cannot explain. It has recently spread, without any help from man, both in Devonshire and in Scotland, so that its former limitation in these areas may be an example of the kind of restriction, referred to above, that happens when a bird is on the edge of its geographical range.

The probable climatic limitations in these examples suggest that many of the species which, although common on the Continent, are absent from England or occur only as occasional stragglers, may be restricted in the same sort of way. The climate of this country is broadly damper than that of the Continent, and is cooler in summer and warmer in winter. Both the first two differences are likely to exclude species which on the Continent are at or near the limit of the conditions in which they can breed successfully. A comparison of the list of British birds with that for Europe shows that while there are several species which breed only near the Mediterranean, which has such a warm climate that we can understand their inability to live here, there are very few which are present in northern France that are not also regularly present in England.

Bonelli's warbler (*Phylloscopus bonelli*), a leaf-warbler which is a close relative of the chiff-chaff and willow-warbler but distinguished from them by its yellowish-olive rump as well as by its voice, is found in France to within a few miles of Fontainebleau, and further to the east as far north as the Ardennes, which are in the same latitude as Cornwall. It has some way to go before it crosses the Channel, but as it is said over much of its range to prefer the oak and pine woods of the hills, ascending to 6,000 feet, it might well be suited once it arrived here. In spite of this it had been recorded in Britain only six times up to the summer of 1960.

The Icterine warbler (*Hippolais icterina*), a member of a genus which is not represented in Great Britain, is rather larger than the leaf-warblers although generally similar to them in habits. It is found over most of Europe as far north as Norway and so can hardly be prevented from establishing itself in England by the temperature, but it could be affected by dampness or other factors. Its habitat is a wide variety of woods and gardens. There are many reports of its occurrence in Great Britain but only one breeding record, for Wiltshire in 1907. It has mostly been seen or captured in autumn, when it is presumably migrating south and has been accidentally blown across the North Sea; this sort of occurrence is not likely to lead to breeding, but anything that increased the population of the French stock, or which led to a deflection of its normal spring migratory route a little to the west, might easily lead to its establishment here. Its congener the melodious warbler (*Hippolais polyglotta*), which prefers damp woodlands, is found in France as far north as the Somme, but has been recorded in Britain rather less often.

The golden oriole seems to be on the verge of becoming a regular British breeding species. It is found over most of Europe, individuals appear regularly in our southern counties, and there are several records of nesting. It likes scattered timber and parkland, habitats which England can provide in plenty, and yet has failed to become a regular breeding bird. It is probably too simple an explanation to say that this is because of persecution. No doubt in the nineteenth century such a brilliant-plumaged bird was shot almost as soon as seen, but in these days, when few people even in the country habitually carry a gun, the numbers in which it arrives should enable it to become established if it otherwise has the power. The truth seems to be, as Newton in his edition of Yarrell's *British Birds* pointed out eighty years ago, that many of the individuals which arrive here make no attempt to breed even when they are unmolested. We can only presume that in some way the ecological conditions are unsuitable for a full sexual life.

These three warblers and the oriole are all summer migrants and have extended their range little or not at all; but the serin (*Serinus canarius*), a resident bird over much of Europe, has in historic times made a large advance northward. It is a pretty yellow finch, smaller even than the goldfinch and lesser redpoll, and is now considered to be a subspecies of the canary although it was formerly ranked as a full species. It is found in a wide variety of woods and gardens, even in towns, and is said to have some preference for coniferous trees. Its extension northward across France has been chronicled by Delamain (1933) as follows:

From time immemorial—the Mediterranean area, including Provence
1550—the Rhône Valley and Gascony
Before 1800—Dauphiny and Burgundy
1875—the Loire
1903—Paris
1906—Champagne
1915—Soissons
1931—Deauville

It reached Germany by the middle of the nineteenth century and made the same sort of spectacular spread there as in France, and it first nested in Sweden in 1942. There are numerous British occurrences but no breeding records. If its advance continues it could become a British species in any year now, but it must be remembered that there have been periods, such as the seventeenth century, when its range apparently altered little. There has been no steady improvement in climate over the four centuries of its known spread, so that there must have been some other factor leading to increase in numbers and so an expansion at the periphery of its range.

Besides the northward expansion of birds found south of Britain, there is the possibility of our winter visitors, which at present breed only to the north, remaining with us for the summer. Three woodland birds which might conceivably do this are the brambling, the fieldfare, and the redwing. The brambling, although in winter largely dependent on beechwoods, has a much wider range of habitat in the breeding season in Scandinavia, and lives in both coniferous and deciduous woods. The scrub birchwoods of the north-west Highlands appear quite suitable for it. There are a few Scottish breeding records, one of them well authenticated, and two separate recent reports of a cock bird remaining in the Midlands of England throughout the summer and showing pairing behaviour with a hen chaffinch.

Any bramblings that stayed here would probably come into competition with the chaffinch, to which they are closely related, but the two species are able to coexist on the Continent.

The fieldfare has not, so far as is known, nested in the British Isles, but the redwing has bred successfully a few times in Scotland and Shetland. Both species breed in Scandinavia in a climate which seems to the human observer not greatly different from that of this country, but the bird may be affected by other less obvious factors. Since birds are known to be influenced in much of their behaviour by light, the length of day could be important, although this would have to be combined with other factors, for the redwing breeds as far south as the Baltic, and the fieldfare in Hungary. The birds may need either a long day or a high temperature, since the southern parts of their range are all areas of continental climate with high summer temperatures. In Switzerland, where the fieldfare breeds sparingly in the mountains, which are cooler than the valleys, the great intensity of sunlight might act instead of a long day. If this suggestion should be the truth, there does not seem much possibility of either bird becoming a British breeding species.

Another group of species which might, but are less likely to, become British breeding birds are those which have a continental type of distribution and only occasionally reach our island. They breed both north and south of us but on the whole well to the east, where winters are colder and summers warmer. The fieldfare might be put in this group except that it migrates to us regularly every winter; the great grey shrike (*Lanius excubitor*), which looks rather like a small magpie, is somewhat intermediate. It is a regular but sparse winter visitor to the east and north of England and has occasionally been seen in summer, but there are no breeding records. Although the typical race, which is the one seen here, breeds only from Norway to central France and north-east Italy, another subspecies, the south European grey shrike, is found in southern France and the Iberian peninsula. There does not seem to be any obvious reason why, as a species, it should not adapt itself to Great Britain.

The nutcracker (*Nucifraga caryocatactes*) is a more typical east European bird whose characteristic home is the taiga or region of coniferous forest, and it is especially common where the arolla pine (*Pinus cembra*) is present. It feeds much on the large seeds of this tree, which weigh about a third of a gramme in contrast to those of most conifers which weigh less than a hundredth of a gramme, and as the total yield of seeds is from 30,000 to 300,000 times as much as for other species, their importance as a food source is very great even though the pine seldom dominates the forest. The nutcracker has a notch in the upper half of the beak, into which the seeds are fitted to be crushed. In spite of this I do not think it can be taken as proved that the bird is limited by the tree. The arolla pine is a plant of marked ecological preferences, occurring only on constantly moist soil and chiefly where the climate is strongly continental, as in Siberia and in the Valais and Engadine; in central Europe it is found only between altitudes of about 5,000 and 8,000 feet. The nutcracker might well be tied to similar climatic conditions. In Sweden, where the arolla pine is not present, nutcrackers live in other types of coniferous woodland but feed largely on hazel nuts, which they obtain from outside the woods. Like the jay, they bury stores of pine kernels or nuts when they are plentiful and dig them up later. Their occurrence in western Europe is mainly by invasion in particular years, a type of irregular migration which has been described above for the crossbill, and is correlated with the failure of the food supply in the birds' homes. There are some fifty authenticated records of the nutcracker in Great Britain, almost all in winter. If, as seems likely, it is dependent on a continental climate, it is unlikely to establish itself here.

The waxwing (*Bombycilla garrulus*) is another bird of the taiga but is not found in central Europe. Like the nutcracker it wanders south and west in winter and in some years there are invasions of this country in considerable numbers. It also is unlikely to become a British breeding bird.

Wherever it can be shown that a species is associated with particular ecological conditions, whether of climate, vegetation, or anything else, the zoologist will want to know what feature it is in the structure or physiology of the bird on which this association depends. For distribution depending on climate one can say very little more than that something in the metabolism of the bird must be specially suited to the environment that surrounds it. There are certain general rules which relate the size and colour and various other features of animals to the climate in which they live, but they are empirical and have many exceptions. Seebohm pointed out long ago that the extreme Chinese and Japanese forms of species or genera which extend across Eurasia often resemble those of western Europe, the forms in central Europe and Asia being different; there is, for instance, a series of nuthatches, variously regarded as species or subspecies, ranging from Spain to Japan, of which the extreme eastern and western forms have reddish-buff breasts, and the intervening continental forms breasts which are nearly or completely white. For the value of the colour of the breast, and even for deciding the problem whether the colour of the breast is produced by the environment or determines the environment in which the bird can live, there is no experimental evidence, but that there is some connexion, based on the climate, seems obvious.

It is equally difficult to say for most species whether their association with a particular type of vegetation is determined by structural, physiological, or psychological characters. Examples of structural features which are related to the habitat are the beaks of the crossbill and hawfinch, which have obvious special functions in extracting seeds from fir cones and splitting the stones of haws respectively, but it is rare that such an exact correspondence can be found. It has been alleged that the avoidance of birches by the goldcrest depends on the weakness of a particular muscle in the thigh, but it does occur in them in winter, and this does not explain its nesting preference for conifers, which can be satisfied by a single yew tree surrounded by oaks. There is a clear connexion between hard bills and seed-eating, but little of more exact correlation. Snow (1954) has shown that those tits which live predominantly in coniferous trees have finer beaks than those which live in broad-leaved woods, but this leaves unexplained the fact that in parts of its range a bird may have an unusual habitat; for example the coal-tit, which has a 'coniferous' type of bill, is in north and west Britain the dominant tit of nearly all woods.

The psychological dependence of an individual on a particular habitat may be no less strong than its structural dependence, but in the species as a whole psychological attachments are probably more easily broken. There is evidence for many species that birds in their first year, even when migratory, tend to return to breed somewhere near the spot where they were themselves bred, and evidence for an even stronger attachment of an adult bird to the site which it has first chosen for its nest; but there is none, so far as I know, to show that individual birds have any inherited preference for the particular type of habitat or nest site (within the range usual for the species) in which they were bred. This would be difficult for a single bird-watcher to obtain, but a combination of ringing and nest record cards with the habitat precisely recorded would enable one to know in a few years if any such preference exists.

That birds can sometimes change their habits and habitats very considerably is well known: the redstart, really a woodland bird, has in the north of England become a bird of stone walls and buildings; while the pied flycatcher, almost confined here to remote hillsides, is in Sweden common in parks and gardens and even in the centres of towns where there are few or no trees, so that I have heard one singing from telephone wires above the sidings of the railway station at Stockholm. Even more striking are the differences in tameness shown by birds in different parts of their range and under different treatment. The British robin (*Erithacus rubecula melophilus*) is confiding and familiar, while the European form (*E. r. rubecula*) is over most of the Continent except Corsica shy and retiring; while the wood-pigeon, under natural conditions a wary bird, has become as tame as it is fat in the London parks. The jay, probably the shyest of all our woodland birds, has recently begun to become approachable in Kensington Gardens, and I have a feeling that jays in general are more readily seen and watched than they were thirty years ago.

The term 'subspecies' is now applied by ornithologists only to a form of a species which is separable from other forms in colour, dimensions, or structure, and which has a more or less well-defined geographical range; it thus has the same meaning as 'geographical race'. The theory is that while subspecies would, if they met, produce fertile offspring, separate species are either sterile when mated together or if they produce offspring these are sterile, but it is very rare for anything to be known in practice about such unions. One of the few cases where there is such information is the cross between the carrion and hooded crows. These two subspecies replace each other geographically, the former being the western form. Where they meet, as they do in Scotland in a wide band from the Solway to the Moray Firth, they interbreed and produce fertile offspring. In spite of this, both the *Handbook of British Birds* and the British Ornithologists' Union *Check List* regard them, against all the rules, as separate species.

The two crows can easily be told apart in the field and this is probably why the books continue to regard them as two species, but fortunately most subspecies are only distinguishable when they are carefully compared in the hand. For this reason they are of little importance to the ordinary bird-watcher. I have introduced them here because where a bird is found over a wide area there are usually forms of slightly different colour, and to these, if they are constant, subspecific names are given. Subspecies are especially common on islands, and in fact many of the birds of Great Britain can be separated from those of the Continent; further, a few species, such as the wren, the starling, and the coal-tit, have developed further subspecies in various of the British islands. These geographical races are generally regarded as incipient species and it is assumed that with time and continued isolation they will become completely separated from each other. Whether there are such entities as ecological races, separated by choice of habitat, or ethological races, separated by behaviour, is a more difficult and doubtful question. Such are known in insects and there is no reason why they should not occur in birds. It is noteworthy that geographical races often show differences in behaviour—the various island wrens, for instance, are said to be different from the mainland form in many ways—and the geographical differences in tameness and choice of nest site in birds such as the robin and redstart described above may indicate at least the beginning of some sort of subspecific differentiation. If such habits and habitat-choices are hereditary, they could in time lead to enough isolation to produce new species.

Wren

13

THE ORIGIN AND HISTORY OF THE BRITISH WOODLAND AVIFAUNA

Because of the lightness and fragility of their bones birds make poor fossils, and so we know much less about their past history than we do about that of mammals or molluscs. Although there is in total quite an impressive list of bird fossils, many of them are fragmentary and specific identification is often doubtful, and over the million years of the Pleistocene period, which is that of most interest for the origin of our present fauna, there is very little indication of evolution of new species. This contrasts with the state of affairs in mammals, but it must be remembered that mammalian bones are better known and better preserved so that if new species have evolved they will be more easily recognizable, and that the mobility of birds, and their migratory habits, make them less liable to the isolation which is now considered essential for the production of new species.

Trees very similar to those at present existing, both coniferous and broad-leaved, were present in the Eocene perhaps fifty million years ago—fossils ascribed to the same genus as the oak, *Quercus*, and the hazel, *Corylus*, have for example been found in Mull—

and the main orders of birds came into existence at this time, with the chief passerine families following in the Oligocene or Miocene. Both the climate and the vegetation of this country have changed several times since then, and it is impossible to trace all the changes that the avifauna has undergone as a result. By the Pliocene, or at least by its end, the plant fossils of Europe are mostly of species which are still found there, and such evidence as we have suggests that in birds too there has been little formation of new species since then. The Canary Isles are considered by geologists to have been formed during the Pliocene and never to have been connected to the mainland. They thus provide an ideal opportunity for speciation, but in spite of this only three out of 42 breeding species are endemic (that is, confined to the islands). In Europe as a whole a much smaller proportion of new species is likely to have developed.

The Pleistocene, the geological period immediately preceding the present, from which it is not marked off by anything except convenience, was characterized in the northern hemisphere by wide fluctuations in climate. In Europe there were four ice ages, separated by mild interglacial periods. Within each ice age and each interglacial there were smaller fluctuations, which were not necessarily the same in all parts of the Continent. At present we are in a phase which corresponds in climate and vegetation to an interglacial, but this does not mean that another ice age is imminent or will even occur at all. Earlier ice ages and interglacials presumably showed in general the same changes in both vegetation and fauna as have been caused by the last cycle. Of direct information on the birds we have nothing; we must therefore deduce what we can from what is known of the vegetation and of other animals. There is still some dispute about the details of this information and it is a field in which research has been very active in recent years, but the main features of the case seem to be fairly firmly established.

At the height of the last glaciation the Arctic ice extended to a line running a little south of the Baltic and across England from the Wash and Humber to the Bristol Channel (Fig. 22). There were possibly favoured pockets in the north of England which were ice-free and the tops of some of the hills probably projected through the ice as *nunataks*, but in general north of this line there was no vegetation and there could have been no birds. A similar but smaller

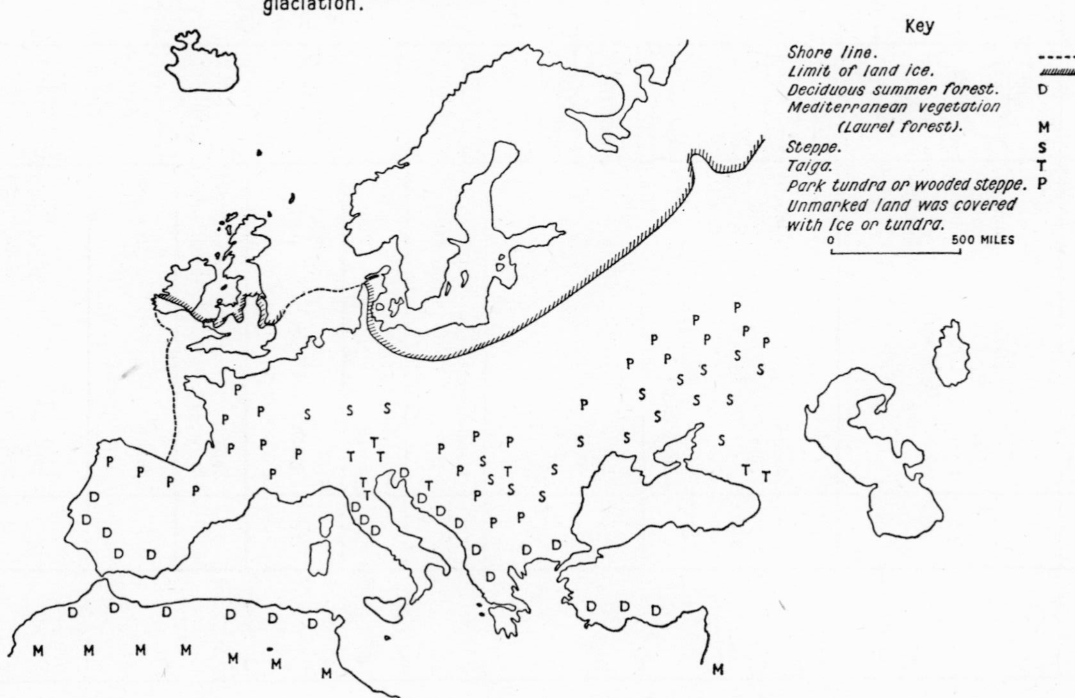

FIG. 22. Europe at the height of the last glaciation, simplified from various authors.

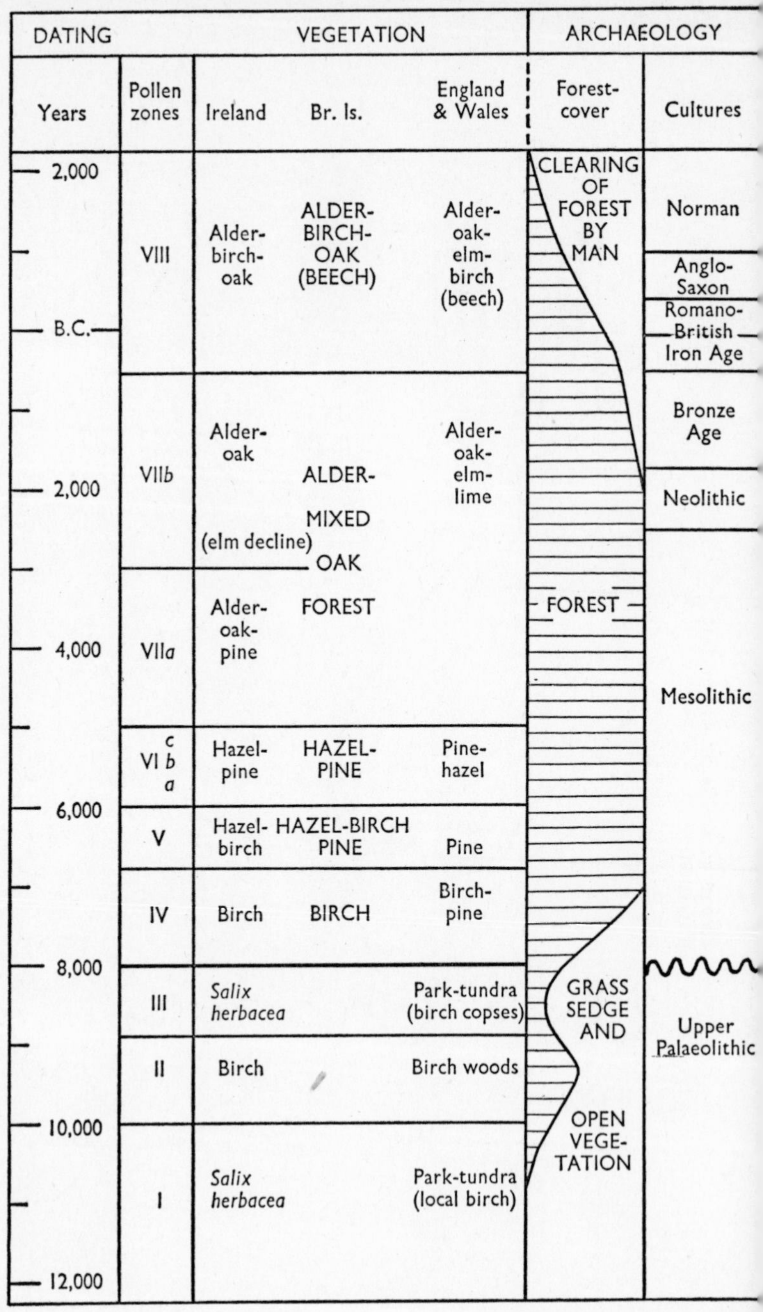

FIG. 23. Tentative scheme of the main events of the late-glacial an
of the British Flora, Cambridg

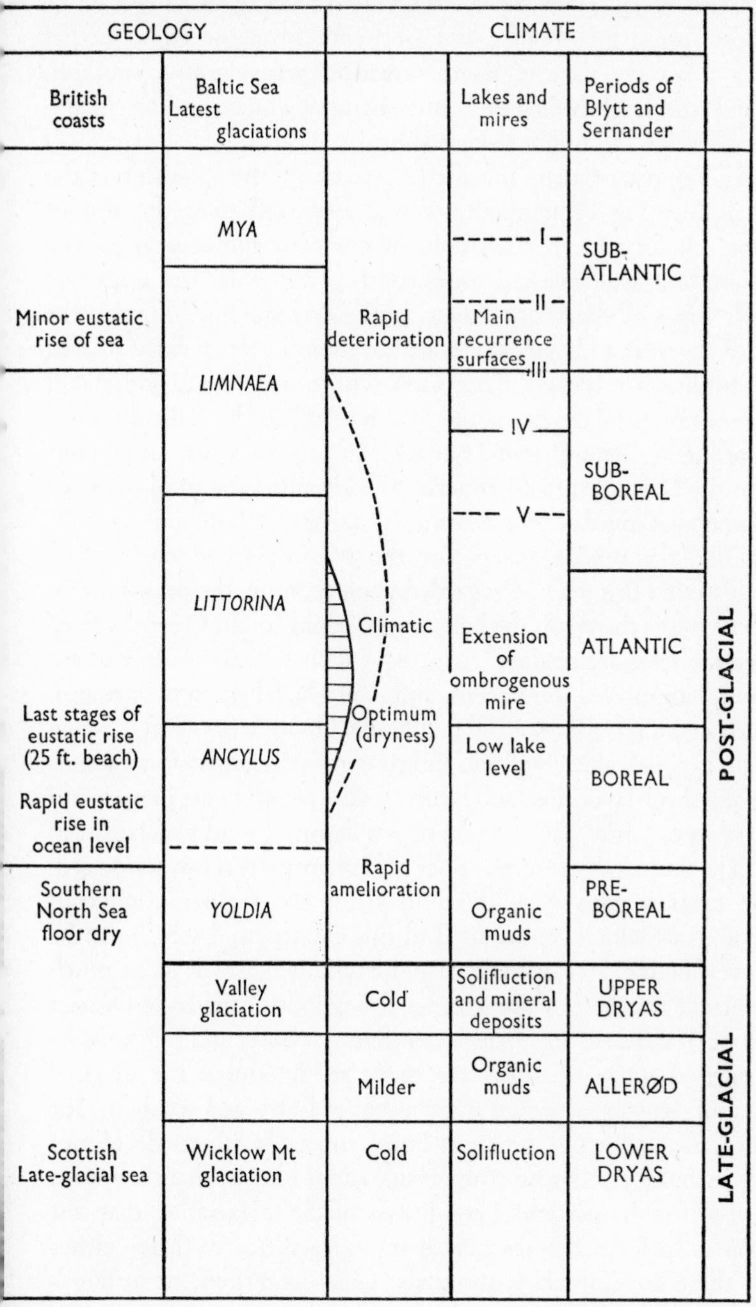

GEOLOGY		CLIMATE			
British coasts	Baltic Sea Latest glaciations		Lakes and mires	Periods of Blytt and Sernander	
	MYA		– – – – – I –	SUB-ATLANTIC	POST-GLACIAL
Minor eustatic rise of sea		Rapid deterioration	– – – – – II – Main recurrence surfaces – III –		
	LIMNAEA		— IV —	SUB-BOREAL	
			– – – V – –		
	LITTORINA	Climatic	Extension of ombrogenous mire	ATLANTIC	
Last stages of eustatic rise (25 ft. beach)	*ANCYLUS*	Optimum (dryness)	Low lake level	BOREAL	
Rapid eustatic rise in ocean level					
Southern North Sea floor dry	*YOLDIA*	Rapid amelioration	Organic muds	PRE-BOREAL	
	Valley glaciation	Cold	Solifluction and mineral deposits	UPPER DRYAS	LATE-GLACIAL
		Milder	Organic muds	ALLERØD	
Scottish Late-glacial sea	Wicklow Mt glaciation	Cold	Solifluction	LOWER DRYAS	

post-glacial periods in the British Isles. From H. Godwin, *History*
University Press, Fig. 29 (1956).

ice-sheet spread into France and Germany from the Alps, so that only a relatively narrow band, covering what is now southern England, the English Channel, and northern France and Germany, was free of ice and might have had birds.

More important than the actual extent of the ice-sheet is the general lowering of temperature that occurred over the rest of Europe. Under present conditions in northern and central Eurasia there are four well-marked zones south of the polar ice, with five possible types of vegetation cover. In the extreme north, frozen for most of the year and typically with the subsoil permanently frozen, is the tundra, a relatively flat region with much water, dominated by mosses or lichens with some low heathy shrubs. This does not now occur in Great Britain, but the flat tops of a few mountains such as the Cairngorm and Braeriach below the level of block scree are somewhat similar. Next comes a narrow belt of birch-scrub, much like the tundra except for the tree-cover, which is often broken so that this may be regarded as an ecotone, the park-tundra. South of this is the taiga, the belt of coniferous forest. Over much of its area the trees are stunted, at most 15 inches in diameter, and are covered with mosses and lichens, and many lie fallen on the ground. The taiga contains some of the smaller deciduous trees—birch, aspen (*Populus tremula*), alder, willow, and rowan—which may form something of a shrub layer, and has a heathy field layer of dwarf juniper and bilberry in the drier parts; or there is a damp ground vegetation of moss. The drainage is generally poor and many parts are waterlogged.

The taiga is thus very different from the regular coniferous plantations to which we are used in this country and which can be seen even better developed in Scandinavia. It has at least as much resemblance to some of the damper fell-woods of the Lake District and of Scotland as to any British coniferous woods, and this must be remembered when attempts are made to determine the original habitat of existing species. Our own redstart and coal-tit, for instance, are at least as much at home in our northern deciduous woods as in our coniferous plantations, and it may be that they were developed for the particular conditions of the taiga rather than for conifers as such; in the absence of the taiga they can thrive either where there are conifers without the taiga-conditions, or in taiga-conditions without conifers.

South of the taiga there are two alternative types of vegetation: under damp conditions deciduous summer forest is dominant, with broad-leaved trees which shed their leaves in the fall; but with a dry climate there is steppe or grassland, which bears trees only in the damp valleys. Almost the whole of Great Britain and western Europe was in prehistoric times covered with deciduous forest, and most of our present woodlands are degenerate remains or copies of this. Steppe becomes the predominant form only at a distance too far east for the warm wet winds from the Atlantic to have any effect on the climate, that is in Hungary and beyond. The Asiatic steppes are ecologically the same as the North American prairie, and readers of R. M. Ballantyne will remember the descriptions of interminable grasslands and the welcome given to the occasional belts of trees which always indicated the presence of water.

The effect of the glaciation was to push all these zones further south and, since Europe was pinched between the polar ice-cap and that from the Alps, to eliminate some of them altogether over a large part of the Continent. At the same time, the atmosphere was drier and steppe conditions extended further west. Fig. 22 shows in broad outline the distribution of the main vegetation types. The most important information on which this map is based is derived from a study of plant fossils. These occur at a limited number of sites and there must therefore be a certain amount of guesswork. The boundaries were not necessarily well marked and the vegetation would have been affected by altitude, so that tundra-like conditions must have held on mountains which projected above the taiga-zone, just as they do today. I have omitted from the map the belt of 'steppe-tundra' sometimes shown as extending across mid-France and Germany, since although it was intermediate in some respects between tundra and steppe, it was grass-covered and so essentially of a steppe nature. The important points to note in considering the state of the woodland bird fauna are that deciduous woodlands were confined to the Iberian, Italian, and Balkan peninsulas; that there was only a narrow band of taiga, all south of the latitude of the Alps; and that most of Europe consisted of steppe, tundra, or park-tundra.

The part of Great Britain that was not glaciated was, so far as is known, entirely tundra; the two known fossil beds, both in the east of England and not necessarily from the time of the maximum extent of the ice in the Full Glacial period, have yielded no trees except juniper, birch, and arctic willows. It must be remembered, however, that the region of Devon and Cornwall, then as now, would have been warmer than East Anglia, and the presence of a thick cover of birch in that region is not impossible. Some entomologists in particular have argued from the distribution of insects that there must have been refuges, perhaps in Ireland or perhaps in land which, like Lyonesse, is now under the Atlantic, where the climate was relatively mild and a richer vegetation survived. Others have attempted to confute their arguments. Whatever the truth of this there can be little doubt that true woodland did not occur in Britain and that at the most and in the most favourable parts of the south-west there might have been some scrub of birch and willow. At the time of the glaciation and for long afterwards England was joined to the Continent, as the map shows. The final break probably came at the Straits of Dover only 7,500 years ago, and perhaps rather later in the southern North Sea.

As the ice retreated and the temperature rose the vegetation zones moved northwards and can be traced in some detail by the analysis of fossil pollen as well as of macroscopic remains. The periods and pollen zones recognized by botanists are shown in Fig. 23. Beds of fossil plants from the Late Glacial of various parts of Great Britain show birches and willows; there are almost no plants which are characteristic of the undergrowth of deciduous woodlands, so that on the whole there was probably a park-tundra, but in the warmer phases there were some closed birchwoods. This is the condition of Lapland at the present time. At the end of pollen zone III some pine was present in the south of England, which suggests conditions similar to present-day Finland just north of the Arctic Circle.

The Late Glacial period ended about 7500 B.C. and was followed by a further improvement in climate, which was not steady but had oscillations. There was probably a time of maximum temperature about 5500 B.C. followed by a recession, and a second period of improvement set in about 4000 B.C. After the Late Glacial period came the Preboreal and Boreal, which were marked by a great increase in pine. There was also much hazel, and there were some other deciduous trees, including oak, which became an important element in the vegetation before the end of pollen zone VI. Following this came the Atlantic period, in which pine almost disappeared and oak forests with much alder became the chief vegetation. During the Atlantic period, or possibly a little earlier, beech arrived, and by the time of the Iron Age it was a common tree, with rather more than its present natural range. There are few records of ash, but the earliest are in Atlantic times, after which it increased, being probably favoured by human clearance of the thicker forests. It is possible that the existing ashwoods on calcareous soils are not a natural climax-vegetation. These changes confirm what one would expect, that as the ice withdrew tundra was followed by park-tundra and this in turn by coniferous forest, and that deciduous woodland developed only at the end, in fact about 7,000 years ago. At about 2000 B.C. neolithic man arrived in Great Britain, and from then on human activities have had more effect than anything else on both the vegetation and the avifauna.

It has sometimes been held that the oscillation of vegetation and climate caused by the ice ages is the cause of migration; that the descendants of the birds which in the settled conditions of the Pliocene nested in the north have for ever striven to get back to their ancestral home, and that driven south four times in a million years they still attempt to return. Such long-inherited memory is unlikely and is not necessary to a reasonable explanation. It is characteristic of the temperate and arctic regions that there is a great difference between their winter and summer, which shows itself not only directly in temperature but indirectly in the destiny of vegetable matter and invertebrates. The result is that there is much more food available for animals, especially the larger ones, in one half of the year than in the other, and if all the animals which can be supported in the summer were to attempt to remain and be active during the winter most of them would die of starvation. Most of the invertebrates pass the winter in special resting stages—eggs, pupae, and so on—or like snails become completely inactive. Mammals may hibernate, sleeping and losing their temperature-control. Reptiles, which cannot stand cold, are for the most part absent. Birds, which have no resting stages and seem to be physiologically incapable, with a few exceptions, of anything like hibernation, make use of their wings and fly away.

If anything needs further explanation, it is not why birds leave the northern countries but why they come back. There seems to be no information on the relative abundance of food in the tropical or sub-tropical regions which absorb our migrants in winter and in the regions to which they return for breeding, but it is at least possible that with the flush of vegetation and insect life in spring there is more for them, at the time when they need it most, here than there. Seebohm and others have commented on the sudden and lush appearance of vegetation and animal life when the ice breaks in Siberia and the winter is over. Presumably natural selection will favour those species which take advantage of food where they can get it. Almost all the species of bird in the arctic and north-temperate regions are more or less migratory. The exceptions are those like the game-birds and woodpeckers which feed on material which is available at all times of the year: the former feed on shoots of evergreen plants such as heather and fir; the latter on the larvae of wood-boring insects which live in the trunks of trees throughout the winter, often taking several years before they become adult. In specially equable climates within the temperate zone, such as Great Britain, conditions have allowed species such as the chaffinch, starling, and blackbird, which are migratory over much of their range, to remain throughout the winter, making only local seasonal movements.

If we make the assumption that the habitat-preferences of birds have not greatly changed since the last ice age, we can suggest with some confidence the steps by which our present woodland avifauna has been reached. How valid that assumption is we do not really know. There is a certain amount of evidence that many of the existing subspecies of birds have arisen since the ice age—this must be true, for instance, of the island forms such as the wrens and starlings, and is probably true where the British forms differ from those of the Continent—and subspecies often have different habitat-preferences. There are even some differences in habitat-preference which are not accompanied by morphological differences large enough to justify subspecific distinction, as for instance in the jay and nutcracker. The existence on the Scottish islands of several species of birds, such as wrens and starlings (endemic subspecies) and blackbirds (no subspecies), which are found on the mainland in woods but live on the islands in heath and on the seashore, should make one wary of being too confident. But over very wide geographical ranges most birds show only minor differences of habitat, and if one does not assume some constancy speculation is impossible.

Apart from any that may have survived in south-western refuges, the first woodland birds to come into Great Britain would have been those of the park-tundra. The fauna of this type of vegetation must have been very similar to that of the birch-scrub of Lapland, which has been described on p. 74.

The redpoll and willow-warbler are species which still breed in this country and are characteristic of the closed birchwoods of our north-western highlands. They may be birds of the park-tundra which have been able to adapt themselves to proper woodlands, or they may be birchwood birds which have extended into the park-tundra where climatic conditions allow. In either case they were probably some of the earliest woodland birds to recolonize Great Britain, and will have been here ever since. The willow-warbler is a highly adaptable species, and is able to live in a wide variety of climatic and woodland conditions. Both species have undergone subspeciation, presumably since the Full Glacial, for the northern willow-warbler (*Phylloscopus trochilus acredula*) and mealy redpoll (*Carduelis flammea flammea*) of Lapland are distinct from the willow-warbler (*P.t. trochilus*) and lesser redpoll (*C. f. cabaret*) of Britain. The brambling, like the last two, breeds in Lapland in park-tundra conditions, in large birchwoods and in conifers, but in Britain is normally known only as a winter migrant . It may well have bred here when conditions were suitable; presumably it needs lower temperatures for breeding than our summers give. The bluethroat is found in Lapland in closed birchwood as well as in the scrub, but occurs in Great Britain only as a scarce passage-migrant on the east coast. Other subspecies breed in Asia and eastern Europe, and one occurs as far west as France; all migrate, mostly to the south-east, some going as far as India. It seems that the origin of the bird is in the east, and that it has never been a resident of Great Britain.

Southern and Venables (1939) found the garden-warbler breeding in birchwoods in Swedish Lapland, but it was uncommon and found only where there was dense undergrowth; even so, its presence there at all is surprising to an English ornithologist since it is scarce in the Highlands of Scotland. It is unlikely to have been present in our park-tundra.

The willow-grouse (*Lagopus lagopus*), which is the most conspicuous large bird of the Lapland birchwood, does not occur in Britain but is closely related to the red grouse (*Lagopus scoticus*); indeed in body it seems to differ only in having a somewhat lighter colouring and in becoming white in winter, characters which in any group of animals but birds would not be used to justify specific separation. It differs also in habitat, for it is found in scrub and woods and regularly perches on trees, a thing which the red grouse rarely does. The conclusion is inescapable that the ancestors of our red grouse came here to live in park-tundra, and when that habitat disappeared they changed their habits to live on moors. In doing so they achieved subspecific or, according to most ornithologists, specific rank. That the red grouse is essentially a northern bird is suggested by the lack of success that has attended most of the attempts to naturalize it south of the Peak District.

Other common British birds present in smaller numbers in the Finnish birchwoods are tree-pipits, crows, reed-buntings, yellow wagtails, willow-tits, hedge-sparrows, ring-ouzels, and cuckoos. All these may therefore have been early immigrants in the Late Glacial, but the present restricted distribution of the yellow wagtail and willow-tit needs explanation. The redwing also is present, and was presumably a regular inhabitant of our first birchwoods. The pine-grosbeak (*Pinicola enucleator*), a scarce breeder in the Finnish birchwoods, is, like the bluethroat, a bird of eastern distribution which is unlikely ever to have bred in Britain.

Yellowhammers, magpies, and fieldfares, which I saw in Norwegian Lapland at sea level but not much higher, and the great tit, which was present in a village, were probably later immigrants to Britain, for the regions where they were present in Norway were warm enough to grow some Scotch firs.

The park-tundra of the Late Glacial, like the Lapland birch scrub and our own fell-woodlands, may also have held some species which, while they are in no way dependent on trees, do not seem to mind trees if they are not too close together and the other conditions are right. The meadow-pipit and wheatear are examples; most at home in regions which resemble tundra, they are found in

IX. Wyre Forest, oak and birch, area 2, in October. See page 115.

X. Wyre Forest, oak underplanted with beech, area 3, in October. See p. 116. The photograph is taken looking into the wood from a clearing, and the grass in the open space in the foreground is not typical.

the more open of the birchwoods both in Scotland and in Finland. The whinchat is another possibility, but I saw it in Finland only on cultivated land. The yellowhammer frequently enters a wide variety of woods, but is a bird of heath not tundra, and if it occurred in England during postglacial times it would have been in the areas, probably chiefly in the south-west, which bore heather and crowberry (*Empetrum nigrum*). From there it may have invaded such woods as there were. The probability of this depends on the time at which it reached Europe, a question which is discussed below.

The park-tundra presumably developed into more extensive closed woods of birch. Most of the birds already present probably persisted in these, although the willow-grouse, as it was then, was apparently unable, in this country, to become used to the new conditions and was driven to the heights. Except for the redpoll and willow-warbler there are no birds distinctive of birchwoods except possibly the black grouse. The German name of 'Berkhahn' and the Dutch of 'Berkhoen' suggest this association, and the Spanish 'Gallo de bosque' shows association with the woods, but in Scotland (and presumably in France, from its name of 'coq de bruyere') it is also found in more open places. Its gradual disappearance from most of the southern counties of England and the failures of most attempts to introduce it probably mean that it needs a relatively low temperature. It may be an early immigrant and a bird of the birchwoods which has only partially taken to the heaths under compulsion.

There was a long period when Great Britain was pretty well covered with coniferous forest, and during this time the woodland birds would have been those which were suited to them. The crested tit, crossbill, siskin, goldcrest, and capercailzie are now more or less confined to this habitat, and probably had their origin in it and spread northwards with it as the temperature rose. The other woodland species, which are found in both coniferous and deciduous woodland, are a more difficult problem as they may have originated in either habitat and spread later into the other. Amongst the common birds which have been suggested as primarily birds of the taiga are the coal-tit, the redstart, the treecreeper, and the great spotted woodpecker, but the evidence on which this view is put forward is rather thin. At present all four species live happily in other types of wood as well, and the coal-tit is the dominant tit of all our northern woods, of whatever type. If they were evolved in the taiga, it is likely, as I suggested above, that they are adapted to the general scruffiness of the woods rather than to conifers as such. The fact that the British avifauna consists of birds that are dependent on shrubs rather than on trees (page 55) may perhaps be explained by the fact that its main lines were determined when these first poor woods were established.

Once the cover of Scotch fir became general, woodland conditions were continuous and change of the dominant species was only gradual. More and more birds would have come in, following either new types of woodland or the generally improving climatic conditions. The last type of woodland to arrive in Great Britain was the beechwood, which was not established until shortly before the land bridge to the Continent was cut, so that if there were any birds characteristic of it they would be expected to be among the last also. In, fact, although the beechwood on account of its structure has a characteristic bird community, it has no characteristic species, for the association with it of the chaffinch and brambling is for winter food, not for breeding.

Apart from any that were connected with the beech, the last woodland birds to come here would have been those which are limited more by temperature than by habitat: chief amongst these is the nightingale. The thick shrub layer that it needs was present very early, in the form of hazel, even when Scotch fir was the dominant tree, but its present restriction to the warm south-east (page 184) suggests that it could not then have survived. At the 'climatic optimum' of the Atlantic period it may well have had a wider range than it has now.

In the southern parts of Europe there is another type of woodland, dominated by evergreen trees which bear flowers, not cones, and have thick leathery leaves, and shrubs of similar type may form the second layer in woods of trees such as beech. This 'laurel forest' is found on the Mediterranean coast and in Spain, but is even better developed in North Africa and in the Atlantic islands such as Madeira and the Azores. It is clearly dependent on a mild oceanic climate. The only tree of this type at all common in Great Britain is the holly, which unlike all the other laurel-leaved trees extends as far north as coastal Norway, but nevertheless cannot withstand persistent frost. It seldom forms societies, but it does so in the oak-woods of Killarney (south-west Ireland) where also a more typically Mediterranean evergreen, the arbutus or strawberry tree (*Arbutus unedo*) occurs. The box (*Buxus sempervirens*) occurs on calcareous soils in a few parts of the south of England. *Rhododendron ponticum* has become naturalized in many parts of Great Britain, and the holm oak (*Quercus ilex*) in a few places in the south-west. The occurrence of the arbutus at Killarney, some hundreds of miles from its next nearest station, together with the shrub layer dominated by the holly, has made some botanists hold that this type of woodland was formerly more widely spread, so as to make the vegetation of south-west England continuous with that of Iberia and the Mediterranean. This could, on grounds of what is believed to have been the temperature at that time, have happened at the 'climatic optimum' of the Atlantic period, when holly was at its maximum, but no pollen of other laurel-leaved trees has been found. Alternatively, though much less likely, the laurel forest which was probably the chief European vegetation of the Pliocene may have persisted on land now submerged beneath the Atlantic.

It is possible, but not very likely, that some of the birds characteristic of this type of vegetation ranged into southern England, but there is little information on what birds prefer it to other types of woodland. Species which are found in it in North Africa and so may formerly have extended into England are the firecrest (*Regulus ignicapillus*) and roller (*Coracias garrulus*). The fan-tailed and Cetti's warblers (*Cisticola juncidis* and *Cettia cetti*), which are now confined in Europe to the lower parts of the Mediterranean coast, are other possibilities. Further, woods of this type, by giving shelter in cold weather, may enable a species to spread northwards further than it would otherwise be able to do. The fondness of many birds, warblers, thrushes, and finches for instance, for roosting in the shrubberies of laurel (*Laurus nobilis*), cherry laurel (*Prunus laurocerasus*), and aucuba (*Aucuba japonica*), so much planted in Victorian gardens, is well known, and Meiklejohn (1952) has published evidence which shows that in the north of England and Scotland, where it is at the limit of its range, the chiff-chaff is commonly associated with *Rhododendron ponticum*. In Italy the bird appears to favour the upland deciduous woods rather than the laurel forests. The exact ecological description of habitats where a bird appears beyond its previously known distribution would test this hypothesis.

Besides the spread from the south, there are two other possible sources of our avifauna, the east and the west. From the east could have come birds of the taiga and the birchwoods, which probably continued to cover a large area of Asia even at the height of the glaciation. There is no evidence that any did so come and it would be extremely difficult, if not impossible, to distinguish between birds that came from the east and those that came from the fringe of coniferous forest that was left in the south-west. It has been suggested that the two very similar treecreepers, *Certhia familiaris* and *C. brachydactyla*, were evolved in isolation when the coniferous forests were divided, and afterwards spread until they met and overlapped. *C. brachydactyla* is found in central Europe and as far west as the Channel Islands, and as far south as North Africa, while *C. familiaris* in various subspecies is now found in Great Britain and over the whole of Europe, Asia south to the Himalayas, and North America. There would thus seem to be no simple explanation of the evolution of the two species and no evidence for any general westward movement. The treecreepers show a very wide geographical range and the occupation of many diverse habitats, but they have remarkably little differentiation. I find it impossible to believe that there is enough evidence even to connect them with one type of woodland rather than another, and their separation may be a result of climatic adaptation rather than of geographical isolation.

The northern woodland avifauna is much the same, except that there may be different subspecies, all the way to the Ural Mountains, and even beyond them there is much similarity. The real natural dividing line between east and west seems to be the watershed between the rivers Yenisei and Lena, at Longitude 100° E. The chance of any of our birds having come from beyond this, or of any coming from there in the near future, seems small, but there is always the possibility of a species suddenly getting so much on top of its environment that it spreads explosively for hundreds or thousands of miles. The azure tit (*Parus cyanus*) thus crossed the whole breadth of European Russia and retreated again in the space of forty years. The greenish warbler (*Phylloscopus trochiloides*), which is a bird of Russia and central Asia, extended its range westward between 1880 and 1930, and by then bred in eastern Germany. Between 1930 and 1950 it spread westward across the whole of southern Finland, following temperature changes in the month of May. A few specimens have been taken in this country, and a further expansion on a slightly larger scale might bring it to us as a breeding bird. Its habitat is said to be open woodland and scrub. The yellow-breasted bunting (*Emberiza aureola*), which is also a scrub-bird, spread from the Urals to Finland between 1825 and 1925, and so could also conceivably reach this country.

Birds which are found in some numbers not far from the eastern shores of the North Sea, and so might manage to cross it, are the nutcracker (which is discussed on page 196) and the black woodpecker (*Dryocopus martius*). The latter, although common in the pine forests of Scandinavia, has never certainly been recorded from this country.

More likely to have come from the east than any of our strictly woodland birds are those which need a combination of trees and open space, especially grass. These conditions, as has been shown above, are found in nature only in steppe country and in the mountains. There was little true steppe at any time in Europe, but it has long been well developed, and still is, in Asia. An eastern source for birds of this sort of habitat is therefore probable. I have already mentioned the starling (page 178), and the rook, which is described as being found in large numbers in the forest islands of the Siberian steppe but which breeds neither in southern Europe nor in most of Scandinavia, is another example. The heron also is probably a bird of the river-valleys of the steppes, where its colonies have been reported as occurring in the same group of trees as rookeries. Its range is somewhat similar to that of the rook, but extends much further south.

Some of the birds of prey, such as the buzzard, which seem to nest primarily in trees but which need open ground for feeding, may also have come from the steppes. So too may a number of other birds which need, or are at home amongst, scattered trees; examples are the woodlark and tree-pipit, whose geographical distribution is not incompatible with this, since they extend well into Russia.

There is no land connexion between Europe and America, so that immigration from the west is much more difficult and less likely than from the east. Nevertheless, the crossing can be made by relatively short hops, by Greenland, Iceland, and the Faroes. The fieldfare, going in the opposite direction, reached Greenland in 1932, and is now established there as a breeding species. Further, there is good evidence of strong-flying land-birds such as lapwings having flown the Atlantic without rest, so that there is a possibility that some of our species could have come from America. The most likely is the wren: the family to which it belongs has only one old-world species, which is found in America as well; but there are many in America, especially in the central parts, so that it probably originated in that continent. Our wren exists in several subspecies: there are forms confined to Iceland, the Faroes, the Shetlands, St. Kilda, and the other Outer Hebrides, and others on the mainland of Europe and on the islands of the Mediterranean. It probably invaded Europe from the north-west and differentiated rapidly into its several subspecies. It would be aided by the fact that it can live in a wide variety of situations, so that adaptation could easily follow the isolation imposed on it by the islands which it used as stopping places. The fact that according to the current theory the island populations must have been isolated for evolution to take place suggests that there was one explosive outburst from America, rather than a steady trickle. This accords with what we know of the way in which other birds have sometimes spread, such as the azure tit and greenish warbler mentioned above. The invasion of the wren could have occurred at a time when the climate of Greenland was better than it is now.

Another American group of birds is the buntings, but since fossils identified as belonging to these have been found in deposits in Germany ascribed to the time of the last ice age, they must have come to Europe before that, possibly in one of the warmer inter-glacial periods.

It must not be thought that the improvement in climate and the retreat of the ice has been steady, for there is both fossil and historical evidence that this is not so. In the early Middle Ages there were human colonies in Greenland which afterwards had to be abandoned because of the cold, and there have been other similar fluctuations. Some of the larger of these have been shown in the record of plant pollen in the peat, but it takes centuries for a new type of woodland to spread and establish itself so that minor changes may not be recognizable in this way. Birds are more mobile and so can be more sensitive indicators of climatic change. There is some evidence that we have been for the last eighty years in a period of rising temperatures. The records from the English Midlands do not show any detectable improvement until about 1925, but those for Iceland and Finland show it beginning at about 1880, the increase being most marked in the winter temperatures. No figures are available for the north of Scotland, but the spread of birds there suggests that the rise began at about the same time as it did in Iceland.

By a piece of good fortune rare in the literature of birds, two volumes of the *Vertebrate Fauna of Scotland* cover Sutherland and Western Ross. The first, by Harvie-Brown and Buckley, is dated 1887, and the second, by Harvie-Brown and Macpherson, is 1904. There are considerable differences between the birds present at the two dates. The chaffinch first bred at Inchnadamph (presumably in the village) in 1877, and by 1887 had become common. A tree-pipit was seen at Inchnadamph in 1873, but this bird spread more slowly; Dobbie does not mention it as present in West Ross in 1897 and it is a bird that could hardly be missed, but it was present in some of the birchwoods of Assynt by 1903. There were no blue tits at Inchnadamph up to 1888, but by 1903 they were not uncommon. An extension of the whitethroat and redstart is also recorded. Since then there have been further changes. By the early 1950s chaffinches were the second commonest and tree-pipits the third commonest birds in the birchwoods, and the treecreeper, absent in 1904, had arrived. The wood-warbler also appeared north of Loch Broom in the 1940s, and by 1951 a few singing individuals were present in the native birchwoods as far north-west as they could go. It was in the more sheltered plantations of beech round Tongue on the north coast by 1947 (Fig. 24).

Whether this extension will continue or not is anyone's guess. Manley (1951), in discussing the recent climatic changes in Britain, likened them to the fluctuations, over periods of twenty years or so, that are known to have occurred several times since the beginning of the eighteenth century, and said that the 1950s might well bring a series of cool, wet summers, as indeed they did except for the brilliant 1959. But he seems to have misread the Icelandic figures, to which he refers, in saying that the rise in temperature began only in about 1925, and he does not mention the circumstantial but strong evidence of the northward spread of the birds. This is as marked on the Continent, in Denmark, Sweden and Finland, as here, and is

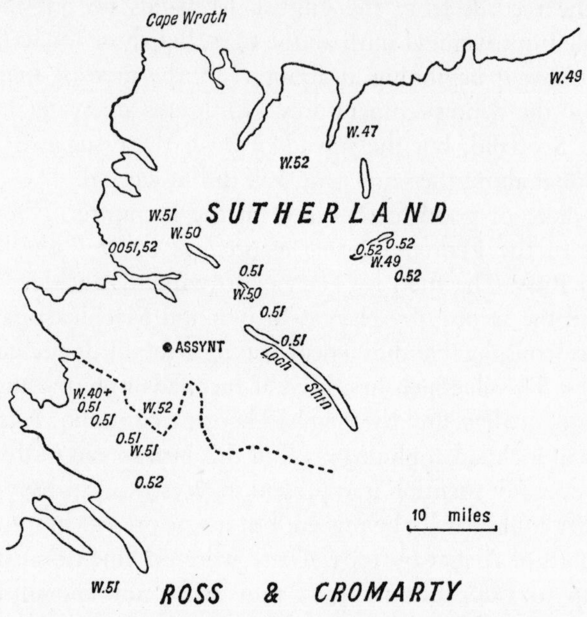

FIG. 24. Spread of the wood-warbler into north-west Scotland.
W = recorded in year shown
O = woods searched but bird not recorded.
Mostly original, some records from *British Birds*, passim.

perhaps most striking in Iceland, which has gained seven regular and two occasional species of breeding birds in the last half-century.

Whatever the climatic changes in the last 4,000 years it is probable that the changes which man has imposed on nature have had an even bigger influence on the avifauna. The effect of man on animal life has been described by Ritchie and all that I shall do here is summarize the chief changes that have been imposed on woodland birds. The destruction of predators and introduction of the pheasant have already been dealt with. Up to the eighteenth century there was a progressive and continuous destruction of woodland, which must have led to a reduction in the numbers of woodland birds. The only compensation was that the cultivated lands round the villages would have provided habitats for the wooded-steppe or park birds which must previously have been rare. Before the Middle Ages the only places likely to support rooks, which avoid mountains, were some of the chalk downs of the south of England, which were possibly always bare. By Tudor times rooks must have been well-established, for Macbeth's lines:

> Light thickens, and the crow
> Makes wing to the rooky wood

clearly describe the flight of rooks to the large winter roosts.

Birds of tree-heath and the upper fringes of woods must always have been present and were probably little affected until the sheep-farming introduced by the Cistercians in the thirteenth century prevented the regeneration of many of the birches and rowans of the hillsides. Sheep-grazing has to be fairly intense to stop trees from growing provided that spiky plants such as briar or thorn or juniper are present, but it is possible that the monks kept enough sheep to do so. Their sheep-walks covered not only the mountainous north, but the Cotswolds and other southern hills as well. The extension of sheep-farming to the low-lying parts of the Midlands by the depopulators under the Tudors would have had a similar effect in destroying many a scrubby field on the outskirts of villages. The impression that one gets from reading Leland, with his repeated references to 'corn, grass, and wood', is that, except for the greater prevalence of arable land then, England must have looked much the same in 1540 as it does now. It is clear also that by then much of the land was enclosed and no longer in the open fields of the Middle Ages.

The eighteenth century saw a great extension of the enclosures, even on the hills, and two other changes in the pattern of the English landscape which must greatly have affected the woodland birds, namely plantation and gardening. The plantations, begun rather earlier in Scotland than in England, began to restore some of the loss caused by the woodland destruction of earlier years. Since many of them were of larch, a new type of woodland was provided, but this seems to have had surprisingly little effect on the fauna. None of the characteristic coniferous forest birds was induced to spread southward by it, but it may have given some encouragement to coal-tits and goldcrests. The Scottish coniferous plantations provided the conditions for the successful re-introduction of the capercailzie, and possibly, though as I have said above I doubt this, for an expansion of the greater spotted woodpecker.

The enclosures divided the old common fields or open sheep-walk by miles of thorn hedge dotted with elms or oaks, and in so doing provided an environment in which woodland birds of many types of habitat-preference could live successfully. The adaptable and wide-ranging species like the chaffinch, tits, and thrushes, birds of parkland or open wood such as the tree-pipit, of wooded steppe like the rook, of tree-heath such as the yellowhammer, and even of dense woodland like the nightingale, are all at home in one or other of its varieties, and their numbers must greatly have increased in the last few hundred years. Lastly, the garden of the gentleman's house, copied on a smaller scale by the tradesmen and professional men of the towns, introduced a variety of new niches combined with an intensity of production of vegetable matter which has led to those woodland birds which can exploit it—robin, blackbird, and throstle, for example—becoming the most numerous as well as the most familiar of British birds.

Since the eighteenth century there has been an extension of small gardens and in the last forty years a great expansion of coniferous planting by the Forestry Commission, but few other changes. The introduction of spruce on a large scale and the consequent raising of the altitudinal limit for successful planting, is progressively bringing woodland birds to areas from which they must have been absent for centuries. In Arkengarthdale Forest in north Yorkshire in the despised Sitka spruce I found in 1953 at 1,500 feet above sea level, without a lengthy search, the following birds: chaffinch, tree-pipit, coal-tit, willow-warbler, blackbird, and hedge-sparrow. A few years before the land was bare moor; none of these birds would then have been present nearer than some thin streamside woods two miles away, and even there they would have been few in numbers. In a quantitative sense the Forestry Commission is likely to have as big an effect on our woodland birds as had the enclosures of the eighteenth century or the suburban gardens of the nineteenth.

Starling

14

SYSTEMATIC LIST

In this chapter I give a summary of the geographical and ecological distribution of the chief birds that may be found in woods in Britain; I have not dealt with the continental distribution but have tried to set each species in its place by a brief reference to the distribution of the family to which it belongs. I have occasionally added a note on other aspects of a bird's life, especially where there is recent work that is not so well known as it deserves to be.

I have given much thought to the order in which the genera and families should be placed. When I first owned and read books on birds they began with the thrushes, then the crows became fashionable, and now the divers have the place of honour. Earlier authors had placed the hawks or the game-birds at the head of the list. The XI International Ornithological Congress made a valiant if foolish attempt to produce a scheme that should be permanent and please everybody: valiant because that word describes all efforts to obtain international agreement, and foolish because as knowledge progresses and opinion changes any static system must become progressively more unsatisfactory. The scheme proposed was little different from what is generally known, for no good reason, as the Wetmore order, which begins with the divers and ends with the finches. This is substantially the same as that used by Evans in 1899 in *The Cambridge Natural History*, which was itself a modification of earlier classifications.

Since such a statement as that the finches are higher than the crows is meaningless, and since it is impossible to express the evolution of the birds in a straight line, the attempt sometimes made to stigmatize the use of any other order as unscientific is naïve in the extreme. The chief function of any classificatory scheme, at least as applied in a book that is intended to be read, is to assist the reader. I have therefore begun this chapter with the passerine birds, which make up most of those in the woods, and arranged them in alphabetical order of families, and within these in alphabetical order of genera and species. The non-passerines follow in alphabetical order of orders. Anyone who knows the Latin names can therefore quickly find any bird without having to learn by heart a long and arbitrary list, and those who know no Latin names are no worse off than they would be on any other system. In the tables in the body of the book I have used alphabetical order of genera, separating the passerines from the others. I have found that this method greatly simplifies my own notes, and I commend it to others. Generic names are changed less frequently than are opinions about the relationships of families, so that the alphabetical system is likely also to be more stable than any other.

ORDER PASSERIFORMES

AEGITHALIDAE – LONG-TAILED TITS

The long-tailed tits are sometimes separated from the true tits (page 251), largely on account of their peculiar nests. All are birds of woodland and scrub in various parts of Europe and Asia.

Long-tailed tit – *Aegithalos caudatus*

The long-tailed tit is widely distributed over the mainland of Great Britain, though rare in some districts, and it thins out towards the north of Scotland. It was present in Caithness in the eighteenth century but many observers have since failed to find it in the northern counties; I have not seen it myself in the birchwoods of Ross and Sutherland, where it is certainly on the limit of its range, and as it suffers heavily in bad winters it is probably often reduced in numbers there. It is not common anywhere and is absent from the fell-woods in both England and Wales. I have a few records from all types of deciduous woods, but none for coniferous plantations or the natural firwoods. Hartley found that at Wytham it fed chiefly in the top of the shrub layer and the lower strata of the trees, and preferred ashes, sycamores, and conifers. It frequents hedges and scrub woodlands in the lowlands but is not often seen in gardens.

ALAUDIDAE – LARKS

The larks are a nearly cosmopolitan group, almost all restricted to steppes, deserts both hot and cold, or other open spaces.

Woodlark – *Lullula arborea*

The distribution of the woodlark has been discussed on pages 185–90.

CERTHIIDAE – TREECREEPERS

The treecreepers are found over almost the whole world except South America, generally in rather thinly wooded districts.

Treecreeper – *Certhia familiaris*

The treecreeper is found all over Britain except for some of the islands, and is not very particular in its choice of habitat. It seems to be equally common in all types of woodland except yew, in which I have not found it, but this may only be because it is an inconspicuous bird and the woods of these trees that I have listed are few. It is also seen in man-made habitats such as gardens where trees are plentiful, but seldom, so far as my observation goes, in woodland ecotones where it would have to fly far from one tree to another. Provided that it has plenty of trees in the bark of which it can search for insects it seems indifferent to their species, height, or diameter, and to the presence or absence of shrubs. I have seen it feeding also on moss-covered boulders, old walls, and a muddy bank on the Severn Estuary, and I have once seen one on the ground. In the hills it ranges as high as the fell-woods, and to reach these it must sometimes fly over the open for some miles. The view that it was originally a bird of the taiga is not supported by any convincing arguments.

The history of the bird's peculiar habit of excavating half-egg-shaped cavities in the soft bark of Wellingtonias has been written by Mackenzie (1959). These holes were first described in 1905 but were not recognized as the roosting-sites of the treecreeper until 1923. They are now found all over Great Britain and Ireland wherever there are Wellingtonias and occur also in Germany and North America. The tree occurs naturally only in a restricted part of California, where it is frequented by a subspecies of the treecreeper, *C. f. zelotes*, but the habit appears to be an entirely new one, produced independently in several different populations.

CORVIDAE – CROWS

The Corvidae are found all over the world except for New Zealand, Polynesia, the Antarctic and some islands, but are rare in South America. This distribution suggests that they originated in Asia. All the palaearctic species are associated with woods, trees, or bushes, but there seems to be a general tendency for them to make use of cliffs and rocks, either as well as or instead of trees. Many species have become commensal with man.

Raven – *Corvus corax*

Thirty or forty years ago the raven was a scarce bird almost confined to a few sea-cliffs and some of the remoter mountains, but since then it has greatly increased. It is now, for such a large bird, tolerably common in Somerset and Devon, in many parts of Wales, and in the Lake District, and there are smaller numbers on the Pennines and other hills, and on the south coast. In Scotland, though it is widely distributed, it is nowhere in my experience so common as it is in Cumberland, where every dale seems to have a pair. This might be connected with the lower density of sheep on the Scottish hills compared with the English, since carrion and especially the afterbirths of sheep form a large part of its food, or may be due simply to gamekeeper-pressure. All the areas where it is common are mountainous or rocky and largely bare of trees, and for many years its nests were almost always on ledges, but with its increase in numbers it has taken once again to the trees, where it used to nest before its numbers were reduced and where it has always nested on the Continent. I have no record from birchwoods but otherwise it seems to use whatever species of tree are present. It occurs both in groves and in large woods and sometimes builds in the tallest trees available, so that its nests are often in conifers. Its method of finding its food, by soaring over open spaces, suggests that its natural home is some sort of tree-grass or tree-heath ecotone, but what sort I would not like to say; the ease with which it has taken to rocks suggests the woodland fringe of the mountains

XI. Sitka spruce in June, Northumberland. The trees, 24 years old, are of poor quality. They have been brashed and thinned. The photograph shows well the horizontal cut-off of the branches and the litter on the ground resulting from these processes.

XII. Nest of chaffinch in May, lichen-covered, in sessile oak. See p. 242.

rather than the grassy steppes. If that is so, its former occurrence in our agricultural lowlands, a habitat to which it has recently returned in many of the Welsh border counties, would be an opportunist utilization of a habitat provided by man. In the Lake District it is commonest at the middle heights, between 1,000 and 2,000 feet above sea level, though it often circles over the dale bottoms. Its altitudinal range in Scotland appears to be much the same. It sometimes goes higher than this, but I have not seen it on the extreme tops.

The normal flight call, 'pruk', resembles the croak of a frog more than any other sound in nature, and is quite unmistakable. There are many other calls and conversational notes, and individuals seem to vary. A sound not recorded in the *Handbook* that I have more than once heard in the Lake District during the aerial gambollings, is a note exactly like a single stroke on a bell, or the sound of a hammer on an anvil. This was mentioned by Dorothy Wordsworth in her *Grasmere Journal* for 27 July 1800, but her observations in natural history were not very good and she ascribed it to the effect of the mountain echo, 'a musical bell-like answering to the bird's hoarse voice'. The same sound is presumably intended by William Wordsworth in *The Excursion*, 4, line 1188, where he refers to the raven's voice as 'an iron knell'.

The habit of roosting communally in large numbers, better known in the rook, is also found in the raven. Like communal nesting, this may be connected with the woodland ecotone habitat.

Carrion-Crow – *Corvus corone corone*, and Hooded Crow – *Corvus corone cornix*

Nothing either in my own experience or in the books leads me to believe that there is any difference in the habits or habitat of the two forms, except that their geographical distribution means that the habitats available to them are somewhat different. Baxter and Rintoul give the transition-line between them as running north-east to south-west through Perth, Stirling, and Ayr; it is not a boundary, as the carrion-crow breeds in smaller numbers to the north of this, as far as Moray and East Ross, and the hoodie less often to the south, even occasionally in the English eastern counties.

The carrion crow seems to be equally at home among deciduous and coniferous trees, and in oak, ash, birch, alder, and mixed woods. I have no record of it in beechwoods and it does not appear in Lack and Venables' lists for these. It seems to be less common in pedunculate than in sessile oak, but this may be merely a reflection of its wider dispersion in the hilly districts where the latter predominates, and of the higher degree of game-preserving in the south. It is sometimes found in large woods, but more often about groves and lines. On the hills the nest is often in an isolated tree, frequently of quite small size, and in the fell-woods the nests are often near the edge. Its altitudinal limit seems to be simply that of trees large enough to contain a nest; Blezard (1943) records nesting in the Lake District up to 1,800 feet above sea level, where there are very few trees indeed; around the tree limit at 1,000 to 1,200 feet there are plenty of nests in many parts of England and Wales. The crow is generally wary of man and when disturbed from the nest it flies off rapidly and silently on the side away from that on which the observer approaches. In places it comes into the more open parts of towns and occasionally forages in quite small gardens. Town nesting has been recorded. Most of its feeding takes place in the open, either on the moors, in agricultural country both grass and arable, or on the seashore.

I have much less information about the habitat of the hoodie, and in parts of its area there is little woodland except birch; it is at home in this as well as in Scotch fir.

Where the two forms overlap inter-breeding is common, and the young of the mixed broods range in colour from all black to almost purely hooded, with all degrees of intermediates (Meise 1928, Stenhouse 1925). This range suggests that the colour is determined by several Mendelian factors, and as the intermediates are seldom seen there is presumably selection of the pure-bred forms or homozygotes, and individuals resembling them.

Rook – *Corvus frugilegus*

The rook is now generally distributed over Great Britain but, except for the rare occasions when it has nested on buildings, is confined to areas where there are trees, and so is absent, except as an occasional visitor, from the upper parts of the hills. In Derbyshire there are many rookeries on the limestone between 1,000 and

1,200 feet, and the highest is at 1,400 feet. There is also evidence from a number of areas that it prefers not to nest at middle altitudes, even when trees are present; Alexander (1933) for instance found very few nests above 400 feet in the Thames basin, but conversely I found in west Gloucestershire (Yapp 1934) that the density of nests on the low-lying land by the Severn was less than half that on land more than 50 feet above sea level, and the same type of distribution has been reported of the Isle of Man. The density of nests over sample areas of about 50 square miles varies from zero up to about 60 per square mile, with an average for agricultural England of about 20 per square mile.

The size and compactness of the colonies varies much. Solitary nests occur and small groups of about a dozen are common, but others range up to hundreds and even, rarely, thousands, although there are none of this size in England. The largest rookery in Britain, at Turriff in Aberdeenshire, has about 6,000 nests, and there are several others with more than 1,000 in the same county. Scottish rookeries are on the whole much larger than those in England. In west Gloucestershire, in Marples' count of the Wirral nests, and in Nicholson and Nicholson's wide survey of the Upper Thames basin, more than half the rookeries had fewer than 30 nests, and in Roebuck's count of Nottinghamshire, Derbyshire, Leicestershire, and Rutland over 40 per cent. of the colonies had 25 or fewer nests. Stewart (1923) found that in Lanarkshire, the north-west of the county, which has much arable land, had many small rookeries, while the north-east, with not more than 10 per cent. of the county's arable land, had about the same number of rooks concentrated into a small number of large rookeries along the river valleys. This suggests that the size of a rookery is to some extent a measure of the density of rooks on suitable feeding grounds.

Sometimes a small colony occupies a single tree, and a big rookery a group of adjacent ones, but in other places the nests are well spread out and there may be distinct little groups of nests within the main colony. This makes it difficult to define a rookery in any very rigorous way. Although the same group of trees may be occupied from year to year, the nests are not always found in the same individual trees, and where the nests at the opposite ends of a colony gradually move further and further apart the rookery may fragment into two. It is generally said that rookeries are very enduring things and this is certainly true of some of the larger ones for which historical records exist. The smaller ones are not so stable. In west Gloucestershire, where the largest rookery had only about 100 nests, I found that the expectation of life of a rookery from its inception was only twelve years (Yapp 1951). Too much reliance must not be placed on this figure, as the period of the survey (seven years) was rather short, but there can be no doubt that many rookeries lasted for only a few years and that even rookeries of 30 or 40 nests could dwindle and disappear very rapidly. Roebuck found that of between 400 and 500 colonies in the Midlands 15 per cent. disappeared in four years, but this is not the whole of the change since there were many rookeries which had a transient existence of less than four years which were not recorded. A low expectation of life at birth is not incompatible with a very long life of a few individuals. Most of the new rookeries in west Gloucestershire started with quite small numbers, but two began with 18 nests, and one with 23. My survey gave no support to the suggestions that rooks prefer to nest near water, or near houses, or that the colonies have a regular spacing.

Except that it likes tall trees, the rook does not seem to mind what species it nests in. In west Gloucestershire elms and oaks had between them 97 per cent. of the nests, probably because they are the commonest trees, and my general impression is that the country as a whole would not show much difference from this. Of the less usual trees I have seen nests in larch and willow, and they have been recorded in Lombardy poplars and in Portugal laurels. Very few rookeries are in woods of any size: one of the largest known to me to contain a rookery is of 48 acres and is also unusual in being an ashwood and from 700 to 800 feet above sea level. By far the commonest situations in England are groves, clumps, and above all lines of trees in hedgerows. It is this choice that makes elms and oaks the most popular trees, since they make up most of the timber trees in this sort of distribution. Nests are occasionally found in suburbs, and even in the central parts of towns. The last nests in central London were in the Temple in 1916; a few pairs nested in College Green, Bristol, until the 1930s. The large winter roosts, often but not always on the site of a former rookery, have already been mentioned (page 163). It has been shown that sometimes the birds which visit one rookery in winter (probably but not certainly those which nest there) divide themselves between two roosts.

Rooks feed in woods and on trees only exceptionally, as when there are many leaf-eating caterpillars on oaks in spring or acorns to be had in autumn; most of their food is taken in the open, and they are thus, like most of their family, birds of the ecotone. All open spaces are used to some extent, including moors, the seashore, and such unlikely places as railway goods yards. Most of the feeding takes place on grassland, but there is some evidence from counts that rooks prefer arable land if it is available; whichever they are using they are in this country dependent on farming. In many parts of England there was an increase in population during the Second World War, which has been connected with the increased amount of land under the plough. Extensive analyses of stomach contents in a wide survey carried out for the Agricultural Research Council showed that, given the method of feeding by digging in grass or fallow or young corn or stubble, both plant and animal foods of various sorts were taken according to their availability. There was thus considerable seasonal change, and the rook is, within its limits, a real omnivore.

Jackdaw – *Corvus monedula*

The usual statement that the jackdaw is resident and common over the whole of Great Britain except the north-west Highlands conceals a very patchy distribution. In counting birds seen from the train between Birmingham and London, whether on the route through Bletchley or that through Banbury, I have seen scarcely any: five journeys for instance scored 491 rooks but only two jackdaws. My impression is that the same is true over much of agricultural England and that the apparent commonness of the jackdaw is due to the fact that where it is present it is a familiar and even impudent bird, readily coming into town parks and even small suburban gardens, where the rook is seldom seen. Where it appears in numbers there is usually and perhaps always a large colony not far away. All such that I know are in rocks not in trees, and suitable sites of that sort occur only in the west and north of England. In Lanarkshire, according to Stewart, large tree-colonies are the commoner.

The jackdaw is hardly a bird of the woods and it appears to like best a combination of trees and cliffs, which may occasionally be provided by any species of tree. If cliffs are present the size of the wood does not seem to matter. I find it impossible to say what was its original nesting site. Baxter and Rintoul, in describing its recent increase in Scotland, say 'adaptability with regard to nesting sites has greatly facilitated its spread', but E. M. Nicholson writes in *Birds and Men*: 'In their distribution jackdaws are sharply limited . . . by their narrow choice of sites for nests.' Since in Scotland it breeds commonly on rocks, in hollow trees, on ruins, in modern buildings, in rabbit holes, and in trees, and in the last makes both open and domed nests, there seems some justification for Baxter and Rintoul's statement. On the other hand there must be something that keeps it from the English Midlands, and shortage of nest sites seems a likely possibility. Most nests are bulky structures of twigs, but those in the smaller holes in trees are said to be lined only with finer material such as grass. It is possible that the jackdaw arose from the general corvine stem as a rock-nester, but never wholly abandoned its liking for trees or the use of twigs in making its nests on ledges, and that nesting in hollow trees and rabbit holes is a much later development. The common building of open nests in Scotland must be a recent habit, for Newton, in his edition of Yarrell's *History of British Birds* published in 1882, knew of only two well-authenticated instances. Whatever the bird's origin it looks as if the Scottish and English populations were developing different habits, and so are on the road to some degree of ecological as well as geographical isolation.

In feeding habits the jackdaw is generally similar to the rook, and is a bird of the tree-grass ecotone. It is much less tied to agricultural land and is rather more of a scavenger, readily taking scraps from dustbins.

Magpie – *Pica pica*

The magpie is found all over Great Britain but is very scarce in some parts of Scotland; this appears to be a local reduction which took place in the nineteenth century, and is generally considered to have been caused by the intense game-preservation which the Victorians imposed on that country. It is now increasing again, and the same is true of many English counties where also its numbers had been reduced, probably in the same way.

It occurs in woods of many different types and I have no indication that it favours either deciduous or coniferous trees. It does not occur in any of my beechwood lists, nor in my birchwood lists except in winter, and it was present in one only of Lack and Venables' 34 beechwoods. It is generally, though not always, to be found on the edges of woods, but when it is inside there is probably always some open space nearby. It is also a bird of ecotones of many types, both natural and artificial, and probably its highest density is found in country with old and neglected thorn hedges. Where the magpie is not persecuted it becomes fairly tame, and will live about houses; it can be found within two miles of the centre of both Manchester and Birmingham, and is as much at home in shrubberies of *Rhododendron ponticum* as in thorns. In the Isle of Man it is common in completely treeless country, where the only cover, apart from buildings, is provided by the stone walls and gorse hedges, seldom more than 4 or 5 feet high, which form the field boundaries. I am informed that it nests in the gorse. I have seen it in November at 1,200 feet in the Pennines, where there are few bushes and no trees in sight.

Magpies, like most Corvidae, are birds of ecotones, and in this country feed mostly on grassland, but they use the association of grass and trees in a different way from the others. They seldom feed far from their cover, and those that nest in hedges avoid using the middle of the fields unless they are very small. When disturbed a magpie flies straight for cover, but this seems to be an individual reaction which is not, as it would be with social birds, copied by others. The birds usually feed in pairs, and if from the train one sees a magpie flying to the hedge, one can usually find its fellow on the ground somewhere near the point from which the first one took wing. In England and Wales the magpie does not frequent the fell-woods, but Baxter and Rintoul quote records up to 1,100 feet above sea level in Scotland. It is difficult to suggest what was its original habitat, as the situations it likes—clearings in woods, and the wood edge—must have occurred very rarely under natural conditions except at the upper altitudinal limit or against marshes, where it is not found. Owen (1956) has shown that the nestlings are fed with animal matter, largely but not exclusively insects, chiefly collected on the ground.

Jay – *Garrulus glandarius*

The jay is found throughout Great Britain except Scotland north of the Great Glen, but has a somewhat patchy distribution possibly partly dependent on game preservation. It occurs in woods of all types, without any preference for conifers or broad-leaved trees. The lists discussed in Chapters 4 to 6 suggest that it is commonest in pedunculate oak and in beech. Shrubs seem to be an attraction for it but they need not be so thick or so high as is sometimes stated, and it lives in some sessile oakwoods where there are none at all. In these woods I have found it at over 1,000 feet in both England and Wales. Goodwin (1956) has given evidence, based on a few trials in aviaries, that before a nest is built the site must be screened, especially from above. The jay makes little use of ecotones, either natural or man-made, but it has recently become a relatively tame park-bird in Kensington Gardens, and is to be found in the precincts of some country houses.

The jay has a peculiar feeding-habit which it shares with the nut-cracker, that of burying seeds for food. Those which the jay uses are acorns, and the habit has been described in detail by Goodwin (1956) and by Chettleborough (1952). The acorns are taken off the trees, from September until they are all gone, and carried away anything up to half a mile or so to be buried in relatively open places (greater distances have been recorded in Germany). One acorn is carried in the beak, and from one to three in the gullet, and they are disgorged for burying. This is generally done in a natural crack or crevice, or under dead leaves, but sometimes a hole is dug with the bill. The acorn is spat out into the hole, hammered in and covered. Only one is buried at a time, the others that are being carried being put down meanwhile. Birds begin to dig up their acorns about a week after burial has ceased, and apparently know where to look for them. Aviary birds find their stores without difficulty.

The jay is an omnivore and especially in spring takes much animal food, but the specialized feeding on acorns suggests that it is primarily a bird of the oak-forests, and the English distribution lists support this to some extent. Nevertheless it is able to live in many other situations and so must be able to survive without its primary food. It has been observed to bury beech-mast, hazel nuts, the seeds of yew, mountain ash and thorn, and various berries on the Continent, and in captivity it buries or hides both soft food and nuts, so that the burying habit seems to be a general way of treating food. It attacks an acorn by holding it down with the feet and biting at it until the shell is pierced; unlike the magpie it does not hammer. Having taken off the shell, it stabs the open beak into the soft kernel and pulls out a mouthful. The nestlings, according to Owen (1956), are fed almost entirely on insects, particularly caterpillars.

EMBERIZIDAE – BUNTINGS

By contrast with the true finches the buntings are an American family, although there are many species in Europe and Asia. Also by contrast with the finches, they are nearly all birds of the tree-ecotone, only a few living in woods and as many more living in places where there are no trees at all.

Cirl Bunting – *Emberiza cirlus*

The distribution of the cirl bunting has been discussed on page 185.

Yellowhammer or Yellow Bunting – *Emberiza citrinella*

The yellowhammer is found all over Great Britain, except some of the Scottish islands, wherever there is a suitable habitat. It does not need trees, being quite content with gorse or other bushes only a few feet high as song posts. I include it here because where woods are present in otherwise suitable districts, as often happens on the hills, it at least feeds in them, though there do not seem to be any records of woodland nests. I have found it as a frequent inhabitant of sessile oakwoods, and less commonly of pedunculate oakwoods, ashwoods, birchwoods, beechwoods, alderwoods, the ancient Caledonian forest of Scotch fir, and yew-woods on the South Downs. Many, but by no means all, of the woods in which I have found it are at or over 1,000 feet above sea level. It is probably commonest on hillsides covered with gorse and scattered thorns, and is also found in the artificial habitat of hedges and hedgerow trees. It is presumably, in origin, a bird of woodland scrub which has been able to make use of the smaller closed woodlands and of the similar habitat provided by enclosed fields, but it is still characteristically a bird of the hills up to the tree-limit.

Reed Bunting – *Emberiza schoeniclus*

The normal habitat of the reed bunting is reed beds where there are no trees, or only scattered willows or alders which do not seem necessary to it, but I have found it in spring in an ashwood in Yorkshire some distance from any water, in a Scottish birchwood, and in a spruce plantation alongside water.

FRINGILLIDAE – FINCHES

In most classifications the family Fringillidae includes not only the finches but also the buntings, birds of a generally different type of habitat which have probably had a quite different origin. The finches proper, or subfamily Fringillinae, have a world-wide distribution but their headquarters are northern Eurasia. They all have relatively large and hard beaks, and feed on seeds, although not exclusively so. It seems that nearly all the British species feed their young on nothing but insects, whatever the adults may eat. Most finches are birds of the woods, at least in the breeding season, but some species, especially in the genus *Carduelis*, have gone out into the woodland ecotones, and most of the British species have been very apt to take advantage of man-made habitats such as farms and gardens.

Linnet – *Carduelis cannabina*

The linnet is a heath bird but is also found where there are scattered scrub trees and bushes, and in winter commonly in hedgerows. It occurs in numbers in some spruce plantations at the thicket stage, especially in the north of England.

Redpoll – *Carduelis flammea*

The race of the redpoll which is resident in Great Britain is fairly easily distinguished from the Scandinavian form by its smaller size and darker colouring, and is known as the lesser redpoll (*C. f. cabaret*). It breeds in most counties but is nowhere common except in the Highlands of Scotland, including the north-west, where there are (or were in 1951 and 1952) numbers in the birchwoods. This is odd because it was apparently not recorded from north Sutherland until 1928; Harvie-Brown and Buckley (1887) say that it was then unknown in the north and west of the county, and Harvie-Brown and Macpherson (1904) add no record. The explanation may be that it suffers fluctuations in numbers. There can be no doubt that it is a bird of birches more than any other tree, although other woods which are not too high, such as willows and the younger stages of plantations, will serve it as well. It sometimes comes into gardens and feeds on the ground on fallen seeds, like a chaffinch. In winter it moves south and is seen in small flocks, usually about a dozen, in places where it does not breed. In Wyre Forest larch plantations and mature oaks seem equally popular, and there is no obvious preference for birches although these are available.

The redpoll tends to be gregarious at all times, and several pairs often nest together. Unlike most social birds it sings, and the song is usually given in chorus. It is a simple but musical trill, like a very high-pitched drum roll, and is given from a perch or in flight.

Siskin – *Carduelis spinus*

As a regular breeding bird the siskin is confined to Scotland, and is there much more abundant on the east side. It has occasionally bred in a number of English counties and appears to be spreading in the north. With this distribution and the fact that it nearly always, apparently, nests in conifers, there can be no doubt that it is a bird of the ancient Scotch firwoods, although it is said now to favour spruce for nesting. In Rothiemurchus Forest it seems to prefer the more open parts, where the trees are scattered, to the closed woods. In winter, when it moves southwards, it is less restricted in its habitat and occurs in woods of oak and other trees. It feeds largely on conifer seeds but also on seeds of shrubs and plants of the field layer. The song is often given in a circling flight above the trees, so that the tendency shown in the greenfinch has here been taken even further.

Greenfinch – *Chloris chloris*

The greenfinch is found all over Britain and though not local in its distribution like the hawfinch, is nowhere really abundant. It likes scattered trees rather than closed woods, but prefers taller ones than the hawfinch. As a song post especially it likes trees of 40 feet or more. The song is also given in quite long horizontal flights from the top of one tree to another, a habit which is incipient in the chaffinch. In winter it tends to flock, and feeds much more on seeds of short vegetation than does the hawfinch.

Hawfinch – *Coccothraustes coccothraustes*

The hawfinch is said to be found in woods, including, on the Continent, coniferous ones, but all that I have seen have been in ecotones of one sort or another—land with scattered hawthorns, orchards, or large gardens. This agrees fairly well with the experience of Mountfort (1957), who describes its British habitat as country with mixed woods, orchards, and hedges; he further says that it is commonest in hilly country and on the belt of chalk that runs from Berkshire to East Anglia and on the Liassic area of the Severn valley, and records it as breeding at altitudes of more than 1,000 feet in Westmorland and Yorkshire. Although it is very local, it is generally distributed over England and Wales and has extended into Scotland as far as Perthshire in the present century.

Its chief food is relatively large seeds, such as those of whitethorn, yew, and cherry, and its presence in woods or elsewhere probably depends on the presence of some of the appropriate trees. Its appearance in some woods has been said to be partly dependent on the crop of hornbeam seeds. It eats not the whole seed, but the kernel only, first splitting the shell neatly into two by means of its enlarged jaw-muscles. Sometimes it takes the seeds off the trees but more often it feeds on the ground. In doing this it shows a commensalism with thrushes, which feed in the trees, eating only the soft fleshy parts of the haws or other fruit, while the hawfinches wait below and eat the seeds that the thrushes drop. The neatly-split shells under the trees are often a useful indication of the presence of hawfinches in a district. Softer fruits such as garden peas and in summer buds and shoots are also eaten, while the young, like those of other finches, are fed on insects, especially caterpillars.

The hawfinch has little territorial behaviour and the song is weak. Various authors have described it in terms which do not agree, some saying that it is musical and others not, so that there is probably more than one type. All the songs that I have heard, given usually from the top twig of a hawthorn but occasionally during a short flight from bush to bush, consisted of a succession of clicking notes, rather like the normal call-note, but with variations, 'tic, toc, tak', etc.

Chaffinch – *Fringilla coelebs*

The chaffinch is the most widely distributed of our woodland birds, being found all over Great Britain (and in fact over the whole of Europe and parts of Asia and North Africa) and in every sort of woodland and in most woodland ecotones. It is equally at home in highland birchwoods, in pedunculate oakwoods with thick hazel, in beechwoods on the chalk with no shrubs at all, and in town gardens. With this wide range it is difficult to decide what may have been the chaffinch's original home, but there is one clue which may have a meaning: it usually covers the outside of its nest with lichens. This could be a mere artistic exercise, done to please or stimulate the cock (for the hen alone builds), just as the bower-birds collect leaves, but this explanation should not be used if a simpler one is available. In the fell-woods the branches of all the trees are themselves covered with lichen, and in this habitat—and in this only—the nest is cryptically coloured, so much so that I have put my hand on a nest without knowing that it was there (Plate XII). The inference is that the chaffinch's nest, and so presumably the chaffinch, was evolved in the marginal woods. It probably became successful for other reasons—a tough constitution, versatility of food and so on—and it is not surprising that a tough bird, used to the mountains, should be able to spread widely given the psychological ability to choose habitats of many different sorts. There is some evidence that the outside decoration of the nest is varied slightly to suit the environment, which is confirmatory evidence that it is protective. The present densities of the bird suggest that the woods of oak rather than of birch are more favourable to it.

The fact that in winter the chaffinch leaves most woods—probably all except those with beech or hornbeam unless artificial sources of food are present—has been discussed on pages 4–5. Many of our winter flocks consist of birds from the Continent, and in recent years much attention has been paid to the migration. There is a general south-west or west-south-west movement on a broad front from Scandinavia to Germany, and then on to France and Spain. Some birds on reaching the coast fly out over the sea, especially where, as in Holland, the coast turns south. It is some of these which arrive here. It has been remarked for a long time that many of the winter flocks are predominantly or wholly of one sex or the other—Linnaeus took the bird's trivial name of *coelebs*, meaning bachelor, from this—but there is much variation and no certain explanation of the phenomenon. The numbers of the two sexes trapped show an excess of cocks in winter in Scandinavia, Holland, and England, but this by itself might only mean that the hens are more wary of taking the bait; some series of counts of flocks suggest that it is a real difference, and more information on this would be helpful. There are some old and general Irish figures which suggest an excess of hens, and the Heligoland trapping results show the same. The sex-ratio in summer in Finland and Holland is 54 per cent. males, which is nearly equality, so that it has been suggested that the hens migrate earlier and further and in particular cross the sea more readily. In the absence of information from France and Spain, and of better figures from Ireland, I do not think that this can be taken as proved. An alternative explanation would be that the hens have a higher death-rate earlier in the winter.

In England the flight lines of migrating chaffinches, like those of many other birds, are often canalized by hills or other physical features into narrow channels, mostly running west or south-west. Hendy found that many of his ringed birds in Somerset disappeared in winter but that they often returned to the garden in severe weather, suggesting that they had not moved far away. One cock and hen paired three years running, although the hen was absent one winter from November to February.

Brambling – *Fringilla montifringilla*

Something has been said of the distribution of this winter visitor on page 195. When it is not feeding in stackyards or on agricultural land it is especially associated with beechwoods.

Crossbill – *Loxia curvirostra*

The distribution of the crossbill has been discussed on page 180. It seems unlikely that such a conspicuous and striking bird would have gone unobserved, especially as it was well known as a winter visitor, so it seems likely that the Scotch breeding population was established not long before it was first recorded. This would mean that subspeciation has taken place rather more quickly than it is usually supposed to do, but when the figures for the two races given in the *Handbook* are examined I do not think that this objection appears very strong. Ten specimens of the Scottish form had a bill-length ranging from 17 to 21 mm. and a depth of 12 to 14·5 mm., while twenty specimens of the continental form (whether from England or abroad is not stated) ranged in length from 16·5 to

20 mm. and in depth from 10·5 to 12 mm. Since Macgillivray records a range for the continental form of 13 to 22 mm. in length and 9·5 to 14·5 mm. in depth, there is clearly complete overlap. The differences in wing lengths given in the *Handbook* are even less. If there are differences in average size between the Scotch and European forms they are no more than could be produced by an accident of the ancestors of the Scottish form, possibly few in number, having slightly larger beaks than the average, or by slight differences in food or other conditions of the environment.

Whatever may be their origin, the Scottish crossbills are found chiefly in the old pine forests, but also live in plantations of spruce and larch; the English nesting birds live in whatever plantations are available, which also happen to be, in Norfolk, mainly Scotch fir. On the Continent spruce is apparently the favoured tree and was largely frequented in England in the invasion of 1956–7. There can be no doubt that the crossbill is a bird of the taiga, outside which it seldom breeds. In the winter it visits other habitats and in its periodical invasions of this country it has more than once been described as a pest of apple orchards, tearing open the fruit and eating the pips.

The striking parrot-like habit of feeding on fir-cones has often been described, but the tropical red colouring of the cock in the sunlight is equally notable. In the young bird the tips of the two halves of the beak meet, but as the bird grows they cross, sometimes to one side, sometimes to the other. This asymmetry is accompanied by a corresponding asymmetry of the jaw muscles, which is such that when the mouth is open the tips come together again. In this position, when the bill is at its narrowest, it is pushed between the scales of a fir cone. The mouth is then partially shut, an action which crosses the tips of the bill and so forces the scales apart. The seed so revealed is picked up by the tongue, which has a horny tip. To be quite fair, since I have not personally studied the matter, I should add that according to a Russian author the cones are opened by a sideways movement of the lower jaw and the crossed bill has no special significance in feeding.

The *Handbook* says that Scotch fir and larch cones are usually torn off and held in one foot while being attacked, while the larger cones of spruce are dealt with on the trees, but this is not an absolute distinction. Of a pair which I watched in Glenmore Forest in 1952 the hen consistently pulled the Scotch fir cones off and held them down to a branch with her left foot, and the cock extracted the seeds while the cones were still on the trees.

Bullfinch – *Pyrrhula pyrrhula*

The bullfinch is found all over Great Britain, and has possibly extended in recent years to parts of Scotland where it was not known before. It is found in woods of many different types, yew-woods, plantations of Scotch fir and larch, beechwoods, ashwoods, and both types of oakwood. I have no summer records from birchwoods. It is found also in the woodland ecotone, especially perhaps in grass with scattered scrub trees of hawthorn and similar trees, and above all in orchards and gardens with fruit trees. In the Midlands it is commonest as a breeding bird in the fruit-growing districts of Worcestershire and Warwickshire. It is much less common in these counties on the land more than 400 feet above sea level, and in all the more industrialized areas.

It wanders in winter, or at least is conspicuous in places where it is not seen in summer. Sometimes the winter birds are in small flocks of about half a dozen, perhaps more often in pairs, suggesting that they pair for life. These winter parties feed on seeds of various kinds and often pick them up from the ground under trees. They feed also in the canopy of both birch and oakwoods; presumably in the last place they must be feeding not on seeds but on buds, with or without parasitic insects. At this time of year I have seen them well above 1,000 feet both in the Lake District and on Exmoor, and indeed they seem to me to be commoner at this altitude than lower down. Hendy (1943) says that he has seen them on Exmoor feeding on the seeds of ling in light snow at 1,200 feet. Many of the Lake District winter birds appear an unusually bright pink, so that they *may* be immigrants from abroad, since the continental subspecies has this characteristic.

LANIIDAE – SHRIKES

The shrikes are an Old-World family, with few species in North America. All the species of the genus *Lanius* live where there are scattered trees and bushes, and have a tendency to prefer dry places.

Red-backed Shrike – *Lanius collurio*

The red-backed shrike is found over most of England and Wales but thins out in the northern counties, and there are no certain Scottish breeding records. Within this area it is very local and seems to have decreased in the last fifty years. It likes places with scattered trees or bushes and must have thorns on which to impale its prey. It seems to prefer sunny banks and warm areas such as railway cuttings and it has been suggested that its European distribution is directly related to climate, since it is commonest in the warm, dry parts of its range and absent from many parts with a damp Atlantic climate. Where it is in competition with the woodchat shrike (*Lanius senator*) it prefers a thick field layer, but in England, where the woodchat shrike does not occur, this is unimportant. The type of country that it likes must have been of very limited occurrence under natural conditions, but now the clearance of woods and abandonment of pasture give rise to scattered hawthorns in grass, and in England thorn hedges give it a reasonable substitute.

The habit of impaling large insects and small vertebrates on thorns to make a larder to which the bird returns is common to all members of the genus. Owen (1948) finds that each pair of red-backed shrikes has up to six such larders and that these may be as far as 150 yards from the nest, though usually nearer. The larder appears to have an aesthetic as well as an economic purpose, for the faeces and pellets of the young and hatched egg shells are often hung up as well as food.

MOTACILLIDAE – WAGTAILS AND PIPITS

This, one of the most cosmopolitan families of passerine birds, is fairly clearly divided, at least in the field, into the wagtails, which on the whole frequent the edges of running or standing waters, and the more lark-like pipits, which have a wider ecological distribution with a general tendency towards open country.

Meadow-Pipit – *Anthus pratensis*

The meadow-pipit is a bird of open country, including the moors and mountain tops where there are no bushes, but it perches on shrubs when these are present, and where open woods are dispersed in its usual habitat it enters these and perches freely on trees.

I have found it on the hills in woods of both species of oak, of alder and birch, and in various mixed woods. It is a fairly common bird of birch scrub in Lapland. In all these places it overlaps with the tree-pipit, and great care is needed to distinguish the two birds, their songs and the long hind-claw of the meadow-pipit (which can be seen only rarely) being the only reliable characters. I have no records of it actually nesting in woods in Britain but it does so in Lapland. It persists in small numbers in coniferous plantations until they are brashed, here also overlapping with the tree-pipit.

Tree-Pipit – *Anthus trivialis*

The tree-pipit is now found over almost the whole of Great Britain, including Sutherland where it is the third commonest bird in the birchwoods, but this has only come about through a great extension of its range in the past seventy-five years (see page 219). I found one bird in the Langwell Woods in Caithness in June 1952. That the tree-pipit nests in woods was stated by Dresser over half a century ago but since then its habitat has been frequently and misleadingly given as being one of scattered trees, for though it does occur in ecotones, whether in park-like conditions or in hedgerows, it is most characteristically in the west and north a bird of closed woodlands, provided there is not a thick shrub layer. Sessile oak, birch, ash, and Scotch fir seem equally acceptable to it, and it occurs also in a few pedunculate oakwoods. It reaches a higher density in many durmast oak and upland woods than I have ever found in the ecotone habitat, and I have no doubt that these were its original home. In the high-forest oakwood of Wyre before the underplanted beech grew up, it was second only to the chaffinch in line-transect scores. It does not demand any great height of tree, and may be found in numbers in scrub birches not more than 24 feet high as well as in mature oaks or firs of 50 or 60 feet. Few trees in Wistman's Wood, where one or two pairs seem to be regularly established, are more than 12 feet high, and it occupies coniferous plantations as soon as the trees show above the grass or heather at a height of 2 or 3 feet. On the other hand its absence from nearly all woods in the Midlands, east and south of England is very striking. It is present but scarce in Epping Forest. I have one record from a Sussex oakwood, but none from beechwoods where its absence is probably due to the absence of a field layer, for the tree-pipit declines rapidly in coniferous plantations when the thicket stage is reached.

In my records it has a correlation (see page 21) of 1·62 with the pied flycatcher. On the hills, the tree-pipit ascends as high as the woods, that is to more than 1,000 feet in semi-natural woods in England and Wales, to nearly 2,000 feet in Scotland, and to the highest coniferous planting at 2,200 feet in South Wales. Its hedgerow distribution seems to be very patchy; in some districts the bird is common, in others never seen, but I have no means of accounting for this.

Wagtails – *Motacilla*

I have occasionally recorded all three species of wagtails—pied (*Motacilla alba*), grey (*M. cinerea*), and yellow (*M. flava*)—inside woods, but though the pied wagtail sometimes makes its nest in trees such as old willows, only the grey wagtail has any regular connexion with them. Its home is fast-flowing, but not cascading, streams in hilly country, and as these are often, and in natural conditions were probably almost always, surrounded and overhung by trees, it must be looked on as a bird of the woodland-stream ecotone. It frequently perches on trees.

MUSCICAPIDAE – FLYCATCHERS

The flycatchers are found over most of the Old World, and have their headquarters in the hotter parts. They are generally woodland birds but their method of feeding, almost exclusively by catching single flies on the wing, demands a certain amount of open space under the trees.

Pied Flycatcher – *Muscicapa hypoleuca*

The distribution of the pied flycatcher has been discussed on pages 190–92. Thanks to the inquiry which was carried out by Campbell (1954–5) we have a better list of the habitats of the pied flycatcher than for any other species. Although it is fairly often found in birches and alders, and was recorded once, in the North York Moors, in beech, and a few times in man-made habitats, the predominant home is the sessile oakwoods. This is so over the whole of its range, from Devon to the Scottish borders. Only in Scotland was it recorded in a coniferous wood, a larch plantation, and that was unnatural in that it had been provided with nest-boxes. In late May 1960 a bird was singing in a small group of old larches in Cumberland, but I was unable to find the nest. The ecological distribution thus confirms in a very striking way the geographical distribution. Whatever may be the reason underlying it, the pied flycatcher is a bird of sessile oakwoods, and is only secondarily found elsewhere. My own impression is that its next commonest habitat is the ecotone of scattered trees, often alders, but usually with birch, oak, and rowan as well, which often line the banks of rivers within its range. It is probably this which has led to the oft-repeated statement that it is found near water. In the oakwoods themselves, which are often on dry hillsides, it is indifferent to the presence of streams.

Campbell sums up the requirements as food supplies, cover, nest sites and nesting material, and perches for song and feeding-sallies, and says that these are given by woods with a general absence or sparseness of a shrub layer, coupled with bare, grassy, or bracken-dominated areas of field layer in most favoured habitats. I would differ from this assessment on two points. Cover is of little importance, since where the bird has spread into man-made habitats such as the neighbourhood of Lake District farms which it has occupied for at least sixty years, it lives very much in the open. The same is true of the hillside ecotones. Secondly, its greatest density both in the Lake District and in Wales is above the limit of bracken, and the chief plants of the field layer are grasses, mosses, and bilberry.

The pied flycatcher has high correlations (page 21) as follows: with the tree-pipit 1·62, with the coal-tit 1·55, and with the wood-warbler 1·62.

The song of the pied flycatcher is very varied, and very deceptive. Sometimes it is unmistakable and at others almost indistinguishable from that of the redstart. Song-like phrases are often used as call-notes. A female at a nest-hole in the Lake District repeatedly called 'tweet-tweet, tui-tui'.

Spotted Flycatcher – *Muscicapa striata*

I have no personal records of the spotted flycatcher in any lowland woods, but Lack and Venables' lists show it in a very few, of oak, beech, birch, and Corsican pine. In the hill-woods, on the other hand, though not common, it occurs regularly in sessile and pedunculate oak, ash, birch, and alder, from Devonshire to Sutherland. In some of these it lives alongside the pied flycatcher and the territories of breeding birds of the two species seem to overlap without producing any friction. In these fell-woods it ranges up to 1,200 feet above sea level. In the lowlands it is a bird of man-made habitats, especially parks and large gardens, and seems to like being near houses. Smith (1952) found that of 197 nests 60 per cent. were against walls, mainly in creepers or shrubs, but these were presumably mostly garden nests. Forty-two per cent. were in holes in trees or in ivy, and this sort of situation is probably the natural one. White (1953) found that in feeding on butterflies the spotted flycatcher was selective, catching the peacock (*Nymphalis io*) and some of the browns (*Satyridae*) and whites (*Pieridae*), and ignoring red admirals (*Vanessa atalanta*), commas (*Polygonia c-album*), and the common blue (*Polyommatus icarus*).

PARIDAE – TITMICE OR TITS

The titmice are found all over the world except for South America and Malaysia and the islands beyond, but are most abundant in the temperate regions, and almost all are woodland birds, the exceptions living in woodland ecotones. The only 'tit' of the British species which does not live in woods, the bearded tit, *Panurus biarmicus*, is now generally placed by zoologists in a separate family.

The tits are the most characteristic birds of the British woods, conspicuous, talkative, and social, and resident or only partially migratory. Mostly microphagous, that is feeding on very small particles, they are very efficient at getting a living even under apparently poor conditions, and between them exploit almost all the situations in the woods. They have been the subject of intense study in the last few years, notably at the Edward Grey Institute, and we know for some of the species living in the neighbourhood of Oxford what they eat, where they get it, how many eggs they lay, what they weigh, both before and after a meal, and many other details of their life. Some of this work has been referred to in Chapter 1 (the life of the blue tit) and Chapter 11 (the flocking habit) and will not be mentioned in detail again. The pattern of the blue tit's life is characteristic of the group as a whole, and although there are specific differences, they are rather differences between averages than clear-cut distinctions. In almost everything, habitat, food, preferred feeding station and so on, there is considerable overlap. It is remarkable that in spite of their social winter life, most, and possibly all, tits pair for life.

Coal-Tit – *Parus ater*

The coal-tit is found all over Great Britain except for some of the islands. It is generally said to be a bird of coniferous woods but this is only true with much qualification. It is much less common in pedunculate oakwoods, ashwoods, and in English and Welsh birchwoods than is either the great or the blue tit, and I have no records from beechwoods, but in the high-level sessile oakwoods of the west and north there are more coal-tits than members of the other two species added together, and the same is nearly true of lowland sessile oak and of the Ross and Sutherland birchwoods. On Speyside the coal-tit is present in the birchwoods as well as the firwoods, and is as common in the former as is the blue tit. It is present in the Sussex yew-woods and colonizes coniferous plantations as soon as they reach the thicket stage. It is also found in deciduous woods in other parts of its range, and according to Turček (1952) is confined to beech at about 4,000 feet in Czechoslovakia although spruce is present.

Hinde says of the coal-tit that it nests on the ground because it lives in coniferous woods where natural holes in trees are scarce, but it seems to me that the opposite is as likely to be true. It is a ground-nester and so requires woodland where there is not too thick a field layer, so that holes under rocks or at the roots of trees are not obscured. These conditions are more often provided in the south of England in coniferous plantations than elsewhere, but in the rocky north and west equally good conditions are provided in the oak and birchwoods, and the coal-tit uses them. Its preference for conifers is thus more apparent than real, and is made to look stronger by the fact that the blue and great tit do avoid these trees—perhaps because they provide fewer nesting sites. The only previous writer, so far as I know, who has not held the conifer-theory of coal-tits is Wilson (1933) who writes of Westmorland: 'The resident cole tits frequent the hardwoods in summer for nesting; these trees afford better nesting places.' In my records the coal-tit has a correlation (page 21) of 1·55 with the pied flycatcher.

It is generally agreed that in winter the coal-tit ranges more widely, and Wilson says that it then goes to the plantations of spruce and Scotch fir. It scores very highly in my winter lists for spruce, with a relative abundance of 25 per cent. in the thicket stage and 35 per cent. in brashed trees. It is probably less often seen in hedges than either blue or great tits. Hartley found at Wytham that it preferred feeding in conifers, but this might be only because his birds had been bred amongst them. It fed at a high level in spring and summer, but dropped to lower levels in autumn and winter. I have often seen coal-tits clinging to the main trunk of a tree, usually fairly low down, and even climbing a little, somewhat like a nuthatch. This habit is rare in other tits.

The presence of coal-tits in a wood can often be picked up by the penetrating call which is generally a single note, quite unlike that of any other tits.

I have observed in England a number of birds which resemble the Irish subspecies (*P. a. hibernicus*), but they do not correspond with it in detail. My records are:

1. Cumberland 23.5.49. One member of a pair singing and holding territory; whole of breast bright yellow.
2. Worcestershire 23.1.53. In flock, distinctly yellowish underparts.
3. Worcestershire 7.10.53. In flock, yellowish-buff breast.
4. Worcestershire 5.4.54. With two long-tailed tits, yellowish breast, but nape-spot white.
5. Worcestershire 22.10.55. Yellow breast, cream nape-spot.
6. Westmorland 3.9.57. Yellow breast.
7. Shropshire 12.5.59. One of a pair, carrying feather, bright yellow breast; other member of the pair yellow but not so bright.
8. Worcestershire 17.6.59. Slightly yellow breast.

The second, third, and fifth of these might be birds of the year in which the moult had been delayed, but this is unlikely, and numbers 1 and 7 were certainly breeding. Further information on the occurrence and distribution of yellow coal-tits would be interesting. Of two coal-tits that I saw in County Mayo in September 1959 one had a trace of yellow on the breast, the other none.

Blue Tit – *Parus coeruleus*

Like the great tit, the blue tit is found all over Great Britain except for some of the Scottish islands, but my records for all types of deciduous wood except pedunculate oak and English and Welsh birch show it to be rather less abundant. It is also widely distributed ecologically and is about equally common in all types of deciduous woods. I have no record from either the South Down yew-woods or the Speyside firwoods, but it is present in the firwoods of Ross. It is as rare in English coniferous plantations as is the great tit, but is more frequently seen in gardens and perhaps more often in hedges. All this suggests that there might be some competition between the two species, but my records give no indication that the presence of one excludes the other, as the correlation between them (page 21) is relatively high at 1·43. Gibb found that at Wytham the blue tits preferred the more open parts of the oakwood, and Hartley that they fed more often in oaks than in other trees. They had a wide feeding range; in the winter they were found at all heights from the shrubs to the canopy but in summer the canopy was deserted. They fed on the ground only when there was an abundant nut harvest, and their favourite stations were the leaves and smaller twigs.

Blue tits correlate highly with redstarts (1·62) and song-thrushes (1·53).

Crested Tit – *Parus cristatus*

The crested tit has a very limited distribution which has been fully described by Campbell (1958); it is nowhere common but is best known in the old firwoods of Speyside, where it occurs up to the timberline at 1,700 feet; from there it has spread out widely but thinly in the present century, especially to the north, to Findhorn and the Beauly Firth; but also to the east, to the valley of the Dee, and west or north-west to Ross. It is apparently now found exclusively in well-grown Scotch firwoods, though it may nest in stumps of deciduous trees such as birch and alder when these are present, and even in fencing posts. Two statements in the 4th edition of Yarrell's *British Birds* on its distribution seem to have been overlooked, both by ornithologists and plant ecologists. They are: 'Mr. Gray informs the Editor that the very old timber, consisting chiefly of Scotch firs and oaks, in this forest, the name of which is more correctly spelt Glenmore, was cut down towards the end of the last century'; and, 'Hoy furnished this work with the information that, according to his experience, it [the crested tit] seems partial to woods where firs and oaks are mixed, the holes in the oaks generally serving it for its nests.' The last quotation apparently refers to continental birds, which are now separated as a distinct subspecies, but taken in conjunction with Gray's statement it may mean that the thin distribution of the crested tit, and its slow rate of spread even now that much of Scotland is covered with well-grown coniferous plantations, are caused by the absence of this particular combination of trees. If Gray's statement is correct, and I see no reason why it should be doubted, botanists must revise their ideas on the natural state of the Speyside forests. At present there are many well-grown and apparently natural oaks along the banks of the Spey itself, but none in the forests. If they were formerly mixed with the firs in the lower parts of what are now the forests of Rothiemurchus, Glenmore, and Abernethy, these would resemble much more than they now do what is known of the natural state of other Scottish valleys.

Great Tit – *Parus major*

The great tit is found throughout Britain except for some of the islands, and has extended its range in the north of Scotland in the last fifty years or so. In England it is found in woods of all the main types, both species of oak, ash, beech, birch, and yew, but is rare in coniferous plantations, except where these are provided with nest-boxes. Possibly, in view of the fact that it prefers to feed low, in bushes rather than in trees, its distribution is determined by the presence or absence of shrubs, rather than directly by the dominant species of tree. This agrees with Gibb's observation, in the somewhat artificial conditions of Wytham, with nest-boxes at two per acre, that the great tits preferred the area of coppice, although this was less marked in a year when the population was high. It is found in a few only of the hill-woods, of whatever species, and is especially rare in them in winter. Most of the Scottish woods for which I have information are birch, and in these, as in the nearest corresponding English woods, it is present but not common. I have no records of it in the Speyside Scotch firwoods, but I have seen it in those of Ross. In England it extends out of the woods into hedges and to some extent into gardens.

The great tit correlates highly with the song-thrush (1·59).

In his study of the feeding habits of titmice Hartley found that the great tit mostly fed on the ground in winter, went to the trees for caterpillars in early summer, to the lower woodland foliage in high summer, and in the autumn fed high or low according to the supplies of food. He decided that of the trees available to it, sycamore was the favourite.

Willow-Tit – *Parus montanus*

The willow-tit is not now regarded as conspecific with the North American chickadee, so that its specific name is no longer *atricapillus* but *montanus*. It has a patchy distribution in England and Wales, and occurs in Scotland, but rarely so far north as Ross. I have not enough records to say anything of its ecological distribution, but as it makes its own nest-hole it needs places where there is rotten or soft wood; it is said to be fond of birch for this purpose, but it is certainly not a bird of the birchwoods as such. It may occur in the same districts, and even the same woods, as the marsh-tit, where the habitats of the two cannot be separated, but in other areas one species seems to replace the other. It is present, but rare, in the Speyside firwoods, and Gibb (1960) found it much commoner than the marsh-tit in the Breckland pine plantations.

The light patch on the wing, given in the books as a distinction from the marsh-tit, is not, in the field, a good character. Of a pair of birds in Worcestershire which were both, by their voice and only slightly glossy black caps, willow-tits, one had a patch clearly visible on the left wing, while the other bird, which was seen just as clearly, showed none. On another occasion of two birds at a nest, both, by voice and glossy caps, marsh-tits, one had a bar on one wing but not on the other.

Marsh-Tit – *Parus palustris*

The marsh-tit is found over most of England and Wales, though it is rare in places and its distribution is patchy, but it is probably absent from Scotland except for Berwickshire, where there are several pairs, and Roxburgh and East Lothian. It is found with some frequency in pedunculate oak, beech, and ashwoods, but it is rare in sessile oakwoods, especially those of the hills, and I have only one record for birch. It is also rare in coniferous plantations. Hartley found that it liked elders and that throughout the year it fed in the shrub layer and on the lowest limbs of big trees. This does not entirely agree with my experience of it in Wyre Forest, where in late autumn it feeds very conspicuously on the buds in the canopy of the sessile oaks. It attacks these vigorously, tearing them to pieces and dropping the bits, whereas the blue tit, feeding in the same place, pecks at the buds but does not tear or drop them. On a still frosty morning the presence of a marsh-tit can often be detected by the sound of its destruction of the buds.

Marsh-tits have long been known to pair for life, and the pairs keep together and hold territory throughout the year, only separating for roosting, when the two birds may, according to Morley (1953), use holes as much as 50 yards apart. The paired birds may join flocks of other tits that pass through their territory, but do not go beyond it. Young birds live in the mixed flocks like the other species.

PRUNELLIDAE - ACCENTORS

This is a small family found in northern Europe and Asia, whose species live mostly in woodland ecotones or in the Arctic-Alpine zone.

Hedge-Sparrow or Dunnock - *Prunella modularis*

The dunnock is found all over Great Britain. The only woods in which it is at all common are those of pedunculate oak, but it occurs also in beechwoods with a shrub layer; it is very rare in sessile oakwoods and birchwoods, and I have no records from ash. It occurs in the natural yew-woods of Sussex, in the firwoods of Speyside and Ross, and in a high proportion of coniferous plantations at the thicket stage, but it is never present at high density. Most birds leave the plantations in winter, and all after brashing. Brown and Buckley connect it particularly with juniper in Scotland. It clearly needs shrubs or thick cover but its relative scarcity in the pedunculate oakwoods suggests that it is limited by something else as well. Its food is mainly animal matter in summer and seeds in winter, and its attraction to the neighbourhood of man—it is fairly common in hedgerows and gardens—suggests that it may be restricted by food supply, particularly in winter.

REGULIDAE – GOLDCRESTS

The goldcrests are hardly different in their structure from the leaf-warblers of the genus *Phylloscopus*, but differ from them in being more tit-like in habits and in not being regularly migratory. They are found in woods all round the northern hemisphere in temperate and arctic regions. They may be looked on as leaf-warblers which have become adapted to a cold climate.

Goldcrest – *Regulus regulus*

The goldcrest is found over almost the whole of Great Britain but is severely limited by its breeding requirements. Its nest is built almost always in conifers, usually attached beneath a branch. Before the planting of the eighteenth century it must have been confined to the ancient fir forests of the north, to the yew-woods of the South Downs and a few other places, and to those deciduous woods which contain scattered yews, such as many sessile oakwoods of the Welsh border counties and some ashwoods and beechwoods. In the first three of these it is still found, but I have no records from ashwoods and beechwoods. Since it lives in woods rather than scrub it can make little use of juniper, though according to Baxter and Rintoul it often nests in this in Scotland where the juniper sometimes makes a shrub layer under the pines. Out of the breeding season it ranges more widely, especially in the oakwoods which are near its nesting places, but it is rare in the hill oakwoods. I have a record from only one birchwood, which contains much oak.

It begins to come into coniferous plantations before they are 6 feet high, and in the thicket stage is third in abundance after the willow-warbler and chaffinch, going to first place after brashing. Its density remains high in winter, with a relative abundance of 23 per cent. for the thicket stage of spruce, and 29 per cent. after brashing.

The normal song consists of a repetition of a very high-pitched note, with a four-note cadence, but the cadence is sometimes varied; it may consist of three high notes or of a single one. I have heard the normal song alternating with a more warbling type, something like the cadence of the usual one repeated and varied, and reminiscent of a sedge-warbler.

The goldcrest usually searches leaves and bark for food just as do the titmice, but I have seen one hovering at a leaf in the manner of a willow-warbler.

SITTIDAE – NUTHATCHES

The nuthatches have a very similar distribution, both geographical and ecological, to the treecreepers, whose habits they parallel to some extent.

Nuthatch – *Sitta europaea*

The distribution of the nuthatch has been discussed on page 184. In England and Wales it is found in some of the highest woods at over 1,000 feet. It has lately shown some signs of increasing and spreading in the north-west, having bred in Lancashire in 1945 and probably 1946, and the north-Yorkshire colony has also enlarged its area and overflowed into County Durham, where the species bred in the early nineteenth century and then became extinct. Some continental authors say that it is a bird of the oakwood, and its northern limit in Scandinavia is the same as that of the oak. Most of my woodland records are for oak, with neither species being favoured, and I have some also for beech and mixed woods. In park conditions, where it is equally common, elm is most often frequented.

The nuthatch normally feeds by running over the bark of trees, usually the larger branches and the canopy rather than the main trunk as does a treecreeper, but I have also seen it on old walls and on the ground, feeding amongst leaves like a tit, and catching flies on the wing. It is unique amongst British birds in having three distinct forms of utterance which appear to be songs. The commonest is probably a very loud 'pee-pee-pee-pee-pee', and the next in frequency a more musical version of the same rhythm, which has been likened to part of a thrush's song. The least common is a trilling whistle, usually of 7 to 10 notes, and often with a pause after the first 3 or 4. There is much variation in all these and I once heard the second variety so modified as to sound like a broken attempt at the song of a chaffinch. As well as the usual whistled call-note it has a less-common repeated tit-like squeak.

STURNIDAE – STARLINGS

The Sturnidae are an Old-World group, reaching America only as occasional visitors to Greenland, and are most numerous in the tropics; the headquarters of the most typical starlings is India, and only three species reach western Europe. All are birds of trees, but they feed on the ground and there is a general tendency for them to become terrestrial. Most nest in holes.

Starling – *Sturnus vulgaris*

The distribution of the starling has been discussed on pages 178–80. As a woodland-breeder it seems to prefer ash and perhaps pedunculate oak, but probably the majority of our birds now breed in or around houses.

The starling carries to an extreme the habit of communal roosting. The usual assemblies contain several thousand birds, many of which fly in from several miles away, the greatest distance recorded being about 30 miles. In the winter of 1932–3 Marples (1934) was able to record 224 roosts in England, his lower limit of size being an estimated 500 birds. They were fairly evenly distributed, but almost all were less than 600 feet above sea level. This agrees with the opinions of several observers that in their flight lines to the roosts the birds avoid passing over hills. Many of the roosts are stable and are used year after year, but others last only for a season or so, and some only for one or a few nights. Sometimes the abandonment of a roost is caused by persecution, but at others the birds desert for no obvious reason. A wide variety of trees and shrubs is used, but Marples found the most popular type to be reeds. This suggests that the original home of the starling might be river valleys, which in the steppes would provide the combination of trees and grass that it needs.

From time to time starlings make a nuisance of themselves by leaving the trees and roosting on buildings in towns. The roost in the West End of London was first mentioned in 1894 but it only became important some time between 1910 and 1920 and is still in existence. The Birmingham roost began in a small way in 1924, but the present large numbers did not come until the early 1940s. Other less well-known town roosts, usually of shorter duration, have occurred in Dublin, Belfast, Glasgow, Leeds, Huddersfield, and Bristol. No systematic investigation of the types of buildings which are favoured has been made, but the classical style seems more popular than Gothic. Paty's Christchurch in Bristol, Gibbs's St. Martin-in-the-Fields, and Archer's Birmingham Cathedral have all been popular, and so have many other city buildings of a vaguely Renaissance type. These all have horizontal ledges on which the birds sit, but in the natural roosts they often cling to near-vertical branches. At times starlings use quite modern structures; they have used power-station condensers and cranes, and for one season in Birmingham sat in rows on tubular steel scaffolding surrounding a building that was being restored.

The time of assembly is about sunset and the arrival of large numbers of birds over the roost is a strange and noisy spectacle. Brown (1946) found that in the autumn the birds began to assemble some time before sunset and took a long time to settle in, but as the days shortened they arrived relatively later and took less time to find their final perches. In December many flocks did not arrive until after sunset, and went straight into the trees. The advantage of this is obviously that the birds are able to spend a greater proportion of the daylight in feeding when it is most necessary for them to do so. The assembly and dispersal of the flocks are visible on radar-screens, dispersal appearing as a series of concentric expanding circles known as ring-angels, each corresponding to the exit of a large group of birds from the roost. The latest study of these is by Eastwood, Isted and Rider (1960). The assembly at some roosts appears as a series of dots converging inwards down a relatively narrow cone, showing that though the birds disperse in all directions they must afterwards concentrate on one side or other of the roost. In addition to these large roosts there are some smaller ones, and some birds never leave the suburbs throughout the year.

For the most part the starling feeds in grassland, and gets its food by digging in the turf. The closed bill is thrust into the soil, and then opened. The bird looks into the hole so made to see if there is anything to eat before the bill is withdrawn. It can do this because the eye is further back than in most birds, and the part of the skull in front of the eye is laterally compressed. The south Pennine moors are regularly visited by flocks of starlings, mostly birds of the year, in June and July; cotton-grass (*Eriophorum*), mat-grass, and wavy hair-grass (*Deschampsia flexuosa*) are all popular. At times starlings feed in other ways, taking for instance caterpillars from trees, and ripe fruit, especially pears. Like rooks, they are as nearly as possible omnivores, but a high proportion of their food consists of leather-jackets.

SYLVIIDAE – WARBLERS

The warblers are small birds, of dull colouring and usually of a pleasant voice. Only two genera are of importance in the British woodland fauna. The leaf-warblers *Phylloscopus* are small and usually greenish and with a simple song. There are many species in the Old World, with a very heavy concentration in Kashmir and some of the other mountainous parts of Central Asia, and most of them live in marginal woodlands or woodland ecotones and some in closed woodlands. They nest nearly always on or near the ground. Warblers of the genus *Sylvia* are larger and brownish, with a more developed song, and also live in woodland ecotones rather than woods, in Europe and Asia.

Grasshopper-Warbler – *Locustella naevia*

The grasshopper-warbler is very local, but is found over most of Britain as far north as the Great Glen. It is hardly a woodland bird, since it lives on heaths with scattered bushes and even a single shrub seems to be enough for it. I have seen it at 1,300 feet on Exmoor and Evans records it at 1,500 feet in the Cheviots, but it is noticeably absent from the Lake District fells.

It comes into coniferous plantations in their young stages and increases to a maximum during the early thicket stage or just before. Even in these it is local, as, though it is common in some Cumberland and Staffordshire forests, I have failed to find it in apparently suitable plantations in Radnorshire and Devon.

Chiff-Chaff – *Phylloscopus collybita*

The chiff-chaff is found over the whole of England and Wales, but while in some areas it is common, in others it is scarce, and it is absent from some apparently suitable places. It has recently extended its range in Scotland: it breeds in some of the lowland counties and there are scattered summer records further north, including one in 1952 for Sutherland. It seems deterred by the Scottish climate much more than the willow-warbler and the wood-warbler, which is rather odd in that it is the only warbler which with any regularity winters with us, which it does most years in the south of England. Its dependence on rhododendrons in its spread into Scotland has been noted on page 215. Its ecological distribution I find difficult to assess. It does not appear common in any of the woodland lists; it is in more than a quarter of the pedunculate oakwoods and of the beechwoods, but is absent from all the latter which are without shrubs. I have records also from a few birchwoods and lowland sessile oakwoods, and from yew. It comes into coniferous plantations in the thicket stage in fair numbers, and stays after brashing has been carried out. There is no doubt that it is common, in some districts, in hedgerows with lines of trees. It is sometimes said that it is, unlike the willow-warbler, largely dependent on fairly tall trees, but this is certainly not always true; there are far fewer chiff-chaffs than willow-warblers in the mature oaks of Wyre Forest, and the same holds according to Beven of the pedunculate oakwood of Bookham Common in Surrey. A chiff-chaff was singing in June 1953 on the cliff at Polperro in dense blackthorn and gorse scrub only 2½ feet high and where the only taller shrubs within sight were about 10 feet, and in May 1955 several were singing in similar gorse on the cliffs of North Cornwall with no trees in sight. When it first arrives in spring its favourite haunt in Wyre is the young larch plantations, but not the tall trees, and it sings quite happily from these. It is found in spruce plantations up to 1,600 feet above sea level.

Wood-Warbler – *Phylloscopus sibilatrix*

The wood-warbler is now found all over the mainland of Great Britain, but is somewhat local in its distribution. It has spread to the northern limits of suitable woods in Scotland only since the late 1940s. It is found occasionally in woods of pedunculate oak and ash, is moderately common in birch, and is one of the characteristic birds of sessile oakwoods. In the latter it is present both in the lowlands and on the fells up to about 1,200 feet above sea level, but in some of the high-level woods, as in the birchwoods, it is subsidiary in numbers to the willow-warbler. This distribution shows that on the whole it avoids woods with a shrub layer, but its occasional occurrence in birches and scrub oaks is at variance with this, since they largely resemble shrubs in themselves. Price (1950) correlates the disappearance of wood-warblers from an oakwood in Gloucestershire with the growth of brambles, but the numbers are too small for the conclusion to be certain. It has fallen markedly in both absolute and relative abundance in the oaks of Wyre since the under-planted beech became thick.

The wood-warbler's status in beechwoods needs examination. The *Handbook* says that its habitat is 'well-grown woods . . . especially beech and oak', and Yarrell (4th edition) that it prefers 'woods containing tall trees, particularly those of oak or beech', but my records suggest that it is rare in beechwoods, as I have found it in only one out of eight for which I have timed counts. As only one of these eight was on the Chilterns, and that, which held no wood-warblers, was visited rather late in the season, I thought that perhaps the wood-warbler was found in this important group of beechwoods and that the statements in the books were based on its occurrence there, but Mr. R. S. R. Fitter informs me that this is not so, as in six seasons he has only one record of a singing wood-warbler in the Chiltern beechwoods, and no evidence of breeding. It can safely be said that beechwoods are not a characteristic, although they are an occasional, habitat. Perhaps the statements in the books are generalized from Gilbert White, who wrote in Letter 19 to Pennant, in which he clearly distinguished the three species of *Phylloscopus* for the first time, that the wood-warbler 'haunts only the tops of trees in high beechen woods'. But I could not find it in the Selborne Hanger, and I am told that it has become scarce in the neighbourhood of Petersfield during the last thirty years.

The wood-warbler avoids conifers; I have no records of it either in the native firwoods or in the yew-woods, and only a few from larch plantations. Armitt (1897-1901), writing of the Lake District, says that it nests on rocky knolls and is, roughly speaking, dependent on oaks, whether in woods or scattered by the side of a gill. These thin lines of trees that run up by the sides of the Cumberland becks are the only ecotones in which I know the wood-warbler to occur.

The wood-warbler has a correlation (page 21) of 1·62 with the pied flycatcher.

Willow-Warbler – *Phylloscopus trochilus*

The willow-warbler is in every respect the commonest and most widely spread of our leaf-warblers, being found all over Great Britain and almost wherever there are trees or bushes. This ubiquity conceals a marked ecological preference, for it is above all a bird of birches. In the relict woods of Ross and Sutherland the willow-warblers are so dense that any accurate estimate of their numbers is impossible; so many are singing at once that one cannot tell where the territory of one ends and another begins, and they make up about a third of the total number of birds. In the lowlands also, although they are found in woods of all types, including all the native and commonly planted conifers, they are much commoner in birches. They are found in fell-woods of all sorts up to the limit of the trees at 2,000 feet, and in ecotones both natural and artificial. May (1949) found that from the beginning of July the young associate in flocks, often with blue and great tits, which they frequently chase. Like all the leaf-warblers willow-warblers feed chiefly by picking insects off leaves and twigs, sometimes hovering to do so, but I have seen one in April feeding on the ground like a hedge-sparrow. Kuusisto (1941), working in Finland, concluded that the willow-warbler preferred birchwoods because they bore a much higher density of the insect food (especially Coleoptera, Diptera, and Hymenoptera) which it took than do the other habitats available to it.

Blackcap – *Sylvia atricapilla*

The range of the blackcap is almost the same as that of the garden-warbler, but it goes a little further north in Scotland; nevertheless Baxter and Rintoul say that it is the less common of the two species in that country. Its ecological distribution is also, at least in outline, similar, for the only woodland in which it is at all common is pedunculate oakwood, where it is more frequent than the garden-warbler, and it occurs in sessile oakwoods and beechwoods with shrubs. I have one record only for birch, a few from ashwoods on the South Downs with much regenerating scrub, and none for a coniferous plantation. Gibb (1960) records it as breeding in small numbers in the Breckland pine plantations. It occurs also in woodland scrub of a park type, especially, but not exclusively, where there is much scrub of thorns and so on. My impression is that in the west of England this is its most popular habitat. It is not, on our present knowledge, possible to distinguish between the habitats of the blackcap and garden-warbler; their food also appears to be much the same and their songs are sometimes, to a human ear, indistinguishable. It is difficult to believe that they are not in potential competition with each other, except that they are widely spread out and do not occupy all the available territories.

Garden-Warbler – *Sylvia borin*

The garden-warbler is local, but is found over most of Britain as far north as Argyll and Kincardine. Like some of the other warblers it has spread north in Scotland in this century, and it appeared over the crest of the main mass of central hills, in Newtonmore and Aviemore, in 1952. Mr. Ian Pennie tells me that he has records of this bird singing in north Sutherland in 1954 and 1960. It is not common in any type of wood but is found in pedunculate oak more than elsewhere, and also occasionally in sessile oak, ash, and beech. It is occasionally found in thick birch and I have a few records from the thicket stage of conifers. Gibb (1960) found it almost as common as the blackcap in the brashed pine plantations of Breckland. It needs a thick shrub layer, and in the oaks of Wyre Forest it is present only where the underplanted beech has grown up to about 10 feet in height.

Whitethroat – *Sylvia communis*

The whitethroat is found over the whole of Great Britain but thins out in the extreme north of Scotland. It is found occasionally in pedunculate and sessile oakwood and in ash, beech, and birch. It is a regular but not abundant inhabitant of coniferous plantations in the early and thicket stages, and a few pairs persist after brashing. It is common in thorn hedges, where it does not seem to need trees, and this is probably now its most usual habitat. Its habit of singing while flying a few feet vertically up into the air demands space above the bush from which it starts, and this is given either by mature woods with plenty of air between the canopy and the shrub layer, or by bushes in the open. I have seen it in dense blackthorn and gorse scrub only 2½ feet high, and at 1,250 feet above sea level on a hillside on Exmoor where there were only a few scattered hawthorns. The usual song is unmistakably harsh, but the sub-song is more musical and quite blackcap-like.

Lesser Whitethroat – *Sylvia curruca*

The lesser whitethroat is practically confined in Britain to England and Wales, and is rare in the north. It is nowhere common and I have not enough information to say anything precise of its ecological distribution. Lack and Venables record it in a few pedunculate oakwoods, but in no others. All my records are from hedges and shrubberies, and it seems to need thick cover.

TROGLODYTIDAE – WRENS

The wrens are a North American family which have spread into Europe and Asia (see page 218). They are birds of the shrub and field layers rather than of the trees.

Wren – *Troglodytes troglodytes*

The wren is found throughout Great Britain and reaches a moderate degree of dominance in natural woods of all types—oak, birch, ash, beech, and yew—but has a lower relative abundance in natural firwoods. It comes into coniferous plantations in the early stages, increases in the thicket stage, and again after brashing. This distribution reflects the fact that it is to a great extent indifferent to trees as such and seldom goes into their branches, though I have seen wrens clinging to the trunks like treecreepers. All that the wren needs is thick cover and vegetation strong enough to support its weight, which can be provided by a field layer of bracken or heather a foot or so high, a shrub layer, or by the brashings in a plantation. It seems to prefer to have the shelter of trees above it, but can live equally well in hedges and even in heathy vegetation with no trees or shrubs, though it seems to use these on the mainland only where it follows the streams up on to the fells, or in other sheltered places. According to Orton its limit in North Wales is about 1,700 feet.

TURDIDAE – THRUSHES

The family Turdidae is now taken to include not only the thrushes proper, but the wheatears and chats and some other birds as well. The young nearly all have a spotted plumage, which in some species is retained by the adult, especially on the breast. They have a world-wide distribution, with headquarters in the north temperate regions of the Old World. The genera *Turdus* (the true thrushes), *Luscinia* (nightingales), and *Erithacus* (redbreasts) are woodland dwellers; *Phoenicurus* (redstarts) has a general tendency towards rocky places, and *Oenanthe* (wheatears) and *Saxicola* (chats) live in open and bare areas.

Redbreast or Robin – *Erithacus rubecula*

The redbreast is found all over Great Britain, including the natural woods of Sutherland and Caithness as far north as they go. It is abundant in the two sorts of oakwood but is much rarer in ash. It is common in the natural yew-woods and firwoods. It enters coniferous plantations in the early years, increases in the thicket stage, and again after brashing. It extends as high on the hills as the woods go. It is also found in artificial woodland ecotones such as hedgerows, orchards, and gardens, but seldom in the natural ecotones with scattered trees. The map given by Beven (1951) for robin territories in a Surrey pedunculate oakwood shows clearly that they are spread along the edges of paths. The robin feeds very largely on the ground, but its distribution shows that it does not need any particular sort of shrub or field layer. Most robins leave the hill-woods, of whatever type, in the winter.

Nightingale – *Luscinia megarhyncha*

The geographical distribution of the nightingale has been discussed on page 184. Almost the only woods in which it is found are pedunculate oakwoods and beechwoods with a shrub layer, and it seems particularly to like the thick hazels of the traditional coppice-with-standards oakwoods. It is also found in thick thorn hedges and in gardens with thick shrubberies. There is a tendency for its territories to be on the edges of woods, and Price (1934) found that in Gloucestershire they tended also to be on the eastern edge; perhaps the bird likes the morning sun.

Wheatear – *Oenanthe oenanthe*

The wheatear is a heath bird which is found also in open hill-woods of birch and oak.

Redstart – *Phoenicurus phoenicurus*

The redstart is found throughout Great Britain and nests as far north in Sutherland and Caithness as there are suitable woods for it, but there are a good many places, apparently of the right sort, where it is scarce or absent. In some ways it has a similar ecological distribution to the pied flycatcher, but it is less restricted; almost any wood that contains pied flycatchers may contain redstarts, but the reverse is not true. Redstarts are characteristic of sessile oak-woods and are found in many birchwoods, both on the hills and in the valleys, but in my records they reach their highest percentage frequency and relative abundance in ashwoods. By contrast they are much scarcer in pedunculate oakwoods and beechwoods. They are plentiful in the natural firwoods of Speyside and Ross and I have records from plantations of larch and Scotch fir which have opened out and come to have some resemblance to the natural woods, but none from the plantations of the Forestry Commission. In the fell-woods they go as high as the trees, that is to nearly 2,000 feet in Rothiemurchus. In the hill-country they range outside the woods into the fields, where they build in the loose stone walls and sing from the isolated ash trees that often grow out of them. In Yorkshire they frequent ruins, and in the south of England occasionally breed in large gardens. Rice (1952) reports that in Wiltshire the redstart is found in woods, gardens, and orchards and on open downland where there is a little thorn, elder, and juniper, but it does not here nest in stone walls, although these are available. In 1951 there were ten pairs in Savernake Forest in old clearings overgrown with old thorns, but none in the more formal grounds of Bowood laid out by Capability Brown.

It has been suggested that the original home of the redstart was the pine-heath, and that it then nested on the ground. It certainly builds sometimes in the Lake District in very similar situations to the coal-tit, that is in cracks between rocks and the ground, and this is a central sort of site that might have led in one direction to holes in stone walls and in another to the more usual holes in trees. What I have written about the distribution of the coal-tit probably applies with even greater force to the redstart; that is, it needs a particular type of nest site rather than a particular type of tree, and any woods, or woodland ecotones, that supply this will do. Judged by its reaction to plantations, it has no liking for conifers as such. It has been said to need space under the trees for its pouncing method of feeding and it does get this in most of the woods in which it is found, but its absence from beechwoods where there is plenty of such space and its occasional presence in oakwoods with a thick shrub layer, shows that this is not an important factor in its distribution. It has a correlation (page 21) of 1·62 with the blue tit.

There is no other common British bird which has such a wide range of song, so that one is continually being deceived. Some individuals sing a simple version hardly distinguishable from that of the pied flycatcher, others are as mellow and for a short time as varied as the smoother passages of the nightingale. Some of this is perhaps imitation, for snatches of other birds' songs are sometimes introduced—I have heard willow-warbler, chiff-chaff, and wren from the same individual.

Whinchat – *Saxicola rubetra*

The whinchat is a heath bird but likes a few bushes as song posts. Like the grasshopper-warbler it is favoured by the first few years of coniferous plantations and in many areas has a higher density in these than on the moors that precede them. It persists in smaller numbers in the early thicket stage. I have seen it inside oakwoods and birchwoods on the fells and at 1,250 feet above sea level on Exmoor.

Stonechat – *Saxicola torquata*

The stonechat is found in the same general sort of habitat as the whinchat but is, I think, satisfied with lower vegetation, or at least with bushes of a more uniform height. Thus I have found it in the cliff at Polperro in an almost level and impenetrable scrub of blackthorn and gorse only 2½ feet high. In accordance with this I have no record from plantations, but in 1959 a cock was singing in the Birkrigg oakwood in Cumberland, using the highest oaks as a song post. Parrinder and Parrinder (1945) found in north Cornwall that gorse was an essential feature of every territory that they examined.

Blackbird – *Turdus merula*

The blackbird is easily the commonest thrush and probably one of our most numerous birds. It is found throughout Great Britain, and has extended its range in Scotland in the last hundred years. In spite of its numbers it is only really common in the woods of richer soils—pedunculate oak, ash, beech, and yew. It is present in sessile oak and birchwoods up to the Great Glen, but in the natural firwoods and the Ross and Sutherland birchwoods it is rare and is greatly outnumbered by the song-thrush. It comes into coniferous plantations in small numbers soon after they are started and increases during the thicket stage, when it slightly outnumbers the song-thrush; after brashing most blackbirds leave.

The correlation (page 21) with the song-thrush in my records is 1·86, which is the highest that I have recorded for any pair of birds.

In the woods the blackbird lives much on the ground, flying into the trees only to sing or when alarmed, but a thick field layer and dead litter seem equally acceptable to it. It leaves some of the fell-woods in winter, but otherwise there seems to be little seasonal movement. It lives in almost all types of woodland ecotone and is commoner in gardens than anywhere else.

There seems to be no information on territory in natural surroundings in England, but in gardens the males may be territorial the whole year round. Lind (1955) found that this was also so in Denmark, but that in woods there were no winter territories. My impression is that the same is true of blackbirds in English woods.

Redwing – *Turdus musicus*

The redwing breeds in Scandinavia in both coniferous and deciduous woods and extends into the scrub birch of Lapland, and is also found in gardens. In winter it lives chiefly in more open places, but as it feeds on haws and other tree fruits it comes into woods where these are plentiful. This is perhaps more noticeable in the north of England, and I have seen it in woods of sessile oak, ash, and birch. It comes into the woods also for roosting.

Song-Thrush – *Turdus philomelos*

The song-thrush is found throughout Great Britain, but in spite of its wide geographical spread and its familiarity in gardens, its woodland distribution is decidedly patchy. It is commonest in pedunculate oak and the birchwoods of Ross and Sutherland, and is much rarer in ash, beech, English and Welsh birch, and especially sessile oak. It is fairly common in the natural pinewoods of Speyside and Ross, especially where there is much juniper, but I have not recorded it in the Sussex yew-woods. This distribution suggests that it prefers soils which are not too poor in lime. It is only in lime-rich soils that earthworms and snails occur to any extent, and it may be that the song-thrush needs a certain proportion of them in its diet; its liking for them is well known and obvious. Hartley (1954) has shown that it feeds much more on yew berries, when it can get them, than on other wild fruits; the yew in the south of England, where these observations were made, is mainly a tree of the chalk, but the absence of the song-thrush from the close yew-woods in the breeding season is in striking contrast to the large number of blackbirds. Turček (1952 and 1955) found that in Czechoslovakia it was confined to spruce at 3,000 feet above sea level, but that in lowland woods its occurrence was linked with low illumination of nest sites, an abundance of molluscs, and an autumnal abundance of berries. These will be provided in woods with a good shrub layer and a high lime-status, which agrees with the British distribution.

It comes into some coniferous plantations, usually rather later than the blackbird, but persists in slightly greater numbers after brashing.

It correlates highly in my records with the blue tit (1·53), the great tit (1·59), and the blackbird (1·86).

Newton pointed out as long ago as 1860 that the term 'resident' and 'migratory' may apply to localities rather than to species, and instanced the song-thrush as a bird which is resident in parts of

England but which disappears entirely from others in winter. I have very few records from woods in winter, and it certainly leaves almost all those on the higher ground and in the north of England, including the plantations.

Fieldfare – *Turdus pilaris*

The fieldfare nests in colonies in Scandinavia in similar woods to the redwing, but it is less of a scrub bird. Like the redwing in its winter visits here it is chiefly a bird of the open fields, especially of grass, but it also visits the Pennine and Lake District fells to feed on berries up to at least 2,000 feet. It feeds also on haws, sitting in the trees, pecking off the berries and dropping the stones, and it sometimes roosts in the canopy of trees in woods. Its woodland nature is shown too by the fact that when disturbed it tends to fly to the tops of the highest trees available—ashes, for instance, not hawthorns; if further pursued it flies off and does not return to its feeding grounds like other thrushes.

Mistle-Thrush – *Turdus viscivorus*

The mistle-thrush is found all over Great Britain but is rare in the extreme north of Scotland. It occurs in a number of pedunculate oakwoods and rather less commonly in sessile oakwoods, beechwoods, and birchwoods, but I have not seen it in ash; Brown and Buckley said that it was characteristic of birchwoods at 1,000 feet above sea level in Moray. I have never seen it in the Aviemore forests, but have a few records from coniferous plantations at both the thicket and brashed stages. It is also found in hedges with trees, and in parks and large gardens, and there are probably more in this type of ecotone than in the woods. It feeds largely on the berries of trees such as holly and yew, and its distribution may be in part determined by the presence of these. It goes high on the hills in search of berries in the fall.

ORDER CICONIIFORMES (ARDEIFORMES)

ARDEIDAE – HERONS

The herons are found all round the world in temperate and tropical regions, and are birds of marshes and shallow waters.

Common Heron – *Ardea cinerea*

The heron, which is found all over Great Britain, with lowest densities on the hills in north-east England and in the Midland plain, is a bird of the tree-water ecotone and presumably evolved in much the same sort of environment as the rook, but exploited the waters instead of the plains for feeding. It comes sometimes to quite small woodland brooks. Like the rook it nests in trees, usually tall, and in colonies, presumably for the same reason. It feeds, however, alone or in pairs, although occasionally half a dozen may be seen fairly close together, particularly on tidal streams.

The numbers of herons' nests in the British Isles have been studied for many years, and in 1954 an attempt was made to cover the whole country; some parts of Scotland were, however, not fully explored (Burton 1956, Garden 1958). Four thousand seven hundred and eight occupied nests were reported in England and Wales, and 1,086 in Scotland. About half the English and Welsh heronries and over four-fifths of those in Scotland contained ten nests or fewer; only three had more than 100 nests. There is a general tendency for the larger colonies to be near large areas of shallow water—estuaries, marshes, or lakes—and there is a strong concentration in Norfolk. All species of tree are used indifferently, provided that they are large enough. Very few English nests are anywhere but in trees, but in Scotland 70 per cent. are on cliffs and 9 per cent. in various other sites such as buildings and reed-beds.

ORDER CAPRIMULGIFORMES

CAPRIMULGIDAE – NIGHTJARS

The nightjars are a small family found over almost the whole world but especially strongly represented in America. They are birds of woodland ecotone, with a tendency to terrestrial habits.

Nightjar – *Caprimulgus europaeus*

The nightjar is found throughout Great Britain but is very local in its distribution and seems to have decreased in recent years. It usually lives in open woodland with a heathy field layer, but I have not enough information to give its ecological distribution very precisely. I have records or information of it in both types of oakwood, birch, and natural firwood, and it probably occurs in other sorts of woodland where the necessary combination of trees and open space exists. In Staffordshire and Shropshire it is now chiefly found in young conifer plantations, sometimes where there is very little or no space between the trees.

ORDER CHARADRIIFORMES – WADERS

SCOLOPACIDAE – CURLEWS, SNIPE, ETC.

The waders are a cosmopolitan group of difficult classification, with long legs and beak. They are terrestrial, living on the shores of rivers, lakes, or seas, but in boreal regions especially several species perch freely on trees; in this country the sandpiper (*Tringa hypoleucos*) sometimes do so.

Woodcock – *Scolopax rusticola*

The woodcock breeds from the English Channel to the north coast of Scotland, but has a most odd and patchy distribution. It has been recorded breeding in every county except Anglesey, but it is common only north and west of the Severn–Humber line and in Norfolk, Suffolk, the New Forest, and the Weald; it is in general absent from Devon and Cornwall, and from most of Wales. This does not correlate well with any features of landscape or any meteorological conditions, but the bird seems to avoid the heavy clays and chalks. In the areas where it is present sessile oak, birch, and Scotch fir seem equally suitable for it, and perhaps more than any others it likes the stream-side belts of alder. It is sometimes present in close-planted Scotch fir and in spruce. Alexander (1946) lists nests also for beechwoods and many in the open, and he found that bracken was especially favoured. A certain amount of dampness in the ground seems to be attractive to it, presumably because of its mode of feeding. Although it is occasionally found in the fell-woods it seems to prefer the valleys. The absence from Wales and the south-west is possibly to be explained by the fact that only within the last century have woodcock become at all common in England and Wales as breeders—or indeed, perhaps, have bred here at all. They have long been known to sportsmen as winter visitors, and it may be that an increase in numbers or a change in habit led to some of them remaining behind. If this were so, the west coast, where the climate is mildest, might well be the last place that they would colonize.

The peculiar nuptial flight, called roding, in which the cock flies several times round a lengthy circuit at about dusk, has been often watched and described, but there is probably more variation than is generally admitted. One which I watched for 35 minutes in Worcestershire in 1952 flew on an irregular figure-of-eight, and the point where the flight lines crossed, which was approximately above my head, was passed in different directions on different circuits. This bird also differed from the books in that it flew higher, at an estimated 100 feet, over open ground than over the trees, when it dropped to nearly their height. Its first circuit was taken much more slowly than later ones.

The woodcock is remarkable for the peculiar position and structure of its ear.

ORDER COLUMBIFORMES

COLUMBIDAE – PIGEONS

The pigeons are a world-wide family, all vegetarian and mostly forest-living, with a tendency to feed on the ground.

Wood-Pigeon or Ring-Dove – *Columba palumbus*

The wood-pigeon is found throughout Great Britain, being commonest in some wooded and agricultural districts in the south. It is plentiful in beech, ash, and both types of oakwood, but is rare in the fell-woods, whether of birch or sessile oak, and in the natural firwoods. There is a very high density in the yew-woods of the South Downs. It comes into coniferous plantations in fair numbers in the thicket stage, but its numbers drop after brashing. On occasions it nests in quite small trees, and cover for the nest seems to be one of its chief requirements. It nests in mixed plantations and ashwoods at 1,200 feet above sea level on the Pennines, and I have found it at 1,150 feet on Exmoor in a line of beech trees which also held a buzzard's nest. It is sometimes seen far from trees, as for instance in north-west Sutherland, although it does not, so far as I know, nest in the birchwoods in that county. It is also a bird of the agricultural ecotones, and its liking for hard seeds is greatly satisfied by man's provision of grain. Murton (1958) has shown that in this environment it suffers very heavy loss of eggs, chiefly through predation by jays and other crows, but this is made up for by the fact that each pair lays on the average five clutches per season.

Stock-Dove – *Columba oenas*

The stock-dove breeds all over Great Britain except in Caithness and the north-west of Scotland, but it is much more local than the wood-pigeon, and in most districts far less numerous. It breeds in both deciduous woods and coniferous plantations, but there is not enough precise information to specify its preferences. It seems not to be present in the yew-woods, and is quite absent from the fell-woods.

In a transect made from the train between Reading and Devonshire, Southern (1944) found that it greatly outnumbered the wood-pigeon on the high chalk downs with grass and small patches of woodland, which suggests that it is even more a bird of the ecotone than is the other. This would I think agree with most people's general impression that it is commonest about farms, and especially where there are derelict buildings.

Turtle-Dove – *Streptopelia turtur*

The turtle-dove is a summer visitor to most of England and Wales, but is rare in the northern counties and in Cornwall and west Wales. There are very few Scottish breeding records. Its woodland distribution is very similar to that of the stock-dove; it is found both in deciduous woods and in coniferous plantations, but I have not recorded it from birch, yew, or the fell-woods. It likes a certain amount of open space, but this is adequately provided by the foresters' rides and fire-breaks. It is also found in agricultural land, especially where the hedges are thick and with many trees.

ORDER CUCULIFORMES

CUCULIDAE – CUCKOOS

The cuckoos are a world-wide group, commonest in the warm parts of Africa and Asia, mostly laying their eggs in other birds' nests and in one way or another destroying the young of the hosts.

Cuckoo – *Cuculus canorus*

The cuckoo is found all over Great Britain. I do not think that it can strictly be called a woodland bird, or even a bird of the wood edge, although it often flies through woods and frequently perches on trees, from which in the south of England it normally sings. All writers agree that its commonest host in Great Britain is the meadow-pipit, and this fits in with the fact that the highest density of cuckoos is found in the fells of the north, where the pipit is abundant. The only true woodland bird which is commonly parasitized is the red-breast, which is a very common bird which is also found in other habitats. Nevertheless, the cuckoo is frequently seen in natural woods of all types, but only rarely in coniferous plantations. On the fells it seems rather to ignore the woods than to use them, flying through them if they come in its way and occasionally stopping to call if it feels like doing so, but not needing them and living much more in the open. It is nothing like so common on the Scottish hills as on the Pennines, but Baxter and Rintoul confirm its moorland nature in saying that it is 'more abundant in the upper lands and hill glens than in the eastern coastal regions'. In other countries it has other favourite hosts, the reed-warbler (*Acrocephalus scirpaceus*) for example in Alsace. The hedge-sparrow and pied wagtail are other common hosts. It is to be noted that none of these is a purely woodland bird.

The usual song and call of the male varies slightly in both pitch and interval from one individual to another, but usually at the beginning of the season the first note is G, and it tends to fall later on to F, E or E flat, and the interval may be anything from a major fourth to a minor third. Sometimes a bird sings with the usual interval reversed, the second note being higher than the first. The water-bubbling call, which is the usual note of the hen, and the 'cuckoo' are occasionally given by the same bird, and as there is a record of a bird calling 'cuckoo', being shot, and laying an egg as it died, it is probable that the hen does sometimes cuckoo.

ORDER FALCONIFORMES

FALCONIDAE – HAWKS

The Falconidae are a cosmopolitan family, mostly living in woods or woodland ecotones, but with a tendency towards rocks and open places.

Sparrow-Hawk – *Accipiter nisus*

The sparrow-hawk is found all over Great Britain but varies much in its frequency. I have seen it or have heard of its being seen in all the common types of deciduous woodland except ash and beech, and in natural firwood and spruce plantations; it may not have been recorded from ash and beech merely because of the small chance of seeing it on any particular count. It is also found in agricultural land. Its mode of hunting demands some space amongst the trees, either such as is provided by the open spaces of the ecotones or the rides of close-planted woodlands. On the hills it goes as high as the trees—1,200 feet in birches in the Lake District and nearly 2,000 feet in Rothiemurchus.

Buzzard – *Buteo buteo*

The distribution of the buzzard has been discussed on page 172. In many parts of Scotland it was completely exterminated, even on the moors, but with the relaxation of gamekeeper-pressure it has begun to spread and increase there as it has done in England and Wales. I know of no part of Scotland, however, where it is as common as it is in the Lake District and in some parts of Wales. On Exmoor in 1953 I found two buzzards' nests only a little more than a mile apart, one in an oakwood and the other in a line of beeches, and in some parts of Devon the density is as high as two pairs on a square mile. On the fells the buzzard seems to prefer oak-woods to birch, but uses these when larger trees are not available.

Merlin – *Falco columbarius*

The merlin is not a woodland bird, but in one Cumberland plantation has taken to beating down the rides like a sparrow-hawk.

Peregrine Falcon – *Falco peregrinus*

The peregrine, now restricted to a limited number of breeding sites on the cliffs of the coast and the mountains, is no longer a woodland bird, but it is possible that, like the raven and the buzzard, it has largely been driven to its present haunts by persecution, since it nests in woods on the Continent and has occasionally done so here. It feeds largely on medium-sized birds such as grouse, pigeons, and jackdaws, and what was said above (page 140) about the maximum possible density of sparrow-hawks, applies even more strongly to the larger peregrine.

Hobby – *Falco subbuteo*

The hobby now has a very restricted distribution in the south of England. It appears to be a bird of the ecotone rather than of woodland. Thompson (1931) found that of 25 nest sites, chiefly in Wiltshire, Dorset, and Hampshire, 17 were in clumps or lines, 1 in an isolated tree, and 7 in big woods. Groups of tall pines or oaks and scrubby downland plantations were all used.

Kestrel – *Falco tinnunculus*

The kestrel is the commonest hawk in almost all parts of Great Britain. It is not usually thought of as a woodland bird but I have occasionally seen it beating through woods, including a part of the Forest of Rothiemurchus in close canopy at more than 1,350 feet above sea level. It is more a bird of the ecotones—agricultural land with hedgerow trees and scattered clumps on hillsides. Though it feeds mainly in the open it often nests in trees and seems to like them to perch on. If there is enough space it can live well inside the built-up areas of towns, as it does within two or three miles of the centre of Birmingham and Manchester. In its hovering it usually flaps the wings steadily, but occasionally holds them momentarily still. More rarely it hangs apparently motionless for some seconds; on every occasion when I have been able to get a good view of a bird doing this it has opened the bastard wing each time that it has ceased flapping, and closed it again as soon as it moved its wings.

Kite – *Milvus milvus*

The kite is now confined as a British bird to a limited area of central Wales. This is a district of open hill with hanging woods chiefly of sessile oak with some birch. About half the nests are in oaks but it cannot be said that the bird really prefers these, for the other half, which have been situated in recent years in beech, birch, Scotch fir, spruce, and larch, are in trees of which far fewer are available. In 1953 one pair, having had their first nest blown out of a beech tree, moved two miles away and built a second nest in another beech. The kite probably needs much the same combination of wood and open country as does the buzzard, but beyond that its real choice, in the absence of persecution, is probably wide. Many of the nests are near hill farms, and it hunts over agricultural land as well as the moors. The food used to be chiefly rabbits, but a good many birds, including rooks and black-headed gulls, are taken by some pairs, and vegetable matter is also used. A kite has been seen eating holly berries from the tree.

The kite, in a good view, is easily distinguished from the buzzard by its forked tail, but also its flapping flight is quite different, having much more wrist-action and being strikingly reminiscent of that of the heron. The screaming call-note, higher pitched than the buzzard's and usually triple, sounds as if the bird broke off, took breath, and began again.

Osprey – *Pandion haliaetus*

The osprey was exterminated in Scotland at the beginning of this century, but a pair has returned and bred for the last few years in one of the few areas that provide its peculiar habitat—tall firs surrounding lakes in which it can catch the fish on which it feeds. The earlier attempts of this pair were frustrated by vandals, but in 1959 young were successfully reared.

ORDER GALLIFORMES – GAME BIRDS

PHASIANIDAE – PHEASANTS, ETC.

The Phasianidae are the central family of the Order, found all over the temperate and tropical regions of the world except for Polynesia, and especially well developed in Asia.

Pheasant – *Phasianus colchicus*

The pheasant was early introduced into Europe from Asia and was certainly present in England in Norman times and perhaps before. It is difficult to determine the distribution that it would take up on its own, as breeding and laying down of stocks, as well as feeding of the birds, still go on. It lives in woods of most types and also in agricultural land where there are belts and windbreaks or scattered clumps and groves which have often been put there especially for it. It is entirely absent from the fell-woods, and I suspect that its range, both ecological and geographical, would contract if protection were to cease. Some other species of pheasant have been released and have become feral in parts of the south of England.

TETRAONIDAE – GROUSE

The Tetraonidae are game-birds which have become adapted to temperate or even Arctic regions, and are found all round the cooler parts of the northern hemisphere. Like all the Order they tend to be terrestrial, but many live in woods.

Black Grouse – *Lyrurus tetrix*

The black grouse was once widely distributed in the woods of England and Wales but has greatly decreased, and introductions in many parts have failed to maintain it. It breeds now only in some of the hillier counties, but is still fairly general in Scotland. It is a bird of the tree-heath and scrub-woods and is generally associated with birches, but sessile oak will suit it instead and there are numbers in the natural firwoods of Speyside. I have one record from a larch plantation.

Capercailzie – *Tetrao urogallus*

The capercailzie became extinct in Scotland about 1780, but birds from Sweden were introduced to a number of places in the nineteenth century and it has now spread through much of the central Highlands from Stirling to Golspie. It lives in the natural pine-forest, which was presumably its original home, and in plantations of pine and larch, including quite young ones twenty-five years old. In winter it lives almost entirely on the buds, shoots, and needles of both conifers, and on the flowers, seeds, and cones of the firs. At other times of the year it ranges more widely and feeds on bilberry and bracken, and even visits stubble. It is said to have become extinct in England about a century before it did in Scotland, but what it lived on until 1680, when there were certainly no coniferous plantations and very few, if any, firwoods, I do not know. In Russia it inhabits oakwoods as well as pine, and in the former it is migratory but in the latter resident.

ORDER PICIFORMES

PICIDAE – WOODPECKERS

The woodpeckers are found all over the world except for Australasia and Oceania, and are all tree-climbing birds, although some feed also on the ground.

Great (or Greater) Spotted or Pied Woodpecker – *Dryobates major* (=*Dendrocopus major*)

The geographical distribution and recent spread of the great spotted woodpecker have been discussed on page 181. My figures suggest that it is about as frequent as the green woodpecker in ash, beech, and pedunculate oak, rather more so in sessile oak, and much more in birch. In Wyre Forest, though it lives in the oakwoods, birch is the tree most commonly chosen for nesting; Wilson (1933), writing of Westmorland, also notes its frequent nesting in birch and suggests, with some reason, that this is because of the cryptic resemblance of the plumage of the bird to the black and silver colouring of the tree. If this is so the birchwoods should be its original home. The great spotted woodpecker is uncommon in coniferous plantations, but it is said to frequent these in Scotland and to have been an inhabitant of the old firwoods of Speyside before they were cut down; the probability referred to on page 254 that these contained many oaks must be remembered. The great spotted appears less in the ecotones and feeds less on the ground than the green, but it is quite at home in both situations. I have seen one feeding on a College lawn in the very centre of Oxford. When disturbed it flew off over Bodley in the direction of the Parks.

Lesser Spotted or Barred Woodpecker – *Dryobates minor* (=*Dendrocopus minor*)

The lesser spotted woodpecker is the least common of our three species, even allowing for the fact that it is less conspicuous than the others. It is local in its distribution, and north of Yorkshire and Lancashire and in some of the western counties of Wales is known only as a straggler. I saw one on the east side of Ullswater in December 1950, and it is possibly established there and in one or two other Cumberland districts. It occurs in oakwoods of both sorts and in beech, but seems to be absent from conifers. Most of the fell-woods are beyond its range, but I found it in November 1953 in Piles Wood on Dartmoor, which is of pedunculate oak and between 850 and 1,050 feet above sea level. In my experience it is commonest in lines of tall trees, especially perhaps hedgerow elms. I have no garden records.

Wryneck – *Jynx torquilla*

The distribution of the wryneck (see page 104) is now so restricted and its numbers are so few, that it is difficult to generalize about its woodland preferences. It seems to be a bird of ecotones, and many of the surviving pairs nest in gardens and orchards.

Green Woodpecker – *Picus viridis*

The green woodpecker is found over all the south and Midlands of England and in Wales, but it thins out in the north and there are few records of breeding in Scotland. It has spread in the Lake District in recent years, especially in the 1940s, and now breeds in Coniston and as far north as Carlisle, but not in west Cumberland beyond Dunnerdale. Since there are old records going back to 1803, this is probably a re-expansion after a contraction similar to that which is known to have happened with the greater spotted woodpecker. It was common throughout County Durham until about 1840, then became rare, began spreading about 1913, and by 1930 was generally distributed. It now breeds in Midlothian.

The lists suggest that it is commonest in woods of pedunculate oak and beech, but it occurs also in sessile oak and ash; I have only one breeding-season record for birch. This may be in part a reflection of its somewhat southern distribution. It is rare in coniferous plantations and the natural firwoods are beyond its geographical range, but it is present in the dense yew-woods of the South Downs. In winter the two or three pairs that are present in Wyre Forest move from the mature sessile oak to an area of regenerating birch and oak some 20 or 30 feet high. Here they dig for food in the nests of the large wood ant, *Formica rufa*, of which there are none under the oaks. The green woodpecker is absent from the fell-woods, but I have a few records from better-grown oaks at about 1,000 feet above sea level in Cumberland and Wales, and Hendy says that it is abundant up to this altitude in the Quantocks. It is also found in parkland and in hedges where there is old and tall timber, and these ecotones are now probably its chief habitat in Britain.

The green woodpecker feeds much on the ground, where it both hops and walks, and is sometimes seen a hundred yards or more from the trees. When disturbed it nearly always flies to these and watches the intruder before flying further off. I have seen it holding on to the vertical face of an old building, and to the leading shoot of an 8-foot larch sapling. Here it clung sideways, with its claws presumably holding round the stem. The usual call note has several variants, including one which sounds rather like the whistling of a wood-pigeon's wings; it bears the same sort of relation to the normal note as does the sound made by an inexperienced person attempting to play a flute to the proper note of that instrument.

ORDER STRIGIFORMES

STRIGIDAE – OWLS

The owls are a cosmopolitan group, remarkable for the wide range of many of the genera and even species, the short-eared owl (*Asio flammeus*) for instance being found over the whole of Europe and western Asia and in north and south America. Most are nocturnal and they inhabit a variety of situations, from plains to the Arctic snows, but the majority live in woods.

Little Owl – *Athene noctua*

This, an introduced species, is now found over the whole of England as far north as a line from Fleetwood to Scarborough, and in Wales except Anglesey. I have never seen it in woods but it is a park-ecotone bird, liking tall scattered trees such as hedgerow elms. It feeds much in the daylight, largely on worms and insects, and I have seen one hovering over a road.

Long-eared Owl – *Asio otus*

The long-eared owl is found over most of Britain but is nowhere common. My only woodland records are from a well-grown spruce plantation, and it is said to be present in the natural firwoods.

Tawny or Brown Owl – *Strix aluco*

The tawny owl is resident all over Great Britain in suitable places, and is easily the commonest of our owls. In judging its woodland distribution from lists of occurrences one must remember that few ornithologists work by night, and that in daytime one is only likely to see it if one goes within about 10 yards of its roost. It occurs in both sorts of oakwood, in ash, birch, and the South Down yew-woods. I have no records from beechwoods but it has been reported from them. I have no reason to think that it prefers any of these to the others. The tawny owl is also found in woodland ecotones, and even in town gardens where there are tall trees.

Barn Owl – *Tyto alba*

The barn owl is found over most of Great Britain except the extreme north of Scotland, but its distribution is patchy. It is not in general a woodland bird, though it hunts over young plantations, and is now generally found about buildings; it is also found in agricultural land with clumps of trees and hedgerows and sometimes nests in hollow trees, so that it is no doubt properly a bird of the park-ecotone. In winter it quite often hunts in daylight, flying low over the ground, sometimes at only 3 to 4 feet.

BIBLIOGRAPHY

There are no books and very few papers that deal with woodland birds synoptically, but there are very many about particular aspects of particular birds. The list which follows includes only those on which I have relied for general information (often not specifically acknowledged in the text) and those which I have thought it useful to mention by name. The omission of a reference does not necessarily imply either that I have not read it or that I have made no use of it or that it is not of scientific value.

1. GENERAL WORKS

BAXTER, E. V., and RINTOUL, L. J. 1953. *The birds of Scotland. Their history, distribution and migration.* Edinburgh, Oliver and Boyd.

CAMPBELL, B. 1953. *Finding Nests.* London, Collins.

CARTER, H. G. 1936. *British trees and shrubs including those commonly planted: a systematic introduction to our conifers and woody dicotyledons.* Oxford, Clarendon Press.

Check-list of the birds of Great Britain and Ireland 1952. London, British Ornithologists' Union.

CLAPHAM, A. R., TUTIN, T. G., and WARBURG, E. F. 1952. *Flora of the British Isles.* Cambridge, University Press.

FORESTRY COMMISSION 1952–3. Census Reports: *No. 1 Census of woodlands 1947–1949: Woodlands of five acres and over. No. 2 Hedgerow and park timber and woods under five acres 1951. No. 3 Census of woodlands 1947–49: Woods of five acres and over: Welsh county details. No. 4 Census of woodlands 1947–49: Woods of five acres and over: Scottish county details. No. 5 Census of woodlands 1947–49: Woods of five acres and over: English county details.* London, Her Majesty's Stationery Office.

TANSLEY, A. G. 1939. *The British Islands and their vegetation.* Cambridge, University Press.

WITHERBY, H. F., JOURDAIN, F. C. R., TICEHURST, N. F., and TUCKER, B. W. 1944. *The handbook of British birds.* (1st revision) London, Witherby. (Quoted as 'the *Handbook*'.)

YARRELL, W. 1871–85. *A History of British birds* (4th edition, vols. I and II edited by A. Newton, vols. III and IV by H. Saunders). London, Von Voorst.

2. SPECIAL REFERENCES

ALEXANDER, W. B. 1933. The rook population of the Upper Thames region. *Journal of Animal Ecology* 2. 24–25.

ALEXANDER, W. B. 1946. The woodcock in the British Isles. *Ibis* 88. 1–24; 159–79; 271–86; 427–44.

ARMITT, M. L. 1897–1901. *Studies of Lakeland Birds*. Ambleside, George Middleton.

BAILEY, N. J. T. 1952. Improvements in the interpretation of recapture data. *J. Anim. Ecol.* 21. 120–7.

BETTS, M. 1955. The food of titmice in oak woodland. *J. Anim. Ecol.* 24. 282–323.

BEVEN, G. 1951. The bird population of an oakwood in Surrey (Eastern Wood, Bookham Common). *London Naturalist for 1950* 30. 57–72.

BEVEN, G. 1953. Further observations on the bird population of an oakwood in Surrey (Eastern Wood, Bookham Common). *Lond. Nat. for 1952* 33. 51–77.

BLACKWELL, J. A., and DOWDESWELL, W. H. 1951. Local movement in the blue tit. *British Birds* 44. 397–403.

BLEZARD, E. (editor) 1943. The Birds of Lakeland. *Transactions of Carlisle Natural History Society* 6. 1–170.

BROWN, F. J. 1946. A Cheshire starling roost, 1944–5. *J. Anim. Ecol.* 15. 75–81.

BROWN, J. A. HARVIE-, and BUCKLEY, T. E. 1887. *A vertebrate fauna of Sutherland, Caithness and West Cromarty*. Edinburgh, David Douglas.

BROWN, J. A. HARVIE-, and MACPHERSON, A. H. 1904. *A fauna of the North-west Highlands and Skye*. Edinburgh, David Douglas.

BURKITT, J. P. 1924–7. A study of the robin by means of marked birds. *Brit. Birds* 17. 294–303; 18. 97–103, 250–7; 19. 120–4; 20. 91–101.

BURTON, J. F. 1956. Report on the national census of heronries 1954. *Bird Study* 3. 42–73.

CAMPBELL, B. 1954–5. The breeding distribution and habitats of the pied flycatcher (*Muscicapa hypoleuca*) in Britain. *Bird Study* 1. 81–101; 2. 24–32, 179–91.

CAMPBELL, B. 1958. *The crested tit*. Forestry Commission Leaflet 41. London, Her Majesty's Stationery Office.

CARPENTER, J. R. 1935. Forest edge birds and exposures of their habitats. *Wilson Bulletin* 47. 106–8.

CHETTLEBOROUGH, M. R. 1952. Observations on the collection and burial of acorns by jays in Hainault Forest. *Brit. Birds* 45. 359–64.

COLQUHOUN, M. K. 1951. *The woodpigeon in Britain*. A.R.C. Report Series, 10. London, His Majesty's Stationery Office.

COLQUHOUN, M. K., and MORLEY, A. 1943. Vertical zonation in woodland bird communities. *J. Anim. Ecol.* 12. 75–81.

DARLING, F. F. 1947. *Natural history in the highlands and islands.* London, Collins.

DARLINGTON, C. D., and MATHER, K. 1949. *The elements of genetics*, p. 360. London, Allen and Unwin.

DELAMAIN, J. 1933. *The days and nights of birds* (translated), pp. 140–51. London, Gollancz.

DOBBIE, J. B. 1898. A contribution to the avifauna of West Ross-shire. *Annals of Scottish Natural History* 1898. 65–75.

DOWDESWELL, W. H., and FORD, E. B. 1953. The influence of isolation on variability in the butterfly *Maniola jurtina. Symposium of the Society for Experimental Biology* 7. 254–73.

DUFFEY, E. A. G. 1947. The change in bird-life during the growth of a Charnwood conifer plantation. *Leics. and Rutland County Report of Wild Birds for 1946*, 9–13.

DURANGO, S. 1956. Territory in the red-backed shrike *Lanius collurio. Ibis* 98. 476–84.

EASTWOOD, E., ISTED, G. A., and RIDER, G. C. 1960. Radar 'ring-angels' and the roosting movements of starlings. *Nature, London* 186. 112–14.

ELTON, C. 1939. On the nature of cover. *Journal of Wildlife Management* 3. 332–8.

EVANS, A. H. 1899. *Birds* in *The Cambridge Natural History.* London, Macmillan.

EVANS, A. H. 1911. *A fauna of the Tweed area.* Edinburgh, David Douglas.

GARDEN, E. A. 1958. The national census of heronries in Scotland 1954 with a summary of the 1928–9 census. *Bird Study* 5. 90–109.

GAUSE, G. F. 1934. *The Struggle for Existence.* Baltimore.

GIBB, J. 1950. The breeding biology of the great and blue titmice. *Ibis* 92. 507–39.

GIBB, J. 1954. Feeding ecology of tits, with notes on treecreeper and goldcrest. *Ibis* 96. 513–44.

GIBB, J. 1957. Food requirements and other observations on captive tits. *Bird Study* 4. 207–15.

GIBB, J. 1958. Predation by tits and squirrels on the eucosomid *Ernarmonia conicolana* (Heyl). *J. Anim. Ecol.* 27. 375–96.

GIBB, J. A. 1960. Populations of tits and goldcrests and their food supply in pine plantations. *Ibis* 102. 163–208.

GILBERT, H. A., and WALKER, C. W. 1954. *Herefordshire Birds.* Hereford, Woolhope Naturalists Field Club.

GOODBODY, I. M. 1952. The post-fledging dispersal of juvenile titmice. *Brit. Birds* 45. 279–85.

GOODWIN, D. 1956. Further observations on the behaviour of the jay *Garrulus glandarius. Ibis* 98. 186–91.

GYÖRI, J. 1956–7. (Examination of bird-associations and surroundings during the winter 1954–5.) *Aquila* 63–64. 41–49. (Hungarian with English summary.)

HARTLEY, P. H. T. 1953. An ecological study of the feeding habits of the English titmice. *J. Anim. Ecol.* 22. 261–88.

HARTLEY, P. H. T. 1954. Wild fruits in the diet of British thrushes. A study in the ecology of closely allied species. *Brit. Birds* 47. 97–107.

HARVEY, L. A., and ST. LEGER-GORDON, D. 1953. *Dartmoor.* London, Collins.

HENDY, E. W. 1943. *Somerset birds and some other folk.* London, Eyre and Spottiswoode.

HINDE, R. A. 1952. The behaviour of the great tit (*Parus major*) and some related species. *Behaviour*, Supp. II. 1–201.

JENKINS, D. 1953. A study of habitat selection of birds in north-west Vesterålen. *Sterna*, Stavanger 9.

JONES, E. W. 1959. Biological flora of the British Isles. *Quercus* L. *Journal of Ecology* 47. 169–222.

KUUSISTO, P. 1941. Studien über die Oekologie und Tagesrhytmik von *Phylloscopus trochilus acredula* (L.). *Acta zoologica fennica* 31. 1–120.

LACK, D. 1946. *The life of the robin.* (2nd edition) London, Witherby.

LACK, D., and LACK, E. 1951. Further changes in bird-life caused by afforestation. *J. Anim. Ecol.* 20. 173–9.

LACK, D., and VENABLES, L. S. V. 1939. The habitat distribution of British woodland birds. *J. Anim. Ecol.* 8. 39–71.

LAURIE, M. V. 1958. The present productivity of forests. *Symposia of the Institute of Biology* 7. 73–78.

LIND, H. 1955. Bidrag til Solsortens (*Turdus m. merula* (L.)) biologi. *Dansk ornithologisk Forenings Tidskrift* 49. 76–113. (English summary.)

MACKENZIE, J. M. D. 1959. Roosting of treecreepers. *Bird Study* 6. 8–14.

MACPHERSON, H. A. 1892. *A vertebrate fauna of Lakeland.* Edinburgh, David Douglas.

MANLEY, G. 1951. The range of variation of the British climate. *Geographical Journal* 117. 43–68.

MARLER, P. 1952. Variation in the song of the chaffinch *Fringilla coelebs. Ibis* 94. 458–72.

MARLER, P. 1956. The voice of the chaffinch and its function as language. *Ibis* 98. 231–61.

MARPLES, B. J. 1934. The winter starling roosts of Great Britain, 1932–1933. *J. Anim. Ecol.* 3. 187–203.

MASUYAMA, M. 1957. An ornithological application of line-grid sampling. *Rep. Stat. Appl. Res.* JUSE. 5. 1–3.

MAY, D. J. 1949. Studies on a community of willow warblers. *Ibis* 91. 25–54.

MEIKLEJOHN, M. F. M. 1952. Habitat of chiffchaff in Scotland. *Scottish Naturalist* 64. 114–16.

MEISE, W. 1928. Die verbreitung der Aaskrahe (Formenkreis *Corvus corone* L.). *Journal für Ornithologie* 76. 1–203.

MORLEY, A. 1940. Recolonisation by bird species on burnt woodland. *J. Anim. Ecol.* 9. 84–88.

MORLEY, A. 1953. Field observations on the biology of the marsh tit. *Brit. Birds* 46. 233–8; 273–87; 332–46.

MOUNTFORT, G. 1956. The territorial behaviour of the hawfinch *Coccothraustes coccothraustes. Ibis* 98. 490–5.

MOUNTFORT, G. 1957. *The Hawfinch.* London, Collins.

MURTON, R. K. 1958. The breeding of woodpigeon populations. *Bird Study* 5. 157–83.

NEWTON, A. 1860. On migratory habits of the song-thrush (*Turdus musicus*). *Ibis* 2. 83–85.

NICE, M. M. 1937, 1943. Studies in the life history of the song sparrow. *Transactions of the Linnaean Society of New York* 4. 1–248; 6. 1–328.

NICHOLSON, E. M., and NICHOLSON, B. D. 1930. The rookeries of the Oxford district, a preliminary report. *J. Ecol.* 18. 51–66.

NIEBUHR, O. 1948. Die Vogelwelt des feuchten eichenhainbuchen Waldes. *Ornithologische Abhandlungen*, Gottingen. 1. 1–28.

NIEBUHR, O. 1952. Die Nachtigall in Niedersachsen. *Biologische Abhandlungen* 2. 36.

NORDSTRÖM, G. 1953. Boniteringsundersökningar över hächfågelfaunan inom tre olika skogsområden under en följd av fem somrar. *Ornis Fennica* 30. 56–67. (English summary.)

NORRIS, C. A., 1960. The breeding distribution of thirty bird species in 1952. *Bird Study* 7. 129–84.

ORTON, K. 1948. in CARR, H. R. C., and LISTER, G. A. *The mountains of Snowdonia; in history, the sciences, literature, and sport.* (2nd edition) London, Crosby Lockwood.

OVINGTON, J. D. 1958. Some biological considerations of forest production. *Symp. Inst. Biol.* 7. 83–90.

OWEN, D. F. 1956. The food of nesting jays and magpies. *Bird Study* 3. 257–65.

OWEN, J. H. 1932. The food of the sparrowhawk. *Brit. Birds* 26. 34–44.

OWEN, J. H. 1948. The larder of the red-backed shrike. *Brit. Birds* 41. 200–3.

PARRINDER, E. R., and PARRINDER, E. D. 1945. Some observations on stonechats in North Cornwall. *Brit. Birds* 38. 362–9.

PRICE, M. P. 1934. A census of nightingales in Gloucestershire. *Brit. Birds* 28. 82–83.

PRICE, M. P. 1950. Influences causing fluctations of warbler population in cultivated lands and oakwoods in the Severn valley. *Brit. Birds* 43. 345–51.

RICE, C. 1952. The redstart in Wiltshire. Report of an enquiry conducted during 1949–50–51. *Wiltshire Archaeological and Natural History Magazine* 54. 327–31.

RITCHIE, J. 1920. *The influence of man on animal life in Scotland. A study in faunal evolution.* Cambridge, University Press.

ROEBUCK, A. 1933. A survey of the rooks in the Midlands. *Brit. Birds* 27. 3–23.

SALISBURY, E. J. 1925. The vegetation of the Forest of Wyre; a preliminary account. *J. Ecol.* 13. 314–21.

SKELLAM, J. G. 1958. The mathematical foundations underlying the use of line-transects in animal ecology. *Biometrics* 14. 385–400.

SMITH, D. SUMMERS-. 1952. Breeding biology of the spotted flycatcher. *Brit. Birds* 45. 153–67.

SNOW, D. W. 1954. The habitats of Eurasian tits (*Parus* spp.) *Ibis* 96. 565–85.

SOUTHERN, H. N. 1944. A transect census of pigeons. *J. Anim. Ecol.* 13. 134–9.

SOUTHERN, H. N. 1954. Tawny owls and their prey. *Ibis* 96. 384–410.

SOUTHERN, H. N. 1959. Mortality and population control. *Ibis* 101. 429–36.

SOUTHERN, H. N., and MORLEY, A. 1950. Marsh-tit territories over six years. *Brit. Birds* 43. 33–45.

SOUTHERN, H. N., and VENABLES, L. S. V. 1939. Habitat selection among birds in a Lapland birchwood. *J. Anim. Ecol.* 8. 114–19.

STENHOUSE, J. H. 1925. Mixed plumages in a brood of hybrid crows. *Scot. Nat.* 1925. 101–5.

STEWART, W. 1923. The rook in Lanarkshire. *Scot. Nat.* 1923. 141–6.

TAYLOR, W. L. 1938. Birds and British forestry. *Forestry* 12. 1–9.

THOMPSON, D. NETHERSOLE-. 1931. The field habits and nesting of the the hobby. *Brit. Birds* 25. 142–56.

THORPE, W. H. 1958. The learning of song-patterns by birds, with special reference to the song of the chaffinch *Fringilla coelebs. Ibis* 100. 535–70.

TINBERGEN, L. 1946. De Sperwer als Roofvijand van Zangvogels. *Ardea* 34. 1–213.

TUCKER, B. W. 1944. The ejection of pellets by passerine birds. *Brit. Birds* 38. 50–52.

TUCKER, D. G. 1947. The mammals and birds of Higham Park. *London Naturalist for 1947*. 109–16.

TURČEK, F. J. 1949. (The bird population in some deciduous forests during a gypsy-moth outbreak.) *Bulletin of the Institute for Forest Research of Czechoslovak Republic.* (Slovak, with English summary.)

TURČEK, F. J. 1952. Ecological analysis of the bird and mammalian population of a primeval forest on the Pol'ana mountain (Slovakia). *Bulletin internationale de l'Académie tchèque des Sciences* 53. 1–25.

TURČEK, F. J. 1954. A contribution to the function of forest bird-population from the point of view of biocoenology and forest managements. *Aquila* 55–58. 51–73.

TURČEK, F. J. 1955. Bird populations of some lowland forests near the Danube in Southern Slovakia. *Acta XI Congressus internationalis ornithologici* 532–6. Basel 1954.

TURČEK, F. J. 1956. On the bird population of the spruce forest community in Slovakia. *Ibis* 98. 24–33.

VENABLES, L. S. V., and VENABLES, U. M. 1952. The blackbird in Shetland. *Ibis* 94. 636–53.

WETMORE, A. 1936. The number of contour feathers in passeriform and related birds. *Auk* 53. 159–69.

WHITE, E. B. 1953. Birds and butterflies. *Entomologists' Record* 65. 55.

WHITE, W. W. 1931. *Bird Life in Devon.* London, Jonathan Cape.

WILSON, J. O. 1933. *Birds of Westmorland and the Northern Pennines.* London, Hutchinson.

YAPP, W. B. 1934. The rook population of West Gloucestershire. *J. Anim. Ecol.* 3. 77–80.

YAPP, W. B. 1951. The population of rooks (*Corvus frugilegus*) in West Gloucestershire, II. *J. Anim. Ecol.* 20. 169–72.

YAPP, W. B. 1953*a*. The high-level woodlands of the English Lake District. *Northwestern Naturalist* 24. 190–207; 370–83.

YAPP, W. B. 1953*b*. The bird community of the fellwoods of the English Lake District. *Northwestern Nat.* 24. 503–12.

YAPP, W. B. 1956. The theory of line transects. *Bird Study* 3. 93–104.

INDEX

Printed in Great Britain by
The Camelot Press Ltd., London and Southampton